Allan Fox   Steve Parish

WILD HABITATS
A NATURAL HISTORY OF AUSTRALIAN ECOSYSTEMS

ABC
Books

Steve Parish
PUBLISHING

Published by ABC Books for the
AUSTRALIAN BROADCASTING CORPORATION
GPO Box 9994 Sydney NSW 2001

Produced by Steve Parish Publishing Pty Ltd
PO Box 1058, Archerfield, Q 4108 Australia
www.steveparish.com.au

National Library of Australia Cataloguing-in-Publication data:

Fox, Allan, 1931- .

Wild habitats : a natural history of Australian ecosystems.

Bibliography.
Includes index.
ISBN 978 0 7333 1947 1.

1. Biotic communities - Australia. 2. Habitat
(Ecology) -
Australia. I. Australian Broadcasting Commission. II.
Title.

577.0994

Author: Allan Fox
Designed by Leanne Nobilio, SPP
Photography by Steve Parish
Additional photography as credited on p. 352

Front cover & title page, top to bottom: Warm light burnishes
rocks on Friendly Beach, Freycinet National Park, Tas; Millaa
Millaa Falls, Atherton Tableland, Qld; Wildflowers blossom in
Uluṟu–Kata Tjuṯa National Park, NT.

Opposite: Sand dunes blaze with blooms of wildflowers.

Pages 4–5, top to bottom: Daintree River, Qld; Otway Ranges,
Vic; Uluṟu–Kata Tjuṯa National Park, NT. *Pages 6–7, left to
right:* Glen Helen Gorge, NT; Fan Palms, Mission Beach, Qld.
Pages 8–9, left to right: Sundial Shell in close-up; Lady Elliot
Island, Qld.

Edited by Kerry Davies; Ted Lewis & Karin Cox, SPP
Project Managed by Andrew Weatherill, SPP
Production by Carol Chandler & Wendy Mansell, SPP
Prepress by Colour Chiefs Digital Imaging, Brisbane, Australia
Printed in China by PrintPlus Ltd

5 4 3 2 1

WILD HABITATS

A NATURAL HISTORY OF AUSTRALIAN ECOSYSTEMS

Text, diagrams and maps: Allan Fox

Principal photographer: Steve Parish

ABC
Books

Steve Parish
PUBLISHING

Contents

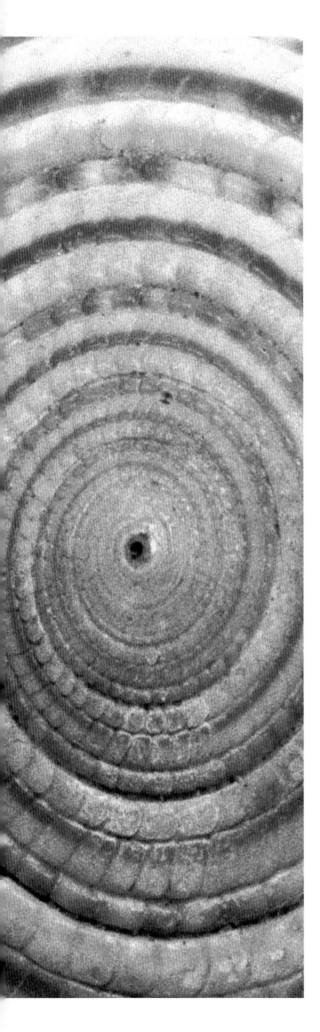

Foreword

We all love to wander in wild places. Who has not been at the end of their tether at some stage in their life and sought the uplift of the spirit or the surge of energy, enthusiasm and creative thinking that is found in green leaves, tall trees, vast brown expanses, mirror-still lakes reflecting the sky, or in the crash of waves on the beach? We welcome the continent's natural blessings on our weekends and holidays, yet what do we really know about the inner workings of these habitats?

In the 35 years that I have been presenting nature to the general public, I have been constantly surprised by how little people — even nature-lovers — know about how habitats actually operate. Without this knowledge, how should we know how to protect such environments from the threat they face from our presence on the planet? Unfortunately, many of us are guilty of taking the natural environment for granted, often in the most senseless ways. Australia is not a "lucky country", it is a fragile country under considerable environmental pressure. As it always has done, the make-up of our environment is changing; however, this time human beings must bear much responsibility for the inevitable changes the Earth will undergo in coming years. The habitats depicted and discussed in this book may alter drastically, some even irretrievably, in the face of global warming and human-induced climate change. Hopefully, by better understanding them, we are better equipped to save them.

This book has been written by a man who has devoted every minute of his waking life to the dual tasks of understanding how Australia's habitats function and encouraging others to get involved in conserving them — in fact, from the 1960s, Allan Fox has been at the forefront of environmental education in Australia. Not only has he strived to understand the complexity of ecosystems, he has also worked hard to excite others about nature and take them on the same journey of understanding, appreciation and preservation. His persistence has created many converts to his holistic approach to landscape — I am one of them and he has profoundly changed my approach to my own work.

Wild Habitats of Australia is a big story and one that must be told in a voice we can all understand. This is Allan's story — a story of an ever-changing, ephemeral landscape filled to overflowing with diversity and drama. However, you must be warned: wild habitats can be addictive places to visit. Each pocket of wilderness draws you in and takes you to a wonderful world of its own — one that may even present you, as it has for Allan and me, with a life-long obsession with nature.

Steve Parish

Above: Charles Darwin, the world-famous naturalist, pictured circa 1840 at Down House in Kent in a painting by George Richmond kept in the Bridgeman Art Library, United Kingdom.

Above: Early Australian explorers and environmentalists, such as Darwin, found a continent populated with mammalian fauna that had evolved in isolation, leading to surprising and distinct characteristics. The clearing of woodlands and the pollution of streams and rivers in the 200-odd years since, has reduced the numbers of both of these unique mammals.

Discovering the Nature of Australia

"Verandah people", Australians have been called — a moniker that suits a life lived largely outdoors. More than 75% of Australians live on the narrow south-eastern coastal strip between Queensland's Sunshine Coast and Adelaide, South Australia. The rest, apart from those who live on Australia's south-west "patio", are scattered thinly across this vast continent. As it was for the Aborigines throughout the past 60,000 years or more, the sheer size and space of the continent demands exploration. This immensity of distance always gave the impression that there was an endless resource of nature and wildness somewhere over the horizon — but was there? A friend who was recently discussing what this book might include made the observation that it could quickly become a historical record of what once was, rather than what is now.

Until 190 years ago, the new settlers from lush old England hadn't even crossed the Blue Mountains — a mere 50 kilometres west of Sydney. Charles Darwin, during his five-year world voyage in the *Beagle*, a trip that totally and irrevocably changed the course of natural science, rode a horse to Bathurst across those mountains just 23 years after the first crossing (1836). He commented:

> *A few years since this country abounded with wild animals; but now the emu is banished to a long distance, and the kangaroo has become scarce … It may not be long before these animals are altogether exterminated, but their doom is fixed.*

The Emu has indeed gone from that country, but like many who make predictions after only a single experience, Darwin was very wrong concerning the kangaroo. He had broken his own rigorous rule: "inferences must be tested again and again against new observations". Of course, he never had the opportunity to return to this continent. Darwin's explanation for the incredible diversity of life on this planet, an idea so revolutionary to science, could have only come after reflecting on countless observations. Five simple, provable ideas lie at the base of his theory:

- Every population of a species is made up of individuals. Each individual is different in ways that make it more or less successfully competitive with other individuals.

- Individuals reproduce themselves as faulty copies, but they also retain major characteristics (that is, kangaroos produce kangaroos).

- Populations live in changeable habitats and under equally variable environmental conditions.

- In life's struggle, habitat provides all of the conditions for the successful life and reproduction of some, but not all, individuals. Successful individuals pass on most of their successful attributes to their offspring.

- In this competitive world, the best-equipped individuals (in getting food and in avoiding becoming someone else's food, while staying healthy enough to rear the next generation) will ensure the survival of the species.

Survival is the measure of success! This process of natural selection has produced the wonderful bounty of biodiversity that we see today. So, why didn't the kangaroos at Bathurst disappear like the Emu, as Darwin predicted? The answer lies in the changes that have taken place to the animal's habitat since 1813. Habitat is the critical word — and the mysteries of habitat, and those of populations of animals and plants, are what this book attempts to unravel.

Habitat is the great provider of life — it, too, is part alive. Habitat must provide nutrition through food and water, shelter from competitors and unfavourable environmental elements, as well as the space that an animal's body and mind demands to remain healthy. The land (including ocean and icefield), soil, water quality and supply must work together with plants and animals as a living system, or ecosystem, to supply habitat needs.

Charles Darwin's challenges in understanding were the same that we face today: how to understand the particular needs of an animal and the changes affecting that animal's environment. By clearing patches of forest and woodland, settlers improved the production of nutritious grasses, created supportive shelter near food and provided permanent water. Kangaroo habitat was enriched by these changes. Our attachment to animals has caused us to introduce laws to protect certain species from over-predation by a dominant introduced species — us! Darwin, the world's greatest naturalist, did not foresee such changes.

In the case of the Emu, the birds' inquisitive behaviour made them a simple target at an early, unsophisticated phase of settlement when settlers were struggling for survival. The Emu's future generations existed in the form of palatable eggs, many of which terminated in human guts. Powerful carnivorous predators, such as foxes, dogs and cats, were introduced and also enjoyed the succulent Emu chicks. The modified habitat didn't provide effective shelter for Emus, despite food and water supply having been enhanced.

Today, we adopt a more environmentally sound approach to learning about wildlife and habitat, seeking knowledge via our ears, eyes, noses, cameras and minds, rather than with guns and spears. Brilliant teacher and conservationist Aldo Leopold writes, "We can be ethical only in relation to something we see, feel, understand, love, or otherwise have faith in." I hope that this book will guide you to understand Australia and to continue your discovery of this vast continent.

Above: Few experiences compare with the face-to-face interaction gained from "going bush" or discovering animals in their natural environments with the aid of a field-based environmental educator.

Above, top to bottom: Galahs; Emu; Red Kangaroo; Eastern Water Dragon. While some animals have benefited from the accessibility of human-created dams and agriculture, many others, such as small mammals and the Emu, have suffered.

Above: Sandstone in Lawn Hill Gorge, Queensland, shows clear fossil evidence of once being laid in a shallow sea bed.

Above: The hard, folded quartzites of the King Leopold Ranges in the Kimberley, Western Australia, demonstrate a history of intense heating and of being under great lateral pressure.

Thinking like a Naturalist about Habitat

Just as much as for any other activity, there is nothing like discovery! This applies to building knowledge about the Australian environment and its inhabitants. Ask any of the many thousands, if not millions, of birdwatchers, insect collectors, anglers or "frog" students how their interest grew. I'd be prepared to bet that their answers will be about going out into the country and searching for, finding and studying their fascinating wild quarry. The many brilliant wildlife television programs, documentaries and books probably stirred that interest along. Books, particularly, help foster an understanding of what one sees in the bush.

However, there are helpful shortcuts to becoming involved with nature — shortcuts that many of us have learned through years of experience. What we see on our journeys makes a lot more sense once we know more about this continent because we quickly learn that life is a game that is almost always played according to the rules.

A QUESTION OF NATURE

No matter where we travel, the land has shape. The Australian landscape is a vast tapestry draped over a crazy framework of rock. Woven into it are wonderful stories, telling in many chapters how the landscape came together. If we can begin to sort out this geological story we will begin to understand not only the nature of Australia, but of every other continent. The rules operating in Australia are the same everywhere — only the patterns that decorate the surface are different.

The scheme that I always use to begin to understand country anywhere, even on other continents and in the oceans, is fairly simple. When looking at a landscape, I ask myself four questions in the following order:

- What is under the surface of this country?
- How was, and how is, this land being shaped?
- What has been, and is, the story of its plants and animals?
- What has been, and is, the story of humans in this place?

In technical terms, I am interested in the country's geology, geomorphology, ecology and anthropology. Heavy words these, but within this set of questions we can explore the story of any place, large or small. Very few of us have the time to fully explore all four questions, so we tend to specialise our interests. Among us are the birdwatchers, rock and fossil hunters, wildflower students, reptile specialists and many others. We are all amateurs, yet at least one of the four questions can be answered in a way that will prove meaningful to all.

As the great Einstein once said, "Keep it simple, don't make it simple!" No matter where our special interests lie, we must always remember all of these questions and think about how they might affect our special interest. How, for instance, does rich volcanic soil affect where we might find lyrebirds? What if this soil is in desert country? The answers we discover will be natural history and, as soon as we ask those questions, we are becoming naturalists. Even humans are part of natural history, because we are a product of all of the natural history that has gone before us. When the human species disappears some time in the future, the natural history of that time will reflect something of our passing. We can see all around us, even now, ways in which we are modifying the rest of life on Earth. So, let us ask those questions, and others, to help us begin to understand life on Earth in our time. With these questions in mind, all travel will be a journey of discovery — certainly there will be no tramping along the roads of monotony!

WHAT IS BENEATH THE SURFACE OF THIS COUNTRY?

First, we must understand that the crust of this planet is in a continuous state of change. At various times it rises, falls, folds, breaks and faults, melts, congeals and crystallises. A place high on a mountain top today may once have been (or may have been many times) at the bottom of the sea. However, the country rock beneath the surface dramatically impacts on the habitat that will be constructed, layer by layer, and species by species, on that particular framework of stone.

IGNEOUS ROCKS

Probably the first kind of rock to have formed on the planet, and still forming, is the fire-formed igneous group. These are the volcanic rocks that form flowing plains, flights of terraces and, in places, the towering, spiry erections of the volcanoes' cores. There are also cliff-lines of "organ pipes", ash beds, beds of shattered rubble (breccia) and basalts. In our travels we will discover these from Tasmania to north Queensland, but rarely elsewhere. The tough, fine-grained volcanic rock of Mount Warning in New South Wales is the solidified core of a massive volcano, from which many cubic kilometres of lava flowed. Layer upon layer of ash and lava from this volcano built like a vast layer cake of igneous rock to form the Border Ranges of the New South Wales–Queensland border.

PLUTONIC ROCKS

The second group, plutonic rocks, also had a molten genesis. Named after the Greek mythical god Pluto, the caretaker of hot Hades, plutonic rocks are buoyant granitic rocks composed of light, melted-down rocky material rich in silicates. Mount Kosciuszko, Australia's highest mountain, was once a massive plume of hot, honey-like molten rock (or magma) that welled up from many kilometres below like an immense blister never reaching the surface. It slowly cooled and hardened beneath the country's rocky "skin". In its slow cooling, minerals making up the magma began to form crystals of silica, mica and feldspar — granite, a plutonic rock, was born. This molten material rose as blisters through the crust, cooling slowly and crystallising. The slower the cooling, the larger the crystals. Millions of years of erosion removed the "rocky skin" and exposed the granite. Plutonic rocks are widespread. Mount Buffalo, Bald Rock, Magnetic Island, the Devils Marbles and Wave Rock are examples from across the continent. Granitic landscapes are those that are smoothly rounded and voluptuous, with arid soils.

METAMORPHIC ROCKS

In the granite's searing rise towards the surface, coupled with other stupendous geologic pressures, surrounding rocks were moved, crushed and fused. They were contorted, faulted, folded, heated and partially melted in the moving. These rocks

Above: Cape Raoul, Tasmania, is composed of fluted columnar dolerite that formed as a vast pool of lava cooled. Seacoast erosion has isolated the spectacular, resistant columns.

Above: Nature's Window in Kalbarri National Park, Western Australia, has been cut through soft, multi-layered sandstones.

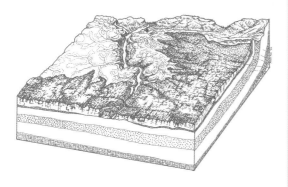

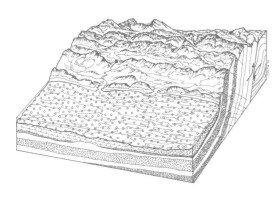

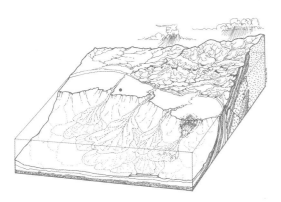

Above: This series of diagrams traces the history of the Lawn Hill area of north-west Queensland. The oldest part is at the bottom, while youngest is the present-day picture at the top. During prehistoric times, the land buckled and a deep basin formed beside a high coastal land. The country was eroding, as it does to this day, and rivers carried the mud and sand into the ocean basin where the sediment settled in layers. First, the heaviest gravel and sand sank; the fine, lighter mud and clay was last to settle. These sediments sifted to the basin bottom, where they set to form conglomerate from the pebbly sand, sandstone and shale from the finer mud and clay.

The basin gradually filled, becoming shallower and shallower and exposed to increasingly brighter sunlight. In this shallow, better-lit, warmer seawater, mats of simple algae plants grew and concentrated the mineral calcium carbonate in their cells. Among these layers, which were rich in animal food and oxygen, lived vast numbers of invertebrates, including polyps of early corals. Again, over millions of years, beds of this calcium-rich material formed thick blankets of limestone.

The top diagram shows the whole area beginning to slowly rise above sea level. Water from slightly acidic rainfall began its long corrosive and eroding effect on the overlying blanket of limestone. Much of it was removed until the rivers reached the red underlying sandstone, uncovering fossil ripples and cutting deeply into the softer sandstone to create today's scene.

were toughened and changed by the heat to become members of another group of rocks — metamorphic, or "changed" rocks, of which slates, schists and quartzites are just some. One could correctly expect these rocks to produce jagged landscapes such as the MacDonnell Ranges in Central Australia, the Flinders Ranges in South Australia, Federation Peak in south-west Tasmania or the King Leopold Ranges of the Kimberley, Western Australia.

SEDIMENTARY ROCKS

The third group are sedimentary rocks, formed from sediment transported by wind, water or ice. All of the glorious sandstones that make up the bedrock of Blue Mountains National Park in New South Wales were once beds of sandy mud in a wide basin of the sea. Uluṟu, in the Northern Territory, is composed of hundreds of metres of sand washed down a raging river system. These are the sedimentary rocks, formed from sediments. Whenever the power of the transporting agent is reduced, the sediments drop out; first the large pieces until, when power is almost gone, even the lightest dust or finest mud settles to the river bed. All rock types, once exposed to the weather, ultimately become sediment to be transported and deposited elsewhere.

Sedimentary rocks vividly portray the history of their time in their many layers, like the pages of a book. There will be the traces of moving water, worm holes, old shell prints, fish bones, corals and a host of other fossils. The formation of sand dunes and holes swept by rushing waters will tell of the dynamic nature of transport. Take time to try to read the pages of these "books" in road cuttings and cliffs. Older times will be at the bottom, unless a great convulsion of the Earth has thrown them upwards. We do not have to travel far to come across sedimentary rock — the stony sheets of Kakadu escarpments, the Blue Mountains, Carnarvon Gorge, Mutawintji, the tilted Grampians and the bent Wilpena Pound all tell vivid tales of aeons of sediment, pile upon pile. There will be pebbly conglomerate, sandstone, shale, mudstone, claystone and, where marshy and peaty swamps were buried, coal. Sedimentary rocks are the libraries documenting the history of our living planet over 4.5 billion years. There are other landscapes, too — the limestone at Jenolan Caves, Windjana Gorge or Yarrangobilly, which is formed from sedimentary rock that was once living coral reef growing in the clear, warm ocean.

Sediment, carried by glacial ice, finishes as moraine or glacial till. The conglomerate or "pudding stone" formed from glacial till is called tillite, with boulders that have flat faces ground on them. We can see these in Arkaroola Creek of the North Flinders Ranges. This grinding by glacial movement produces a particularly fine mud that settles out as varve shale. All rock, no matter what kind, over time is weathered, eroded, transported and deposited to form sedimentary rocks in the process known as the Cycle of Erosion (see page 16), which is a continuous process of change, acting everywhere across the planet's surface.

So, the framework for the continent is constructed of these groups of rocks, all with vastly different properties and histories.

Right: South-west Tasmania comprises a very complex landscape. Here, around a tarn in Southwest National Park, towers of very resistant quartzite have undergone numerous periods of intense pressure and heating. They have been folded, faulted, uplifted and intruded upon by minerals — many of economic value, such as copper, gold and tin. Glacial ice, too, has added its touch, carving deep lakes, cirques, tarn-scoured pavements and U-shaped gorges. Erosion by heavy rains added further detail to this craggy vista.

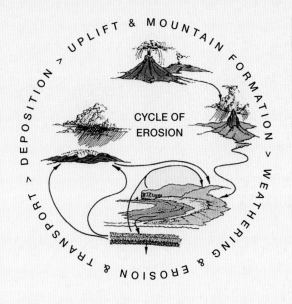

CYCLE OF EROSION

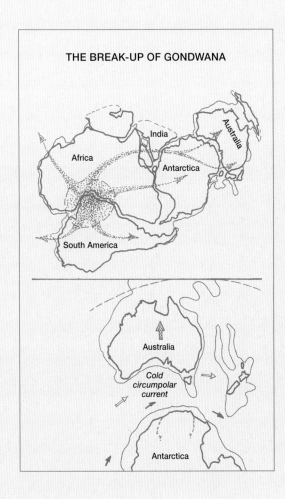

THE BREAK-UP OF GONDWANA

Above: Australia was the last continental mass to separate from Gondwana, leaving the Antarctic some 50 million years ago. Flora and fauna became isolated on this great Australian raft that drifted some 4500 km from the ancient Gondwana relict. This drift completely reoriented the continent's habitats, placing northern Australia within 11° of the equator and under the influence of the north-west monsoon and the South-East Trade Winds. Tasmania and southern Western Australia came under the influence of winter westerlies. A large area in the mid-latitude low-pressure belt, coupled with low physiography, produces Australia's arid interior. This radical readjustment of climatic influences over 50 million years of relative isolation allowed the evolution of our unique flora and fauna.

THE CYCLE OF EROSION

When rocks are placed under great pressure, as when movements in the crust bury them many kilometres deep, they become plastic in the extremely hot environment. In this way, metamorphic rocks form when the grains soften, run and stick together, making slate from shale; schist and gneiss from granite; quartzite from sandstone and, with more heat, hornfels. Nearer the surface, under cooler conditions, such movements crush and break the strata. Under subsurface hot conditions, minerals frequently become able to move about, minerals to like minerals, and create masses of crystals of pure minerals. Super-heated water dissolves the minerals, creating metallic compounds. These hydro-thermal and very active compounds permeate the mobile, crushed and fractured rock bodies. Thus the hard, laminated layers of contorted metamorphic rocks may contain ore bodies, such as one finds in Broken Hill's Barrier Ranges (silver, lead and zinc), the underlying rocks of Kakadu (uranium and gold) or the ranges of Mount Isa (copper). Many of these very resistant toughened rocks are ancient and represent Australia when life was little more than single cells.

Landscapes have originated from geological cycles that have been occurring continuously since the Earth was young. Materials are shunted around by erosion, by geologic, wind and wave transport, and by vertical upheavals. The whole surface of the planet is afloat on a hot plastic foundation heated by radioactive processes. The Earth's crust is organised into great rafting plates (very similar to the skin on porridge), which are in the process of either separating or colliding. About 50 million years ago, one massive piece, the Australian Plate, separated from the Antarctic landmass that scientists call Gondwana. Much earlier, India, Africa and South America had broken away from Gondwana. Until the breakup began, that group of continents shared systems of life and a heritage of plants and animals.

Like a great "Noah's Ark", Australia, carrying its Gondwanan plant and animal communities, broke free and has been rafting northwards at a speed somewhat faster than our thumbnails grow. Australia's breakaway cleared the Southern Ocean and opened a seaway that allowed the cold polar ocean current to spin around the planet without being warmed by south-flowing tropical currents. Southern Hemisphere climates became much colder. In the meantime, travelling north, Australia entered warmer and warmer climatic belts as it moved closer and closer to the tropical Asian area. All the while, the continent pushed up a vast bow-wave of rock before it, in the form of New Guinea. Much of its leading edge, however, was forced downwards, perhaps 100 kilometres, beneath the plate north of us. That part is now melting down and fuelling the Indonesian volcanoes to the north, as well as creating future wells of magma to form granite.

As Australia drifted northwards, the plate passed over massive "hotspots", great turbulent wells of fiery pressurised fluid magma. These subsequently burst through the surface, producing a chain of volcanic areas that created Cape Hillsborough near Mackay (33 million years ago), the Bunya Mountains (24 million years ago), Mount Warning (21–24 million years ago), the Nandewars (19 million years ago), the Warrumbungles (16 million years ago), Mount Canobolas (10 million years ago) and Mount Macedon (6 million years ago). Another line of hotspot-fed volcanoes runs south through Middleton Reef and Lord Howe Island in the Tasman Sea.

WEATHERING WATER

Wind and running water alone are very inefficient cutting agents, but when combined with the incising tools of ice, sand or gravel, their potency is dramatically increased. Consider the many gaps the Todd and Finke Rivers have cut through the resistant quartzite of the MacDonnell Ranges of the Northern Territory or the grand gorges of the Franklin, Gordon, Mitchell, Cox or Grose Rivers. Consider also how the form of the Murray River changes from the roaring, boulder-strewn upper Murray, or Indi in its High Country canyons, to the vast, muddy floodplains of the slow-moving, sinuous lower course. The water cycle, however, is not as simple as erosion alone. Water is the universal solvent and may also be acidic or alkaline in its chemical reactions. Under warm conditions, water is more chemically active. The rocks of the surface are not normally of pure single elements; they are almost always mixes of numerous minerals, all of which are variously soluble — particularly if the watery solution surrounding them has increased chemical reaction caused by its acidity or other dissolved chemicals. With the development of bacteria, plants and simple animals, acids secreted by those organisms to aid in the uptake of soluble food also acted to break down rock surfaces. Plants and animals have other actions that assist in "detailing" the landscape's form. Animals such as wombats, rodents and even Platypuses actively burrow, while the gentle power of fungi can lift a slab of concrete as it grows and tree roots can dramatically widen rock cracks, allowing water to work its way into a rock mass. However, chemically active water dissolves most rock components, rotting the rock and allowing wind, water-freeze and running water to break into the rocky mass in a process known as weathering. Weathering and erosion are the two allied processes that shape the landscape. Each rock type reacts at a different rate and way in the weathering and erosion process.

All sloping lands retreat before the power of weathering and erosion because gravity drags any loosened objects — whether a whole mountainside, a boulder, a grain of rolling sand or water — to a lower level. It is not possible to contemplate a world without gravity. All of the materials of this spherical planet are held in place and even sorted by mass (weight) by billions of years of gravity at work. Gravity holds our atmosphere in place and gives our planet life. These weathering agents then etch the land's surface and, together with the agents of erosion and the force of gravity, cause the resistant rocks (not necessarily the hardest) to become isolated and stand out. If there is an inherent resistant structure in the rock this will usually give the landscape a "signature". Granite is shaped into a rounded landscape; alternating sandstone and shale into plateaux, tablelands and mesas with vertical cliffs; limestone into holes, ravines and water-sharpened points; metamorphic rocks into twisted and chaotically sharp ridges.

The land's surface also has an edge exposed to the sea. Sometimes these seas crash against headlands where mountain ranges run into the ocean, or lap at arcing beaches that connect the headlands, divorcing the placid waters of lagoons and forming barriers that front wetlands and undulating heathlands. These beaches are the bay-mouth sandbars deposited in the quiet waters behind protective headlands that formed after rises in sea level. There will be much dynamic detail on the seaward side of these features: channels, rips, bars, dunes, berms, wave-cut benches, reefs, bommies, potholes, sea stacks, islands and sand cays. All of these are playthings of wind, water, waves, drifts, currents and changing sea levels.

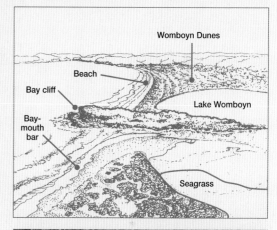

Above and diagram below: Bay Cliff, Womboyn Lake and the Womboyn Dunes of Nadgee Nature Reserve, NSW, illustrate many of the processes of coastal landscapes, such as beach formation, development of bay-mouth sand barriers, influence of rock islands on channel development and the stabilising effect of vegetation.

Above: Waterfalls such as Apsley Falls, NSW, are also known as nickpoints, where a river that has had its base level lowered cuts its channel back upstream at times of low sea level.

Above: The middle time period of the Lake Mungo eastern lunette dune in the Willandra Lakes World Heritage Area, New South Wales, (the so-called "Mungo Unit"), was the richest in animal and Aboriginal fossils. During this 20,000-year period, commencing about 45,000 years ago, the lakes filled with water and aquatic and wetland life abounded, attracting much mammalian life, including Thylacines and humans.

HOW WAS, AND HOW IS, THIS LAND SHAPED?

Weathering, erosion, fretting, shaping, building and reshaping of the landscape is going on everywhere about us in a continuous process. If rebuilding processes had ceased, the land would have been at sea level long ago. Fortunately, our planet is a very active place thanks to the pressures and heat generated below the crust. It is the eternal conflict between mountain-building processes and the water-charged atmospheric blanket enclosing the planet that gives our land its form.

Earth, however, is not an independent entity. The sun provides energy in the form of light and heat, and combined with the forces of gravity drives the great material cycles, including air and water. The cycle of mobile water through its various forms — liquid, vapour, condensation and ice — does much of the shaping. The unequal heating of the air mass from equatorial regions to the poles, combined with the spin of the Earth, builds high- and low-pressure belts that drive the world's wind systems. These global movements are diverted and pushed off course by the local topography of the landscape — its mountains, plains, deserts, ice fields and vegetative cover — in conjunction with the heat of the surface and the spin of the Earth. So many factors are crucial that when one tries to arrive at an answer to the "how" questions, we frequently find more hidden questions. What is important is to realise that it is moving air and moving water, either as fluid or solid ice, that cut and shape the Earth.

WHAT HAS BEEN, AND IS, THE PLANT AND ANIMAL STORY?

Life on Earth began in the warm, murky seas, so let's venture from life's origins in the seawater back into the dunes. The edge of this habitat is under constant attack from the sea, which can be truly wild. The weather is dominated by a deep low-pressure system a couple of hundred kilometres offshore. Closely spaced heavy seas are pounding the beach, their turbulence loosening the sand and, with the wash, cutting and dragging the beach sands offshore. These destructive phases are short-lived and as long as the quieter, constructive seas that replenish the sands keep pace with storm-wave destruction the beach will remain in place. However, a sea-level rise or fall or a change in the climatic patterns will change this balance. But this belt of beach is an impermanent land of conflict, a "no-man's land"— the environmental conditions here will not sustain life permanently.

A few metres above this belt, the environmental conditions are dramatically different. Beach sand is mainly silica and particles of shell liberally coated with sea salt. The surface is dry, parched during daylight, cooled during the night. It is swept by sand-blasting, salt-bearing winds and dotted with "islands" of old decaying seaweeds (algae), smelly dead sea squirts and other seaborne litter. These islands are outposts of life, miniature oases, populated with decaying micro-organisms and providing shelter from moisture loss, ultraviolet radiation, sand blast, sea birds and nocturnal predatory crustaceans. They are home and habitat for a myriad tiny crabs and amphipods, as well as for flies, beetles, spiders and centipedes. Already a miniature system is living here, but living dangerously, for it can be wiped out by a high tide or a single storm wave. Most occupants here have short life cycles.

Far enough up the beach these "islands" trap numerous seeds of various local plants blowing across the dunes. Few will germinate here; those that do survive only a short time because of the lack of soil nutrients, excessive salt and exposure

Above: A Red-capped Plover at nest on Jane Spiers Beach, Nadgee Nature Reserve, NSW. These birds are very susceptible to predation by Lace Monitors and their eggs by Silver Gulls.

Above: Typical ocean beach on Tamboon Beach, Victoria, shows the wave cut berm lying in front of the Coastal Spinifex vegetated frontal dune, a favourite nesting site for sea birds.

Above: Acacia, Banksia, Monotoca, Melaleuca and tea-tree species flourish further back from the frontal dune at Tamboon Beach, on successively higher dunes and sand masses pushed back by prevailing south-westerly winds.

Above: Coastal Spinifex runners form a colonising, binding network across the new sands of the frontal dune.

Above: Ghost Crabs are common tropical beach occupiers that tunnel out shelters and scavenge the tideline nocturnally.

Above: Pigface is another early coloniser of the dunes. Its thick, succulent leaves are a useful adaptation in its exposed habitat.

Above: New Holland Honeyeaters are just one species of honeyeater that feed on coastal banksias and bottlebrushes.

to sand blasting. The nature of the site will select out any survivors and these will require special adaptations. Perhaps Beach Spinifex runners may survive burial here, the silvery, hairy and slender flexible leaves will withstand sand blast by strong coastal winds. At each of the buried nodes along the runners, roots will venture out in search of food and moisture. So plant nourishment might be coming from much higher up the frontal dune slope. Already the spinifex is beginning to mat down the sand, to hold some of the drift and to cool it beneath its shade. The smooth beach is beginning to become hummocky. Some leaves will die and begin to build an organic layer, enhanced by an increasing amount of blowing litter trapped by the matted network. Environmental conditions are changing. Insect life increases in number and variety in this new, more complex habitat. In the early morning light, the prints of foraging, pallid Ghost Crabs are becoming mixed with the tracks of small mammals and reptiles.

A belt of water-storing, fleshy leaved plants such as Pigface and Beach Scaevola, along with hairy or down-covered leafed plants and those that crowd close to the surface (such as the Pennywort, Correa and the Beach Wattle), begin to form a densely packed mat of plants with a strong canopy. The growing tips of this canopy are constantly pruned by the onshore wind. Any sand dropping into the calm air beneath the protective canopy builds up on the floor. So the slope on the now-protected dune front steepens and takes on the sleek, streamlined form of the wind track. Now Coastal Tea-tree, melaleucas, leucopogons, monotocas and Coast Banksia can find enough shelter and nutrients to join the dune plant community, particularly in the shale beyond the crest. With this very dense cover stopping sand from sliding and moving, extremely steep sandy slopes develop. Wildfire or other major disturbances to this cover very rapidly destabilise the dune, causing a "blow-out" that may take 100 years to stabilise again.

Coastal dune scrub communities provide excellent shelter and varied food resources, and so are prime habitat for possums and swamp wallabies. If there are grasslands, heathlands, woodlands or forests nearby, the scrubs provide shelter for Red-necked Wallabies and Grey Kangaroos. Eastern Whipbirds and numerous

Above: Eastern Grey Kangaroos busily feed on a "kangaroo lawn" of couch grass along the beachfront of Pebbly Beach at Murramarang National Park, New South Wales.

honeyeaters are common in the flowering season. These dense, dark, closed communities have little ground cover except where openings occur in the canopy. In the better lit places, Blady Grass, Lomandra, shrubs, Bracken Ferns and mosses flourish.

In the shelter of the windbreak afforded by the frontal dune, shrubs take on scrub and tree form with a canopy around 15 metres high, its upper surface still following the wind's streamlining path. Soil moisture, organic soil in the depression and low moist flats behind the dunes provide the prime environment for a number of woodland and forest eucalypts with a tall understorey of Old Man Banksias and a dense heathy groundcover of pea and wattle species, grass-trees and Epacrids. Dominated by eucalypts, the Red Bloodwood, Peppermints, Blackbutt and the Sydney Red Gum (*Angophora costata*), this is a bright, sunny world. It is alive with the calls of numerous birds — Crimson and Eastern Rosellas, Australian Magpies, ubiquitous Willie Wagtails, the White-throated Treecreeper, Golden Whistler and numerous seasonal honeyeaters — and the rasping screech of Yellow-tailed Black-Cockatoos. Digging marks the passing of a foraging Long-nosed Bandicoot, interrupted in its search for beetle larvae by a lumbering black monitor lizard, now dozing along a branch above, its speckled coat camouflaging it perfectly against its fire-seared roost.

Dappled sunlight becomes even more shady in the cool gullies where the rocky hills meet sand. Here, male lyrebirds build their dancing mounds while the females scratch in the damp litter, rich in mould, for worms and amphipods (a tiny crustacean). The dry, "cinnamon" smell of the open woodland has become the smell of damp, turned soil. High in the rotting heart of an ancient Blue Gum, entered via a hollow broken limb, a black and white furry ball, the Greater Glider, sleeps off a hard night's treetop travel in search of succulent young leaves, the odd insect and eucalypt flowers. This is a patch of wet sclerophyll forest — forest because its trees are tall, with their trunks longer than the canopy is deep, wet because that is its environment, sclerophyll because the trees' leaves are leathery and wax covered to avoid water loss.

Above: Crimson Rosellas are very common along the NSW and Victorian coast and frequent wetter areas in inter-dune swales.

Above: Possums and gliders inhabit eucalypt forest bordering coastal regions.

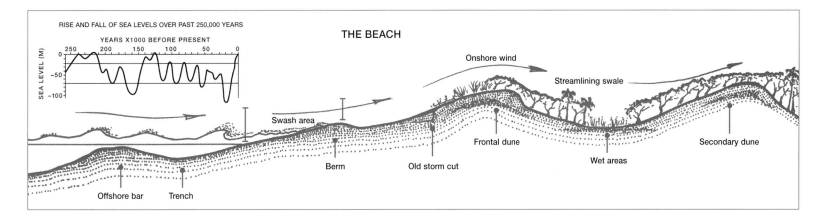

The Sand Dune Story

Constructive waves and currents drive sand ashore. On warmer, windy days, onshore winds roll and lift individual sand grains, pushing them up onto the drier, higher surfaces to shape a dune. Each dune will have a slope smoothly rising to a crest, over which the incoming sand grains tumble and fall to form a steep slope in the calm air behind the dune's crest. Once the dune has formed, the first rains will soak in and a wet zone will form in the dune's core; some water may also collect on the inter-dune swale floor. Organic debris, such as leaves blown into the quiet inter-dune air, all falls down between the dunes, gradually building up the organic matter in the damp, sandy soil. Plants thrive in this warm, moist, quiet place and in places a kind of "rainforest" may develop.

Meanwhile, pioneer plants such as Pigface, spinifex, convolvulus and acacias colonise the more unstable areas, holding the dunes in place — unless stormy seas sweep the beach and undercut the dune. Plant surfaces exposed to the sand blast are cut and wind-pruned to fit the flow pattern. So the coast is shaped. However, global warming and rising sea levels destabilise the dune-creation process. If sea-level rises continue, saltwater will sweep far inland, covering coastal plains and smothering some of our most fertile and populous lands.

What, Then, Is Habitat?

During our short journey so far we have cut through seven different communities of plants and habitats: the oceanic, pioneer, heath, scrub, woodland and dry and wet sclerophyll forest communities. Environmental conditions of each are quite distinct. Temperature, humidity, soil moisture and the soil's chemical mix, quality of the air, exposure to damaging wind and diurnal environmental changes are components that are in a variety of mixes. Imagine the incredible diversity of plant communities there must be to fit all of the possible environmental conditions that exist over a continent the size of Australia — particularly as it has been changing its position not only over the past 50 million years, but for many millions of years before that, along with changing global climates. The reason for the plant world's success is a combination of the time spans involved and the capacity of plants and animals to adapt. Look at the varied forms of plants discovered in just a short one-kilometre ramble — algae that are able to live submerged in the sea; long, trailing spinifex that can survive being buried and gains its nutrients 30 metres from its pioneering shoots; tiny leafed, densely packed melaleucas and tea-trees that can withstand strong prevailing winds and yet have a vast leaf area; the wax-covered, leathery-leafed (sclerophyllous) eucalypts, designed to keep water loss to the minimum; the epicormic shoots buried beneath insulating bark of the Bloodwood tree; and lignotubers below ground level to avoid being killed by fire in the very flammable dry woodlands.

The power of organisms to adapt is a characteristic of life. It is part of the fact that no natural offspring is a perfect copy, or clone, of its parent. Such changes or errors will all be tested by the environment because competition is also a universal characteristic of life, primarily because plants and animals are able to produce far more young than the planet's resources can possibly sustain. A few genetic errors will give the recipient a better chance of competing for their habitat's sustaining resources and of protecting themselves from their competitors. In the case of a wallaby, the "enemy" might be a dingo, but most likely its greatest competitor for necessary resources at times of drought will be a sibling. So, given time, all of these successful generational changes in body form or behaviour, small as they may be, accumulate to build new varieties of plants and animals that are more effectively adapted to new and changing habitats. These new varieties eventually become the more effective breeders.

But why give plants so much emphasis? Simply because without green plants life as we know it — including human life — would not be possible. As far as we animals living under the energetic glow of the sun are concerned, plants are the base of all food chains.

Two and a half billion years or more ago, photosynthesis appeared in bacteria, allowing them to mine the energy of sunlight. Bacteria began their long ancestral journey at a time when the planet's atmosphere was dominated by hydrogen

Left: Queensland's Frankland Islands — five islands composed of jagged outcrops of metamorphic continental rock located approximately 10 kilometres off the mainland 45 kilometres south of Cairns — represent a diverse number of habitats. Fringing reefs, mangroves and coastal vegetation surround the islands; in the interior, dense rainforest flourishes set back from the coast. The varied habitats attract an equally assorted mix of species, including numerous sea bird species as well as the fruit-eating Pied Imperial-Pigeon and nectareous honeyeaters.

sulfide ("rotten-egg" gas released from volcanoes) and when oxygen, deadly to those early life forms, was present in only a tiny trace. This long journey of the bacteria not only ultimately generated food and usable energy for the rest of the biosphere, but radically changed the composition of the air that now sustains today's life forms. Part way along this journey, the most efficient of some thousands of bacteria species developed — blue-green cyanobacteria, which could tolerate the gradually increasing amounts of oxygen. These bacteria flourished in damp and watery places, where they incorporated the hydrogen atoms from water into their microscopic bodies and released molecular oxygen gas into the air. Slow build-up of oxygen and reduction of hydrogen sulfide (the early bacteria consumed the hydrogen in this gas) in the atmosphere gave advantage to the blue-green cyanobacteria, which soon swamped earlier types of bacteria. Release of oxygen dramatically increased. Purple, red, brown and blue-green mats of oxygen-producing bacteria began to cover the floor of marine and freshwater shallows and the damp land surface, and knobbly hummocks of stromatolites grew like millions of miniature minarets in the shallows, just as at Hamelin Pool, in Shark Bay, Western Australia, today.

However, the rapid increase in atmospheric oxygen was seriously slowed by its role in the oxidation and reduction of metals in the rocks and seas. Between 2.2 and 1.8 billion years ago the predominantly brown and black rocky surface of the Earth became yellow and reddish, principally from the oxidation of iron, the fifth most prevalent element. Oxygen sped up chemical reactions. Rusty, iron-rich sediments and bacterial wastes settled to ocean and lake floors, building up many hundreds of metres of the iron ores magnetite and haematite. Some have been more recently uplifted and are now in the ancient Pilbara Hills of Western Australia, with Mount Tom Price, discovered by Lang Hancock, now providing the material for Toyotas and Holdens, railway tracks and ocean liners.

Once this early abundant supply of surface iron, copper and other metals had been largely oxidised, atmospheric gaseous oxygen began its rapid build-up from levels of something like one part in 100 billion to one part in five today.

The process of photosynthesis was the great revolutionary happening that switched on the development of higher forms of life. Without the "green fire" of photosynthesis, which powers the entire realm of higher life, we would not exist, the rainforest would not be, the colourful world of flowers would not be, and the teeming life of the coral reef would never have evolved. Humans, through our dependence on plants and our own ancestral story, belong to, and are part of, the biosphere. We are chapters in a continuing story that still has probably a billion or so more years to run. Yet there is one crucial system that explains our existence, the dynamic ecosystem. Many other cycles and systems flow and feed into it, but the rules of life's big picture, what we see around us and what has been before our time, relate back to that core system. What makes the ecosystem sometimes difficult to understand is that the systems never stand alone but interact with each other as part of the great mosaic of life on this planet. Mobile animals and the physical flow of materials, such as water in the water cycle, nitrogen in the nitrogen cycle or phosphate in the phosphate cycle, cut across but link these living systems. Pothole life on the tidal benches and island life, both isolated ecosystems, are good places to begin to explore the interdependency of life. Once we understand ecosystems, the story of life begins to gather meaning as we explore the world around us.

Above: Living stromatolites in the hyper-saline Hamelin Pool, Shark Bay, Western Australia, represent an ancient life form that helped produce today's oxygen-rich atmosphere. They are composed of sheet upon sheet of sticky single-celled cyanobacteria, upon which sand adheres in layers.

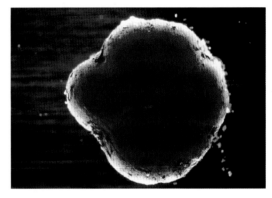

Above: Bacteria enabled photosynthesis to occur, effectively kickstarting higher life on this planet.

Bacterial Symbiosis

As well as initiating photosynthesis, bacteria had yet other crucial tricks up their slimy sleeves! They are masters of symbiosis — the ability to develop relationships with other organisms that allow them to become almost a part of those organisms and to assist in the life of that organism, yet retain some of their own identity. They have this ability because bacteria have been entering into stable relationships with one another for several thousand million years; their bodies can easily lose and acquire genes, a process that generates rapid genetic change. Bacteria have no antibodies protecting them from invasion, but they have a very large range of chemical activity. Thus they can readily "infect" other organisms. Recent studies of the DNA of cells and some of their component parts (such as the plastids, miniature living packets), containing the bundles of green chloroplasts in plant leaves, have shown that the plastid and the plants have different genetic histories. Plastids, through their green chlorophyll, trap sunlight energy and with it create sugars from water and carbon dioxide. The power locked up in the produced sugar is used in the miraculous chemical reactions that link and lock the minerals, water and gases, absorbed by the roots and leaves, to become living, organic matter. Plastids have bacterial ancestry! (Yet another reason to use antibiotics more wisely than we do, as many bacteria are not only friendly, but essential components of life.)

CREATION OF A UNIQUE HABITAT

Let's look at the genesis of Lord Howe Island. In the beginning, there was a massive marine volcano. Ultimately it broke through the ocean's surface and its pile of lava and ash became large enough to resist the sea and become a stable island. Immediately, the surface began to weather and to be shaped. The rocks were a pot pourri of numerous chemicals, including phosphates, silicates, sulfates, nitrates and other things necessary to feed plant life. The wind, ocean currents and birds carried in a variety of seeds as well as bacteria and numerous invertebrates, including insects and spiders, far more species than the environmental conditions of the island could sustain.

Meanwhile, the tail end of the warm East Australian Current, like a great conveyor belt, carried in a vast array of colonising eggs and swimming larvae of reef-building corals, crustaceans, molluscs, sea stars and many more animals and plants to become established on the "new" reefs of resistant lava. Vagrant turtles nested on the beaches. Early on, life on Lord Howe Island was a huge lottery, but steadily complexity grew, creating the sustaining habitats discovered by Lieutenant Ball in 1788: palm forest, temperate rainforest, shrubland, freshwater lagoon wetlands, tussock grassland on the land and a number of marine reef and lagoon systems.

The base for all of these systems, each with its unique habitat, food and shelter, is the plants. These were the only organisms with the bacteria that could convert the minerals of the old volcano into organic food to sustain and grow the animals. Land plants are at the producer level. Through their energy-grabbing chlorophyll in leaves and some stems, they create food that is consumed by a second level of life in the ecosystem: herbivorous animals such as the grasshoppers, emerald pigeons and wood hens. These then provide meat for a third level of consumer: carnivores, such as kestrels and, unfortunately, human-introduced ship rats. Some of these third-level consumers will be omnivores, eating a mix of plant and animal food, and some insectivores. Because of its isolation, the top predatory carnivores never reached Lord Howe Island. On the mainland of Australia common predators were quolls, Wedge-tailed Eagles and dingoes, along with humans. Because energy is lost in the form of heat at each level of consumption and conversion, the rise in level means that there must be less living matter (biomass) at the new level. There are fewer animals on the top levels but, no matter what level of life, they all in the end depend upon the plant base of this pyramid.

However, there is still another level, which if it didn't exist would cause a bankruptcy in the bank of soil nutrient resources. That is the decomposer level, and it underlies the continuity of the system in breaking down the dead carcasses and waste products so that the nutrients can be recycled. Here, bacteria and fungi, along with numerous invertebrates come into their own. So the materials are recycled. Energy, on the other hand, is lost in the form of heat generated in animals living, moving and reproducing. Only plants have the power to recharge the living system by utilising the light energy from the sun.

The essential animal metabolism in living, moving and reproducing places heavy demands on animal anatomy, physiology and behaviour. For survival, they need the service of efficient legs and feet, movement technique, economic use of energy and maintenance of body temperature, communication, effective thought processes, survival strategies for hunting (and surviving the hunt), effective attracting and mating mechanisms and technique, and effective care of the young. The trials of life and living in the context of that living system, the ecosystem,

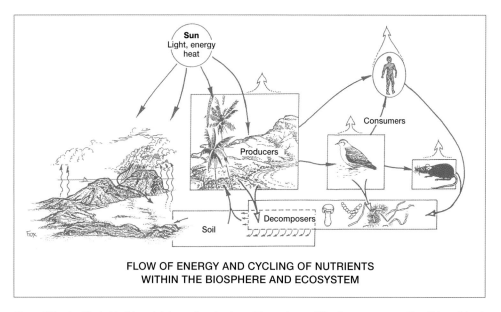

**FLOW OF ENERGY AND CYCLING OF NUTRIENTS
WITHIN THE BIOSPHERE AND ECOSYSTEM**

Above: This simplified pictorial model shows the structure of the systems of life, the ecosystems of Lord Howe Island. All ecosystems use energy from the sun to drive the metabolism of all living things. Nutrients provide minerals, from which molecules of living matter are made. These nutrients progress through the ecosystems in a series of cycles. Life does not create or destroy the minerals, but merely temporarily uses them. Plants are the only organisms that can convert sunlight to usable energy.

Plants, then, are the producers of ecosystems, while all animals are the consumers that depend on consuming plants. Second-order consumers are omnivores, such as rats, which eat a mix of plants and prey on animals. Those that live solely on other animals, such as many sea birds, are carnivores. Mineral wastes — faeces, urine, salty perspiration and decaying carcasses — are finally deposited on the ground where fungi, bacteria and invertebrates decompose this waste, putting minerals once again into circulation. When the mineral cycle is short-circuited, diverted or broken, the ecosystem is threatened. Much human activity and trade is engaged in short-circuiting and diverting massive amounts of mineral nutrients.

remove the ineffective characteristics and their organic carriers through natural selection. This selection and refining process has produced the incredible living diversity and beauty of life about us. This book is about those systems, of which we are a part.

Scientists of our premier research organisation, the CSIRO, have provided a logical base by which we can organise our travels and discoveries. For ease of reference and categorisation, I have broken down the immensity of the Australian continent into environmentally sensible units. The large geographic divisions (see the map on the following page) will give you an idea of why we have grouped areas into the following habitats:

- oceans;
- forests;
- woodlands;
- scrublands and shrublands;
- heathlands;
- grasslands and herbfields;
- the extremes.

Broadly, on the basis of environmental and ecological factors, these large areas are broken into units that make the planning of discovery tours a simpler and more effective task.

Left and right: Lord Howe Island was created from a volcanic eruption that occurred approximately 7 million years ago. The island's high mountains, Mount Gower (*right*) and Mount Lidgbird (*left*), were once deep down in the core of a giant volcano that had collapsed in on itself. These mountains are all that remains of the deep pool of hard lava that filled the bottom of the pit. Over time, forests formed on the rocky slopes and over two-thirds of the island remains natural forest that includes larger tree species such as Banyan Trees and Kentia Palms.

LEGEND

1. OCEANS

Mangrove forests

2. FORESTS

Tropical rainforest

Subtropical rainforest

Warm-temperate rainforest

Cool-temperate rainforest

Cloud forest

Wet sclerophyll forest

Dry sclerophyll forest

3. TALL AND LOW WOODLANDS

Monsoon & tropical woodlands

Temperate & other eucalypt woodlands

Riverine woodlands

Semi-arid shrub with savanna

Arid & semi-arid low woodlands

4. SHRUBLANDS AND SCRUBLANDS

Mallee

Acacia – Mulga

Acacia – Brigalow

Saltbush/Bluebush

5. HEATHS

Wallum

Temperate

6. GRASSLANDS AND SEDGELANDS

Northern grasslands

Desert grasslands

Temperate grasslands

Cool-temperate grasslands

Cold-climate grasslands & sedgelands

7. EXTREME HABITATS

Alpine herbfields

Salt lakes

Plant Basis for Australian Habitats

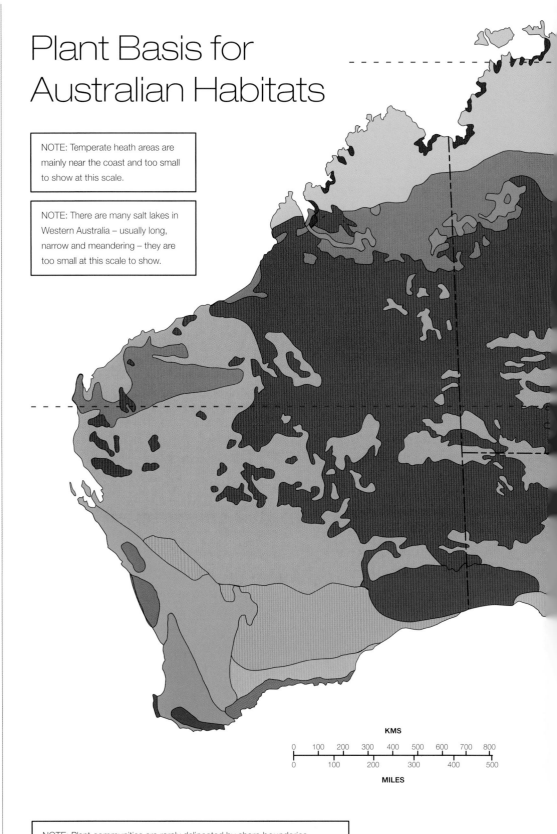

NOTE: Temperate heath areas are mainly near the coast and too small to show at this scale.

NOTE: There are many salt lakes in Western Australia – usually long, narrow and meandering – they are too small at this scale to show.

KMS

| 0 | 100 | 200 | 300 | 400 | 500 | 600 | 700 | 800 |

| 0 | 100 | 200 | 300 | 400 | 500 |

MILES

NOTE: Plant communities are rarely delineated by sharp boundaries. Wildlife also wander across boundaries and find boundary edges to be rich habitats, providing the best shelter as well as diverse food resources. Small-scale maps of this kind should be used as a guide only.

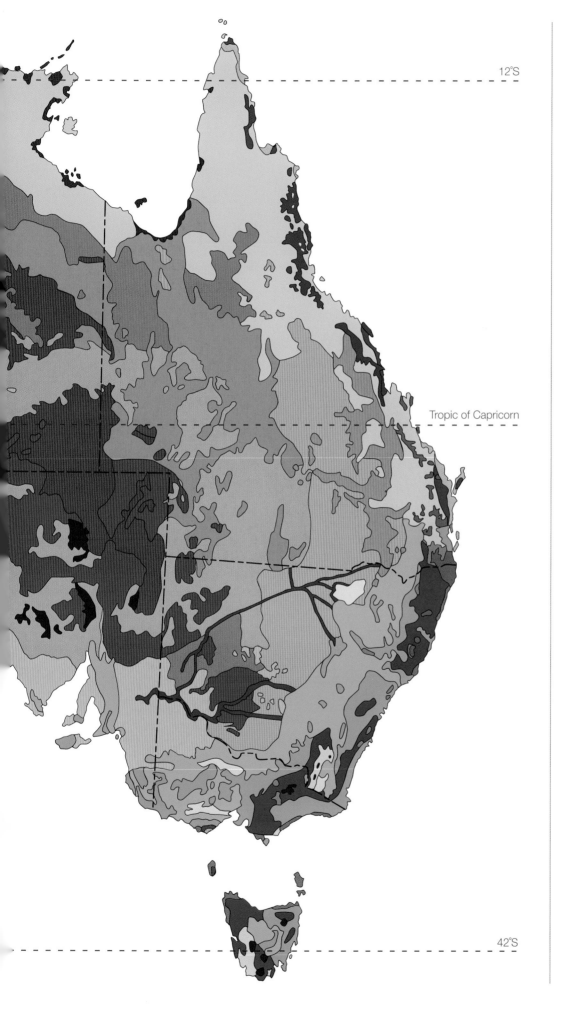

12°S

Tropic of Capricorn

42°S

Australia's Oceanic Connection

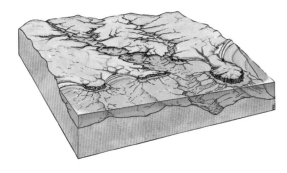

Above: The sea never stays at one level for very long. For about 6000 years the ocean remained at its present level; however, it has now begun to rise. When sea levels rise coastal valleys are flooded, creating new habitats and landscapes. Sydney Harbour, the Derwent River, Moreton Bay and the Swan River are classic examples, all of which have been very useful to humans, both as harbours and delightful coastlines upon which to live. However, rising sea levels may put an end to that as well as destroying and changing older landscapes, wiping out terrestrial vegetation and forcing dependent animal life to move (if it can find suitable habitat nearby) or die out.

Previous pages: The White Shark, a powerful predator, among a school of herbivorous food.

Above: Humans and sealife are inextricably linked. Children are drawn to aquariums and to shoreline rockpools where they can come to appreciate and understand the marine ecosystem.
Right, top to bottom: The rugged Southern Ocean coast of Cape Leeuwin–Naturaliste National Park, WA; spray forms on a wave's crest, Jervis Bay, NSW; Krill, the crustacean staple of the Southern Ocean and the main diet of whales.

Australia's Oceanic Connection

Australia's 200-nautical-mile Exclusive Economic Zone, proclaimed in 1994, is over 11 million square kilometres in area, excluding Antarctic waters, and is the third largest in the world. The total area of the continental shelf around our continent, as defined by the 1982 United Nations Convention on the Law of the Sea, is 14.8 million square kilometres. These waters include a great range of geographic, geologic, oceanographic and biological features and around 12,000 islands … Australia's marine domain is a part of the interconnected world ocean, which covers 71% of the planet. Australia's seas encompass all five of the world's ocean temperature zones: tropical (25–31ºC); subtropical (15–27ºC); temperate (10–25ºC); subpolar (5–10ºC); polar (-2–5ºC)…

"Our Sea, Our Future", State of the Marine Environment Report for Australia (2000).

Somewhere beyond 5 billion years ago, when masses of dust and gaseous elements congealed into fiery, planet-making blobs circling about a massive incandescent globe, our solar system was born.

The most magical density and variety of gases was found in the third planet, Earth, and, from 4.6 billion years ago, gravity compacted this planet's interior, where decaying radioactive elements maintained meltdown. Iron was dragged towards the centre, forming a dense core. Above this core, a blend of lighter elements composed a mantle and a rocky crust, a 5–80 kilometre thick "skin" floating on a scorching, pressurised, viscous "ocean" of magma. Magma frequently broke through the crust of silicates (largely quartz and feldspar), and rose as volcanoes and huge rifts that released lava and vast chimneys of steam. Bombarded with icy comets and shrouded in thousands of metres of "volcanic" rain cloud, the Earth's lowlands flooded, producing the first oceans, which gradually accumulated salts from the eroding crust.

COSMIC CONTRIBUTORS TO OCEAN LIFE

By 3.8 billion years ago, life, in the form of micro-organisms, had begun to evolve in the Earth's warm oceanic soup. A by-product of the existence of these simple life forms, largely cyanobacteria and algae, was the build-up of oxygen in the atmosphere — a build-up that was instrumental in the development of all species living today. Early species required very little oxygen, but today we can only be nurtured in an atmosphere containing around 20% oxygen. In the stratosphere, 15–50 kilometres above the Earth, ultraviolet light in sunlight converts oxygen into ozone gas, which absorbs ultraviolet radiation and shields the planet.

Four planetary circumstances dramatically affect the ocean, the atmosphere, and the species that live within them. First, the Earth spins on an axis, taking 24 hours to complete the cycle of daylight and darkness. Second, the planet circles the sun in approximately 365 days; linked to this is the third circumstance — the Earth's axis is tilted 23.5º, producing the four seasons. Fourth, the gravity of the moon circling the Earth drags the oceans into low and high tides on a regular basis.

Above: Manta Rays, gentle giants of the deep, are found throughout the world's tropical oceans.

Because the sun's light and heat strike equatorial regions directly, with only a "glancing blow" on polar regions, the oceans and atmospheric conditions of equatorial regions are hotter. The air in these places expands, grows less dense and lighter and consequently rises. Air pressure is lessened. North and south of this low-pressure belt lies cooler, denser and therefore high-pressure air, which pushes into the tropical low-pressure area.

WINDS, WAVES AND CURRENTS

Moving air is wind, and as the Earth rotates wind is pushed towards the west. In the Australian mid-summer, the sun is directly over the Tropic of Capricorn (running through Rockhampton, Alice Springs, Newman and Coral Bay). The north-west monsoon blows in to northern Australia's low-pressure belt, while the south-easterly winds remain far to the south.

In mid-winter, the sun is almost directly above Karachi and Hong Kong. Winter is northern Australia's dry season, when the South-East Trade Winds blow northwards across the Tasman, Arafura, Timor and Coral Seas, and the Indian Ocean towards India. These winds drain pressure from the southern mid-latitudes, which have their air pressure replenished by the Roaring Forties (westerlies that continuously circle the planet). The winds' energy creates surface wave systems across the seas and oceans — waves that build in magnitude as the distance travelled (wind's fetch) increases. The cold, circumpolar Roaring Forties and Fifties down south have the longest fetch, producing the wildest seas, particularly where they whistle past Cape Horn.

Varying water depths and exposure to the sun's energy over time have rendered oceans a massive heat sink that moderates the planet's climate. The spin of the Earth and its atmospheric winds, along with heat-generated water convection movements, govern the worldwide circulation of ocean currents and their regional eddying effects in response to land masses and water depths. Around this continent, the East Australian Current pushes warm tropical waters (at a magnitude of 30 million cubic metres a second!) down the east coast — acting as a great conveyor belt for warm-water organisms that have colonised southern reefs, such as those of Lord Howe Island in New South Wales. The weaker Leeuwin

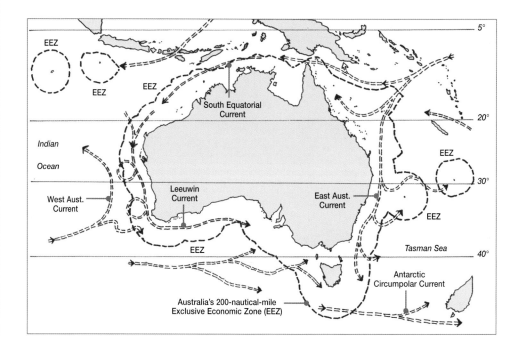

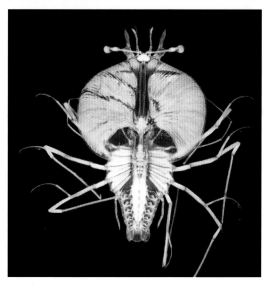

Clockwise from top: Reefs around Basile Island, in the Houtman Abrolhos group, are warmed by the south-flowing Leeuwin Current; Western Rock Lobsters rely on warm waters for their life cycle; lobster larvae suffer high mortality during El Niño years; Australian Sea-lions at the northernmost limits of their range in the Houtman Abrolhos Islands.

Current is a similar force that ferries warm water down the Western Australian Coast, feeding the reefs of Ningaloo and the Houtman Abrolhos Islands, where rock lobster larvae (among other marine species) begin their life cycle.

The most dramatic indicator of the ocean as climate regulator is El Niño. In normal years, the Pacific Peruvian waters drift west to Indonesia and New Guinea, feeding the monsoon with increased moisture to water Australia. In an El Niño year, warm surface currents move eastward, away from Australia, causing storms in the central Pacific and drought in Australia. Ocean currents are an arterial system, keeping waters mixed in temperature and salinity. Without this circulation, the waters would stratify out into a permanent, deep layer of icy, dense and almost lifeless super-nutrient-rich water, upon which would lie a brackish soup.

Above: An ocean's nutrient value is enhanced by the leaching of minerals from eroding rock, such as the pillars of the Twelve Apostles in Port Campbell National Park, Victoria.
Right: A school of pelagic fish form a dense circle in the tropical waters of the Great Barrier Reef.

Where Are They? The island continent of Australia straddles the Tropic of Capricorn (23.5°S). This location ensures that northern surrounding waters are a warm body maintained by the South Equatorial Current, while southern oceans are continuously cooled by the Antarctic Circumpolar Current. The south-flowing East Australian Current and the Leeuwin Current of the west mix these water bodies producing a warm-temperate mass between about 30°S and 45°S.

What Do They Look Like? Deep green and blue waters with surface wave systems (swell) that reflect local and distant weather conditions. These are typically tropical waters affected by the winter South-East Trade Winds and summer north-west monsoon, with periods of intense cyclonic disturbance from December to April. Southern temperate waters are affected by easterly moving weather fronts and, south of 35°S, by prevailing westerly winds with violent incursions from further south during winter.

Critical Conditions: Habitat requirements differ for sealife species according to the following variables: water turbidity, chemical (nutrient) content, dissolved oxygen, water temperature, depth, daylight penetration, water pressure, and water turnover and renewal.

What Are the Threats? Australia's oceans, like all oceans, either benefit or suffer from residues dissolved in waters running from the land. Increased use of agricultural and industrial pollutants, along with rising global temperatures and over-fishing of large predaceous fishes and invertebrates, threatens oceanic ecosystems. River systems also experience build-up of clay muds as well as sand, hindering flow to the oceans.

Warm-temperate and Tropical Oceans

HABITAT AND BIODIVERSITY

Oceans have supported life for millennia, possibly longer than any other habitat, allowing time for marine environments to become populated by life forms that have adapted to suit rigorous environmental conditions. In the oceanic water column, life is arranged in layers, depending upon light penetration, water temperature, nutrients and the availability of oxygen and pressure. The warm-temperate and tropical water masses that wash western, northern and eastern Australia are generally low in nutrients. No major pockets of nutrient-rich deep waters exist there and the run-off from the ancient, leached land is low in nutritional content, limiting biodiversity. Paradoxically, tropical inshore waters, dominated by highly productive mangroves, seagrass and coral communities, experience a greater level of biodiversity because resident plants and animals have become highly adapted to low nutrient levels. Surprisingly, at the sustainable productivity level, the cool-temperate waters of Australia's south are much more productive than tropical waters.

Habitat diversity is, quite obviously, dependent on an ocean's geography. Australia's narrow continental shelf — the outer shelf of which begins its plunge to abyssal depths of 4000 metres or more from a depth about 150 metres — covers approximately 2.5 million square kilometres. Covered by layers of alluvial sediment, sand and shell debris that is broken at irregular intervals by reefs of continental rock, extinct volcanic forms (known as seamounts) and marine canyons, the continental shelf provides a substrate environment that is critical to the survival of a multitude of invertebrate species. The archetypal example of this complex oceanography is situated 100 kilometres south of Tasmania; here, in 1000 metres of water, a 35 square kilometre area is covered by about 50 conical seamounts that average 200 metres in height. An abundance of invertebrate life, such as plant and animal plankton, worms, sponges and crustaceans, occupies this territory, which is also the principal habitat of the Patagonian Toothfish (*Dissostichus eleginoides*), and Orange Roughy (*Hoplostethus atlanticus*).

Like that other highly diverse ecosystem, the tropical rainforest, oceanic habitats and their incredible diversity of organisms utilise the majority of the system's nutrients, leaving the ecosystem highly vulnerable to any major disturbance that may remove sections of this living nutrient bank.

THE MARINE WEB OF LIFE

Only 3.5 billion years of evolution, and endless adaptive experiments in form and behaviour, could have fashioned such a complex, interwoven web of organisms! Like terrestrial habitats, marine ecosystems are built upon tiny plants. Marine flora, like its land-based cousins, uses chlorophyll to convert the sun's energy into organic energy, which is used to assemble living tissue from nitrogen, phosphorous and silica in seawater, coupled with the "building blocks" of life — carbon, oxygen and hydrogen. Other essential elements, some in minute quantities, are

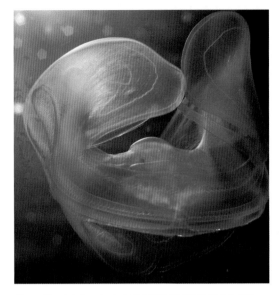

Above: Comb jellies, such as this Venus's Girdle Comb Jelly, may resemble sea jellies but they are actually dissimilar enough to warrant their own phylum, Ctenophora. These luminous ocean denizens are not equipped with stinging nematocysts but use their sticky tentacles to trap their prey.

Organisms of the Temperate and Tropical Oceans

Warm seawater was the "soup" in which most life on our planet had its foundation. From this matter, over hundreds of millions of years, a green algae (plant plankton) evolved — a plant that lived together with a green bacteria, and that, in their combined living, produced the gas oxygen, which changed the atmosphere and allowed more complex life to develop. These more complex organisms went on to colonise the planet as we see it today — our incredible "blue planet" of life.

Classic Plants: Phytoplankton (diatoms, dinoflagelates and nanoplankton); algae such as *Sargassum* spp.

Classic Prey: Zooplankton (herbivorous and carnivorous species, protozoans and larval stages of invertebrates and fishes).

Classic Fishes: Albacore; Barracuda; Bonito; Cobia; Yellowtail Kingfish: Shark Mackerel; Spanish Mackerel; Black Trevally; Big-eye Trevally; Teraglin; tuna (various spp.); Wahoo; marlin; sailfish; Bronze Whaler shark; Tiger Shark.

Classic Mammals: Killer Whale; Sperm Whale; Pilot Whale; Bottlenose Dolphin; Common Dolphin; Long-snouted Spinner Dolphin; Striped Dolphin.

Right: Whale Sharks, the world's largest fish, survive on a diet made up of some of the oceans' smallest residents, including small fishes that float with the zooplankton. They are true residents of the open ocean and, consequently, little is known of their lifestyles. The annual migration of Whale Sharks to the warm, sustaining waters of Ningaloo Reef, Western Australia, is helping marine biologists learn more about these vulnerable, migratory behemoths.

also required for the health of these "pastures of the sea": micronutrients, vitamin B12 (particularly in spring by diatoms), iron, copper, selenium and manganese. In upper sunlit waters, phytoplankton rapidly deplete the water's nutrients. Unless sustenance is replenished by in-flowing waters, upwellings, input from the land's rivers or the recycling processes of the ecosystem, the glut of underwater plants rapidly becomes a famine. In deeper, darker waters, the lack of light keeps populations of diatoms at a low level, but their role is supplemented by other tiny producers — dinoflagellates, which have miniature, whip-like tails that power them along. These exquisite, microscopic swimmers can move towards the surface during the day to increase their exposure to light. Overall, there is much less production in these deeper, darker waters. Countless larger (but still tiny) animal plankton, called zooplankton, graze on the phytoplankton. In turn, they are devoured by other carnivorous zooplankton, including hydroids, sea stars, gastropods and crustacean larvae. Krill, the larger consumer of phyto- and zooplankton, frequently forms immense masses, particularly in Antarctic waters.

Swimming among the larger zooplankton (although still less than 1 centimetre long!) are massed populations of fishes and larger crustaceans, the result of prolific egg-laying by adults. Here, nature experiences a "Catch 22". For fishes, crustaceans and other marine animals, laying vast quantities of eggs (usually in late spring–early summer when the zooplankton is at its richest) is insurance: hopefully, some will survive the gauntlet of predators. However, with prolific egg-laying comes risk. Shortly after massed hatching, competition for food between siblings may deplete the zooplankton food source, leaving most of the hatchlings easy pickings for other predators. Regardless, some do survive their first few days and join the predatory herds of plankton to drift with the flow of current and wind-driven waves. Just how vital a resource plankton is can be illustrated by the dietary requirements of just one of the largest of the zooplankton: the sea jelly. A single sea jelly can clear zooplankton from several cubic metres of water in just one hour!

There is no escaping the rules of predation — they apply equally to larger pelagic (surface-living), bony and cartilaginous fish, and even to birds and mammals. This aquatic, "tooth and claw" microscopic world is every bit as violent as the Serengeti. Thus, schools of silvery pilchards and sardines follow and feed off streams of plankton, themselves attracting larger predators, such as tuna, which must consume 25% of their body weight each day to maintain their activity and growth. If a school gets too big, the challenge is in finding an adequate food supply. Larger (but fewer) predators prey on tuna, including dolphins, Bronze Whaler, Mako and

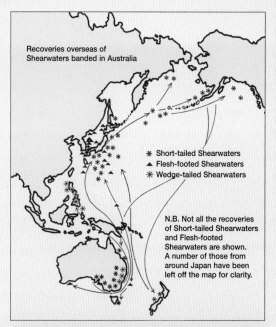

Recoveries overseas of Shearwaters banded in Australia

* Short-tailed Shearwaters
▲ Flesh-footed Shearwaters
※ Wedge-tailed Shearwaters

N.B. Not all the recoveries of Short-tailed Shearwaters and Flesh-footed Shearwaters are shown. A number of those from around Japan have been left off the map for clarity.

Above, top to bottom: A dense school of anchovies comes under sudden attack by plunge-diving Wedge-tailed Shearwaters; the coral cay of Heron Island, on the southern Great Barrier Reef, Queensland, provides important nesting sites for these birds. *Right, top to bottom:* Shearwater species are remarkably well travelled — this map shows the extent of their range; Wedge-tailed Shearwaters courting on Heron Island, Tropical North Queensland.

The Short-tailed Shearwater — an Amazing Oceanic Wanderer

A few years back, during early October, I was sitting on Osprey Lookout in the Nadgee Nature Reserve searching the sea for the last of the Humpback Whales migrating back to Antarctic waters. Soon I became aware of dark clouds of large birds leap-frogging their way over the sea. They would alight in "rafts" upon the water, feeding, then, as they were passed by others, taking off and with a fluttering flight dropping ahead of the raft. I began to count one such nearby raft of birds and finally came up with 900. There was a vast "river" of bird rafts slowly leap-frogging their way southwards. After counting over 100 such groups, I realised that this procession was never-ending. Many squid, small fishes and crustaceans were eaten that day — and the next — and so on for four more days.

The birds were the long-winged, sooty grey Short-tailed Shearwaters, rebuilding their energy supplies after their incredible trans-Pacific flight from Alaskan sub-Arctic summer feeding and moulting areas 12,000 kilometres away! Since the third week in September they had returned to their nesting areas on a sandy Bass Strait island, cleaned out their nesting burrows, then flown out to sea to feed and build up their condition to allow their eggs to develop. During the last ten days of October the bird pairs will return to their familiar nesting burrow to lay an egg, which hatches after nearly two months. Over the next three months, the chick becomes heavier than the parents. When the parents desert the chick to begin their extraordinary flight across the western Pacific to the Bering Sea, the chick fasts until it has slimmed down to flying fitness. Without parental guidance, it too heads northwards, along with millions of its young cousins, towards the Bering Sea — a remarkable journey! Aborigines and European settlers took hundreds of thousands of these unprotected chicks as culinary delights.

Birds of the Temperate and Tropical Oceans

The distribution and local abundance of sea birds depends upon the interaction of surface water zonation, abundance of food and habitat space preferences. The amount and type of food available to birds in an area is related, in an indirect fashion, to the concentration of nutrient salts (mostly phosphates and nitrates) dissolved in the water. The nutrients are taken up by microscopic plant and animal plankton, which, in turn, are consumed by larger invertebrates and fishes, creating the food chain.

Classic Birds: Black-winged Petrel; Wedge-tailed Shearwater; Flesh-footed Shearwater; Sooty Shearwater; Short-tailed Shearwater; Streaked Shearwater; Little Shearwater; Southern Giant Petrel; Northern Giant Petrel; Sooty Albatross; Wandering Albatross; Royal Albatross; Black-browed Albatross; Yellow-nosed Albatross (race *bassi*); Shy Albatross (race *cauta*); Common Diving-Petrel; Wilson's Storm-Petrel; White-faced Storm-Petrel; Red-tailed Tropicbird; Masked Booby; Red-footed Booby; Brown Booby; Great Frigatebird; Lesser Frigatebird; Crested Tern; White-fronted Tern; Arctic Tern; White Tern; Bridled Tern; Noddies.

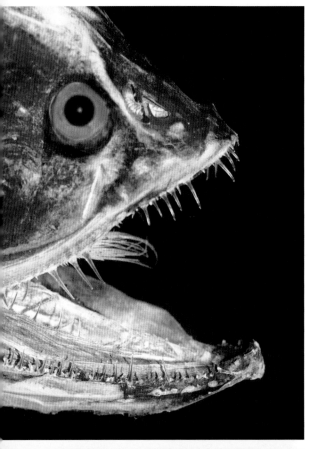

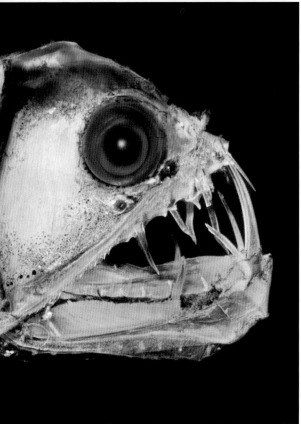

Tiger Sharks. The giant Whale Shark, which annually visits hunting grounds off Ningaloo Reef, Western Australia, feeds by sifting zooplankton from huge volumes of water funnelled through its colossal mouth. The Whale Shark's huge shadowy bulk is rendered almost invisible due to its beautiful, speckled blue pattern and smooth gliding motion, which allows for a surprise attack on masses of plankton.

Baleen whales, such as Humpbacks and Southern Right Whales, spend summer in the Krill-rich waters of the Antarctic, where they build up fat reserves by consuming 4–8 tonnes of Krill each day. The latent energy stored in Krill-built fat fuels their annual winter migration to the warmer southern, western and eastern shelf waters of Australia, where they will mate and birth their young. These gentle, migratory giants appear off the Australian coast from May to August and depart for their Antarctic home from September to December. Migratory sea mammals, and the violent whaling history attached to them, provide perhaps the most dramatic reminder that effective management of the oceans, and their vulnerable species, is an international responsibility. Humans worldwide must respect and conserve these continuously flowing, living resources that lap all continents.

STRATEGIES FOR SURVIVING THE HIGH SEAS

The sea's surface, ruffled by waves and refreshed by currents, is an interface penetrated from above by air-breathing, marine-organism-fed birds, seals, turtles and reptiles. Beneath the surface lies a top layer of sunlit waters, stretching down 50–100 metres (the depth of the majority of the continental shelf) and gradually dimming at its deepest reach. Massive loads of plankton (albeit patchy), sardines, pilchards, herring, tuna, shark, marlin and the like frequent these surface "larders".

Inhabitants of this teeming world have adopted novel ways of keeping themselves buoyant and close to the surface, with its riches of food and energy. These include diminutiveness, air bags (Portuguese Man-o-War); jelly (sea jellies); and foam (cuttlefish). Counteracting their vulnerability in the light, comes an assortment of behaviours, speed, form, colour and transparency — even the ability to change hue and pattern. Ironically, larger predators of these small, stealthy creatures also need subterfuge. Dolphins, Bronze Whalers, Makos and Tiger Sharks use colouration not for protection but for discretion — to avoid discovery by their prey. Counter-shading is the most common strategy. Seen from above, brownish, bluish-grey or barred colouring resembles the dappled light of sun streaking the water; when observed from below, white undersides match the brightness of the water's surface.

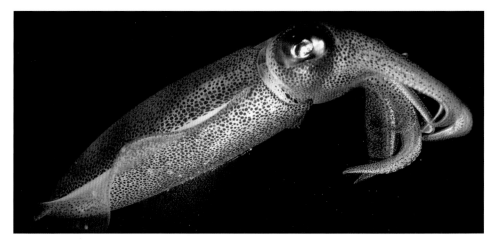

Above: Squid have adapted a remarkable method of avoiding predation. Like many Cephalopods, they are able to change their body colouring and patterns rapidly to camouflage themselves to their surroundings. If that fails to deter predators, they release a cloud of obscuring ink to mask their getaway.

Above, top to bottom: Deepsea Fangjaw (*Gonostoma bathyphilum*); Sloane's Viperfish (*Chauliodus sloani*). The ocean depths inspire a bizarre collection of deepwater dwellers with modified features that enable them to withstand limited light.

Above: Sperm Whales (females are pictured here with a calf in tow), are the largest of the toothed whales. Preferring temperate waters to the tropics, they are commonly seen in deep offshore waters around Australia. Pods infrequently venture into shallower waters and often strand if they do. *Right:* Sharks patrol the submarine world.

On the dimly lit continental shelf live burrowers, worms and wandering shellfish, such as scallops and crustaceans. Here, too, are sedentary adult sea pens, corals, and sponges, as well as the specialised fishes that feed on these animals.

The darker, "twilight zone" of colder waters, down to depths of 1000 metres, is the haunt of metallic, compressed-bodied, big-eyed, huge-jawed monsters of the fish world, many with their own light-emitting organs called photophores. Hatchetfish, slim-bodied lancetfish, needle-toothed viperfish and fangjaws, along with other grotesque creatures (at least to our unaccustomed eyes), reside here and are beautifully adapted to living and hunting in perpetual darkness. Other inhabitants of the depths are those that can withstand great pressure changes when swimming either towards or away from the surface, such as squid, cuttlefish and the Sperm Whale. Buoyancy regulation is achieved by the use of air-filled swim bladders, oil-saturated organs (such as the liver in sharks and flesh of mackerel and Bonito) or by fat storage (particularly blubber in sea mammals).

Deeper still are even more extreme and bizarre adaptations. In a pitch-black abyss of immense pressure, dense saltwater and intense cold, far offshore near the mid-ocean rifts and ridges, are the volcanic "black smokers". In constant night, these special habitats are heated by hydrothermal vents and "smoking" clouds of minerals that provide the chemical energy to maintain life in the absence of sunlight and photosynthesis. These very exclusive communities exist oblivious to the sunlit world above, but nevertheless obey the universal rules of ecology.

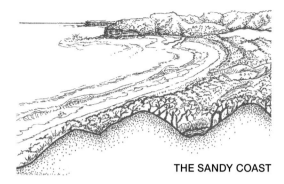

THE SANDY COAST

Where Are They? Beach and dune communities fill the gaps between the rocky headlands of the coast. Back-beach dunes are built and shaped by onshore winds working on beach sands.

What Do They Look Like? Sweeping sandy coastlines smoothed by the long-shore currents and constant turbulence of the waves. Along the east coast, the main ocean current (East Australian) flows southwards, causing the south end of the beach to curve sharply against the headland; hence the smallest sand grains are on a headland's southern extent.

Critical Conditions: Beaches are affected by storms, sea level and waves. Dunes are shaped by wind, sand supply, salt and fire.

Best Examples: *Vic* — Ninety Mile Beach (Gippsland). *WA* — Eighty Mile Beach (south of Broome). *SA* — Head of Bight (Yalata) and Coorong Beach are the longest, but can be as short as 100 m.

What Are the Threats? Build-up by river-carrying clay muds and sand. Immediate threats to the beach are from beach mining and from other coastal developments that cause instability of the frontal dune, such as from resort and urban development. Ultimately, beach processes are indestructible and so in the long term unsuitable development will be destroyed by nature.

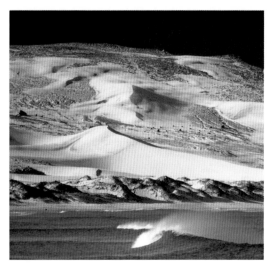

Above: Dunes of snow-white silicates meet the ocean off Fitzgerald River National Park, WA. *Right:* Lighthouse Beach, protected by the headland of Sugarloaf Point, NSW.

Beach and Coastal Dune Communities

Land this morn very sandy. We could see through our glasses that the sands which lay in great patches of many acres each were moveable; some of them had been lately moved, for trees which stood up in the middle of them were quite green, others of a longer standing had many stumps sticking out of them which had been trees killed by the sand heaping about their roots. Few fires were seen. Two water snakes swam by the ship; they were in all respects like land snakes and beautifully spotted except that they had broad flat tails …

Joseph Banks, off the Fraser Island coast, 18 May 1770.

Beaches are what mountains are destined to become. As soon as land is thrust upwards above the oceans and exposed to the elements and the atmosphere, weathering and erosion begin. Loose fragments of rock (usually silica in the form of quartz grains), if not dissolved in run-off water, are ultimately transported by rivers or wind to the sea, where they mix with shoreline rock particles and the pulverised calcium carbonate of shells, bones and corals. Concentrated and conveyed by waves and the shoreline currents of tumultuous seas, they form coastal beaches and dunes.

Australia's tropical coasts are generally calm, with the exception of the period from December to April, when powerful cyclones and hurricane-force winds can whip up wild seas and cause storm surges. At these times, brief as they are, vast coastal changes can occur. In tempestuous times, fringing and offshore reefs, beaches and (on muddier coastlines) mangrove forests, act as shock absorbers for the pounding seas. On Australia's "soft" southern coasts, only the beaches and frontal dunes protect the country behind; there, on the sloping, absorbing beach, wave energy is dissipated. During high seas, destructive turbulent water sweeps far up the beach, cuts into the dune barrier and drags sand offshore. After the storm, when waves become lower and more widely spaced, the sea slowly pushes the lost sand back onto the beach, where it will again settle. The slower, sand-returning waves will, on the way to shore, collect into channels and scour out deep courses or "rips", leaving sandflats between the channels. Such sea-floor geography, which evolves between periods of high seas, provides a much richer habitat for marine organisms — pipis, worms, whiting and flathead on the flats; Tailor, Mulloway, Australian Salmon and large predaceous fishes in the trenches and channels. Tide levels and wave turbulence determine the use of these offshore waters by marine species.

Onshore winds at low tidal levels move freshly accumulated dry sands to form back-beach sand dunes. The shape of a continent, composed by its country rock in conjunction with the rise and fall of sea level (as has occurred many times over the past millennium alone), can dramatically affect the supply of sands for coastal dune formation. The world's highest coastal dunes are on Fraser Island in Great Sandy National Park, Queensland. The island's location — on the far eastern continental edge, rising off a wide, sand-covered continental shelf — meant that when sea levels dropped (falling, for instance, 120 metres around 20,000 years ago) a vast source of available sand was blown by the South-East Trade Winds into huge dunes. As sea levels rose or fell over time, further dunes (or barriers if you like) were built upon older dune systems. As Joseph Banks observed, the dunes

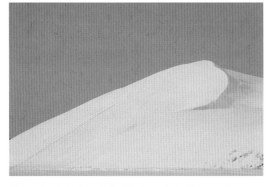

Above, top to bottom: Lake Wabby and the Hammerstone sand blow, Fraser Island, Queensland; destructive storm wave on Nadgee Beach, New South Wales; enormous, shifting sand dunes change the face of Fraser Island over time.

Best Examples: *Qld* — Stradbroke Island; Fraser Island. *NSW* — Myall Lakes National Park. *Vic* — Cape Howe; Croajingolong; Point Hicks; Ninety Mile Beach. *Tas* — Wineglass Bay (Freycinet National Park); Henty Dunes (Strahan); Bay of Fires. *SA* — The Coorong. *WA* — Eighty Mile Beach.

Sounds: Clamour of the sea; cries of sea birds.

Smells: Salt smell of the sea; decaying flotsam (seaweed and cunjevoi); musty sea bird guano in nesting areas.

Sensations: Sting of sand blast; cold water.

Right: Sparse vegetation knits together dunes in South Australia. *Opposite, top to bottom:* Low-growing shrubs are best-suited to this sandy, salty, vertiginous environment; Pandanus trees are common colonisers of beach dunes, seen here on Heron Island, Qld; red soil contrasts with the sapphire sea of Shark Bay, WA.

were unstable and "movable", particularly if bushfires had removed the supporting vegetative cover. Transient, shifting sands are highly susceptible to wind erosion, often causing bare patches or "blows". Erosion that occurred on Fraser Island during drought sometimes removed sands from land below the normal water table. Consequently, when normal rainfalls resumed, these depressions formed freshwater soaks, swamps and lakes known as "window lakes". "Barrage lakes", such as Lake Wabby, formed when shifting dunes moved across watercourses. When lagoon bottoms became sealed and hardened by built-up organic oils and matter from decaying vegetation, "perched lakes" formed. Fraser Island is Australia's best example of these communities, but other massive dunes, with incredibly steep, vegetated slopes, occur along the Croajingolong coast behind Point Hicks, Victoria. These were built from sands blown in by prevailing south-westerlies off a much wider continental shelf at the eastern end of Bass Strait.

Apart from the coastline fronting the Gulf of Carpentaria, Australia's northern seacoast from Broome in Western Australia stretching around to the southern end of the Great Barrier Reef in Queensland, does not have dune development on the grand scale of that further south. These environments are better suited to mangrove forest and mudflat development (discussed at length in later chapters) because of the subdued seas (cyclones aside!) and the mud generated by river systems that carry large loads of wet-season sediment along the coast.

In the Introduction, colonisation of coastal dunes, such as those of Croajingolong, was described in detail. The early phases of the colonisation process remain the same around the continent. So, in south-west Australia the primary colonisers of harsh coastal and dune environments will be similar species to those of the east coast. When the colony becomes stable, the species begin to vary from west to east and from temperate to tropical environments. Even then, they will, in most cases, have evolved a similar structure in order to adapt to the similar conditions; however, having been born from separate ancestors their similarities will be more akin to cousins than to siblings. Successive plant and animal inhabitants produce more-complex communities as the dunes age. In the south-east, the "classic" wallaby may be the Swamp Wallaby; in the west, the Quokka fulfils a similar role. In the east we find the Eastern Quoll, which is matched in the south-west by the Western Quoll, and the Northern Quoll in the tropics. Coast Banksia (*Banksia integrifolia*) vegetates the south-east, with Cutleaf Banksia (*Banksia praemorsa*) and *Dryandra* spp. in the west. Bird species are somewhat of an exception, being infinitely more mobile, with numerous species able to cross the continent.

A Sand-mining Story

The 1500 kilometres of coast from Sydney to Fraser Island contains beaches that are more than silica sand. Like all beaches, their sands have come from the decay of inland mountains. It is believed that the granite rock of the New England region and younger rocks towards Rockhampton carried the heavy minerals rutile, zircon, ilmenite and monazite. For the past 200 million years or more these minerals have been eroded from the mountains and washed down the streams, and long-shore currents have spread them along the beaches.

Being very much heavier than silica sand, these sands were winnowed out by wave, current and wind action into thick layers of black sands that we find in the beaches. Back in 1870, gold was also discovered mixed in these heavy layers — so the sand-mining industry for gold, platinum and tin began. The richest areas were quickly worked out. Then, in 1925, black rutile sand and ore of titanium and zircon were discovered. The first titanium mining began in earnest in 1933 at Byron Bay, but the real value of titanium was only acknowledged during World War II, when strong, light metal was required for jet engines, rocket parts, atomic reactors and even spectacle frames. When lead oxides (primarily in lead-based paint) were found to be deadly if ingested, titanium oxide became the new white-base pigment. The scramble to mine the beaches began and soon Australia was producing 90% of the world's supply.

The mining process was first to find the ore bodies that were usually in the beach and dunes. Then the scrub and forest was dozed and burned. The topsoil was dozed into great stockpiles, as it held a rich seed store and nutrients. A great hole was dug to the water table, then a massive dredge floated on top. Using a couple of giant sand and water pumps, the dredge dragged itself forwards devouring the dune in front. Within the dredge, the heavy mineral was separated and the waste sand and water sprayed onto the dune behind (see picture opposite). Bulldozers reformed the dune shape and spread the stockpile of topsoil over the top. Mats of brush and fertiliser were laid on top to stop erosion so that, in theory, the surface would regrow. However, the dunes were never to return to their natural condition, although it sometimes appears that way. Fortunately, many fine national parks, such as Fraser Island and Myall Lakes National Parks, were established before all of these beaches were irrevocably altered.

Left, top to bottom: "Model" dunes of coarse sand on a large dune blowout behind Point Hicks, Victoria; perched dunes on the top of the Zuytdorp Cliffs, Zuytdorp National Park, Western Australia. *Below:* Massive blowouts engulfing forests on Fraser Island, Queensland.

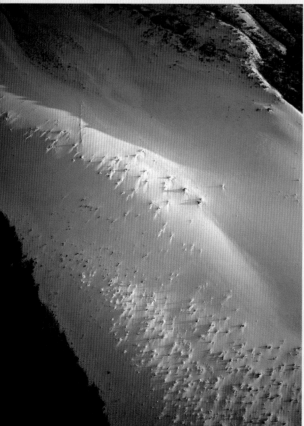

Above, clockwise from top left: Rutile and zircon sand-mining dredge, near Lake Macquarie, New South Wales; the great dunes of Cape Howe, on the New South Wales–Victoria border, regularly change their shape; the dune field behind Shelburne Bay on Cape York, Queensland, is a source of pure silica for computer chips.

Above, top to bottom: Tropical perennial Beach Morning Glory, (*Ipomoea pes-caprae*), growing on the Cobourg Peninsula, Northern Territory; Beach Spinifex on Fitzgerald River Beach, Western Australia.

Plants of the Beaches and Coastal Dunes

Plants of this habitat must counter difficulties such as high exposure to wind; loose, porous "soil"; extreme solar radiation levels (including UV, heat and intense light); flooding by seawater or by intense freshwater rain; and high salinity. Sand blast can potentially shred soft tissue. Pioneer plants of this habitat are those that can draw on resources far from the high tide levels. Beach or Coastal Spinifex is the classic form, with extremely long runners that have many growth points at nodes, which can begin to grow roots if buried. Seeds are in large globular masses and are admirably suited to dispersal by the strong onshore winds.

Classic Plants: Coastal Spinifex; Marram Grass; Festuca; Beach Morning Glory (*Ipomoea pes-caprae*); Sea Rocket; Pennywort; Scaevola Fanflower (various spp.); Pigface; Coastal Wattle; Beach She-oak; Coast Tea-tree; Coast Banksia; Moonah Paperbark; Iron Grass, *Lomandra* sp.

Tracks and Travels

Six of the world's seven species of marine turtles frequent Australian waters. Loggerhead, Green and Hawksbill Turtles come ashore at Heron Island. The huge Leatherback visits Sydney's Middle Harbour and Broken Bay. The smallest species, the Olive Ridley, along with the only turtle restricted to Australian waters, the Flatback Turtle, nest on Bare Sand Island near Darwin.

My most vivid memory of these gentle giants was on the northern beach of the Lacepede Island Nature Reserve, about 150 kilometres north of Broome in Western Australia. Approaching the beach we noticed dozens of "bulldozer-like" tracks running up the beach (see the photo opposite), before numerous near-shore disturbances became obvious. The breeding season was in full swing. At times there were as many as three male Green Turtles fighting to mount a single female! The unfortunate females were having great difficulty in slipping a breath in before being sunk by yet another male. A number of exhausted females were resting in the beach swash, but would not attempt to clamber up the beach in daylight — that would be done sometime later during an evening high tide.

The frontal dune above the beach resembled a battlefield, its surface pitted with hundreds of nesting hollows. Many of these shallow hollows were real nests, but many others were employed simply as decoy holes. Later, while walking the beach, we noted not only the massive tracks of adults but the unmistakable tracks of hand-sized, miniature baby turtles fanning out from pits within the nests.

There were other tracks too — various herons, Jabiru, Beach Stone-curlews and numerous gulls, terns and crabs. Hovering above, with long black wings and forked tails, were hundreds of "pirates" of the air, the Lesser Frigatebirds, cruising above graceful Brown Boobies. The occasional pecked-out soft shell of a tiny turtle hatchling is a reminder of just how unlikely making it to the sea really is, especially when predators await. Perhaps just 5% of each nest of around 50–100 eggs would ultimately reach adulthood and breeding condition 30 years later. What happens to the sea turtles during those 30 years remains largely a mystery. One thing scientists do know is that female turtles make incredible migrations, sometimes many thousands of kilometres, back to what is thought to be the beach of their birth, to breed and lay their eggs.

Classic Organisms: *Wet beach:* Sea Worm; Pipi; Soldier Crab; Crested Tern; Silver Gull; Little Stint and numerous migratory waders. *Dry beach:* Sand Hopper; Shore Slater; fly larvae; Ghost Crab; Red-capped Plover; pipits; Masked Plover; Beach Stone-curlew; Little Raven; White-bellied Sea-Eagle. *Frontal dune:* Grasshoppers; cockroaches; millipedes; ants; Golden Web Spinner; Noisy Friarbird; Yellow-faced Honeyeater; Tawny-crowned Honeyeater; New Holland Honeyeater; White-fronted Chat; Brush Bronzewing Pigeon; Eastern Whipbird; Little Penguin (nesting); Swamp Harrier; Nankeen Kestrel; Flecked Garden Sunskinks; Lace Monitor; Ground Gecko (Eastern Australia); Diamond Python; Bush Rat; Swamp Wallaby; Quokka; Agile Wallaby; Common Ringtail Possum; Eastern Quoll (Tasmania); Western Quoll; Northern Quoll; Dingo.

Above: Pied Oystercatchers are often seen foraging for pipis and other bivalves near the tideline on the beaches of Fraser Island, Queensland.

Above, clockwise from top left: Crested Terns are among the most common avian species of the coastal waters; Agile Wallabies of the woodlands and monsoon forests regularly feed on tropical beach grasses; Red-capped Plovers can be found around sheltered beaches and coastal estuaries but also make their homes around salt lakes and brackish watercourses; Australian Sea-lions frolic at Seal Bay, Kangaroo Island, South Australia; a female Green Turtle returns to the sea after laying eggs on Heron Island in Queensland; Ghost Crab at Kakadu, Northern Territory.

Above: Crevices and rockpools on Australia's rocky coasts are prime habitat for numerous invertebrate species and crustaceans. Animals that dwell in this intertidal zone require shelter from intense sun, predators and pounding surf.

Where Are They? Wherever coastal ridges of country rock run, or once ran, to the sea's edge.

What Do They Look Like? The rocky headlands and cliffs have their softer parts etched out, revealing the structure of the rocks and the land's geology. Different rock types produce differently shaped shorelines and reefs. Granite creates rounded surfaces and spherical "tors". Horizontal sandstone with shale beds produces vertical cliffs and flat tidal platforms with deep rifts. Slates, and other metamorphosed folded rock, forms jagged, broken cliffs and fold-shaped sea caves. Volcanic beds and flows lead to terraced cliffs, columnar formations and boulder beaches.

Critical Conditions: Coastal rock formation is dependent on the degree of exposure to high-energy seas, light penetration of water, water depth, temperature, and country rock type.

What Are the Threats? Principal threats to these communities are from the pollution of the seawater by chemicals from industry and agriculture, as well as seaside development and urbanisation, over-fishing and change in sea levels caused by global warming.

Rocky Coasts, Islands and Reefs

It is here, on the continent's rocky coasts, islands and reefs, that the land fights a losing battle with the sea. Constant sorties, waged by ocean wave and current, blow apart and grind down the continent's rocky skeleton. The water's erosive weapons are explosive compressed air, rolling boulders and abrasive sand. The present attack, which has given rise to the coast as we know it, commenced 6000 years ago when the rising sea reached its current level.

The ocean's relentless attack begins with the isolation of any high country, which is left marooned, forming islands. Ceaseless pummelling causes the shorelines to retreat until only the most resistant rock is temporarily left. The islands, gradually submerged, become reefs swept by wild seas, at first only during high tides and storms. But nothing can stop the persistent waves. Eventually, when only submerged country rock is left, some form of peace is achieved for that place, now experiencing only the relatively gentle sweep of the currents. The submerged cliffs, caverns, crevices, hollows and heights of rocky reefs become anchor holds for seaweeds, and for plant and animal crusts and growths. Soon this brightly lit environment, bathed in highly oxygenated and nutrient-enriched water, is transformed into a super-rich food source and shelter for marine flora and fauna.

If the surface of the continent didn't also have its own processes of land creation — uplift, folding, volcanicity and more — billions of years ago the oceans would have entirely consumed all of the land. The coastline shows much evidence of restless sea levels, none more vividly than the grand "drowned valleys" of Sydney Harbour (NSW), Port Davey and the Derwent estuary (Tas) and King George Sound (WA). In some places, undersea volcanoes erupt and finally build large enough piles of ash and lava to create the new country rock of temporary islands, such as Lord

Above: Using glowing light organs situated at the side of their mouths, Pineapplefish (*Cleidopus gloriamaris*) scan the sea floor of shallow coastal reefs down Australia's east and west coasts, searching for and attracting prey. *Opposite:* South Solitary Island Lighthouse, off Coffs Habour, New South Wales, is surrounded by a crucially important marine reserve that protects a rare warm-water community. The island is a reserve for nesting sea birds.

Above, top to bottom: Cape Leeuwin Lighthouse, Cape Leeuwin–Naturaliste National Park, WA; aerial of Montague Island, NSW; Tomaree Head, Port Stephens, NSW.

Best Examples: *NSW* — Lord Howe Island; Fingal Point; Cape Byron; Smoky Cape; Seal Rocks area; Yacaaba Head; North Head; Coalcliff; Green Cape; Point Perpendicular; Broulee Island. *Vic* — Point Hicks; Wilsons Promontory; Cape Schanck; Shipwreck Coast. *Tas* — Freycinet National Park; Capes Raoul and Pillar; Tasman Island; south-west coast. *SA* — Cape du Couedic; Seal Bay; Deep Creek Conservation Park; Stenhouse Bay; Port Lincoln; Streaky Bay. *WA* — Cape Arid; Cape Le Grand National Park; Fitzgerald River National Park; Denmark Greens Pool area; Walpole area; Augusta area; Rottnest Island; Geraldton; Houtman Abrolhos Islands; Kalbarri.

Sounds: Waves and wind.

Smells: Sea salt; "sweet" stench of rotting seaweed.

Sensations: Exhilarating wildness.

Howe Island in New South Wales. Regardless, islands — no matter how beautiful or permanent they appear — have always been temporary features!

FORMATION OF ROCKY COASTS, ISLANDS AND REEFS

The shape of shoreline features, like the shape of a landscape anywhere, has a large bearing on the types of plants and animals that will grow and breed there. Country rock, as the building material, is the foundation of environment.

Granite tends to produce smoothly rounded rocky coast, as evidenced at Gabo Island and Wilsons Promontory (Vic), the South-West (WA) and Freycinet National Park (Tas). Horizontal sedimentary rocks of sandstones, shales and some limestones break down to provide vertical cliffs and masses of sand and, where there are layers of soft shale, caverns and masses of broken scree slope — the best examples of these features are the Nullarbor (SA), Sydney Heads and Jervis Bay's Point Perpendicular (NSW), Eaglehawk Neck (Tas), Port Campbell (Vic), and Kalbarri (WA).

Depending on the chemical mix of the lava, volcanic flows — such as those that occurred at Fingal, Lennox Head and Kiama (NSW), and Tasman Island and Cape Raoul (Tas) — will produce stunning vertical columnar cliffs or steeply rounded coastline with tunnels and blowholes.

Folded, resistant metamorphic rock, such as hardened sandstones, slates and quartzites — as at Womboyn and Narooma (NSW) and Tasmania's south-west — are jagged coastlines with anticlinal sea caves, usually with numerous joints, dykes and faults that erode to become trenches. Any rock-fishing enthusiast knows that deep trenches lure crustaceans and fishes.

Because rocky coasts, islands and reefs are shoreline "battlefronts", any organisms wishing to colonise them successfully must be able to find shelter or a firm anchor to withstand the relentless assault of seawater. In the hostilities, the intertidal area, or littoral zone, is "no-man's-land". Very few animals or plants can endure spending half the day submerged in water and the other half parched and sunbaked in the open air. Even fewer can survive periods battered by the sweeping waves or washed by freshwater downpours, not to mention the violent temperature changes. However, organisms such as barnacles, limpets, mussels, the Sydney Coral Worm (*Galeolaria* sp.), periwinkles, cunjevoi and seaweeds require sharply defined environmental conditions — conditions that are all individually met in the littoral zone.

Above, left to right: Algal species flow with the currents in the intertidal zone; black bivalves, bordered top and bottom by barnacles — both are inhabitants of the rigorous littoral zone and must weather the extreme conditions.

Above, clockwise from top left: Salmon Holes, Torndirrup National Park, Western Australia; Cape Byron Lighthouse and headland, Byron Bay, New South Wales; horizontal sedimentary rocks create the plunging cliffs of North and South Heads, Sydney, New South Wales; the precipitous dolerite cliffs of Cape Raoul on the Tasman Peninsula, Tasmania; Windmill Bay to the south-west of Cape Willoughby, Kangaroo Island, South Australia; Wilsons Promontory National Park, Victoria, is the southernmost point of Australia's mainland and is composed of granite rock.

Above: Australian waters (especially shallow rocky pools) harbour a number of blue-ringed octopus species, all are dangerous to humans. Like many Cephalopods, they have remarkably adaptable colouration. When threatened, vivid blue rings signal their deadly intent. *Below:* Leafy Seadragons inhabit rocky reefs and sandy-bottomed patches near weed-covered reef in southern Australia, from Wilsons Promontory, Victoria, to the south-west of Western Australia.

On most rocky shorelines, during calm periods the low tide exposes clearly distinct zones and their particular plants and animals. Rock type provides the physical environment. Horizontal sedimentary rocks offer special mid-tidal sanctuary — this is because they erode in sheets, producing wide benches with deep potholes, pits and "gullies" cut by abrasive, rolling, rotating and spinning pebbles that are propelled by the swash.

LIFE IN THE PUDDLES AND POOLS

As kids, we all delighted in the mysteries lying hidden in rockpools. The joy to our discoveries was in the way each pool differed from the next. Those near the high-tide line were warmer, often with freshwater dribbling in from the cliff behind. Occasionally, dabblings in these pools revealed the bleached, crusty form of a rock crab, scattered rock oysters and little, if any, brown seaweed, although streamers of "hairy" green algae waterweed would grow near the freshwater trickle.

Nearer the mid-tidal area, the potholes are much more full of life. The water is cooler and clearer, with dense, beaded strings of floating, olive-brown Neptune's Necklace (*Hormosira banksii*) shading the sides and partially hiding the lairs of rock crabs. Here, too, lingers the flashy, venomous blue-ringed octopus and, anchored in corners and under overhangs, the smooth meat-red domes of anemones. Looking closer still, the water teems with tiny planktonic animals. Perhaps a small piece of pink-speckled bottom lifts suddenly and darts away, settling as a tiny, beautifully camouflaged fish among a cluster of limpets.

Nearby, a sandy surface on the brown rock bed is covered with a tangle of wandering "finger-painted" tracks — evidence of the nocturnal wanderings of vegetarian Zebra Top Shells or maybe Crow or Nerita Shells. The harder the search,

the greater the variety — sea stars; a large, carnivorous ribbed triton nestled among the bottom pebbles; Tube Worms in a rock crack; a low-slung, eight-plated chiton clamped tightly to the surface and packed into a crevice running towards low water; and masses of purple-tinted mussels. This venerable wealth of rockpool life is just a small percentage of the ocean's living offerings; most marine animals are resting, awaiting the night.

Each pothole and rockpool is a microcosm of the larger, wilder world of the rocky coast, and each pool differs because the mix of environmental conditions also differs. These conditions are water depth, the degree of tidal flushing, the incursion of freshwater, rock type and texture, shading, temperature, volume and the available "pool" of plant and animal species present in the region.

ZONAL ZOOS

Success around the rocky reefs and shorelines depends upon becoming adapted to living a rigorously zoned life — that is, if the rocky environment remains neutral; it is not necessarily always so. If the sea bed is of gravel, pebbles or even boulders, the waves will tumble these about as they do at Little Pebbly Beach, near Batemans Bay (NSW) or any other boulder beach. Any living thing risks being ground to pulp. In contrast to rolling and tumbling rounded boulders, fields of enormous angular boulders, when jammed and locked together, become almost immovable and also provide protective shelter in their caverns and gaps. Out on deepwater sandy beds (at depths of 5–20 metres), large isolated boulders and reefs that appear as dark-shaded patches on emerald-green seas, form almost perfect habitat for rocky-coast marine communities and the larger marine animals.

Life in the water column of the rocky shoreline at low tide must survive wild, broken water. This complex micro-community is based on clumps of strongly attached "rubbery" cunjevoi, with its hairy, intricate mini-caves and tunnels. Also populating this zone are crabs (from pea-sized to Red Bait Crabs and even Gardener Spider Crabs) along with their crustacean relatives the shrimps, immature rock lobsters and various worms, muricid whelks, numerous hydroids (almost "pastures" in some places) and myriad microscopic egg masses and miniature animal larvae. In the tidal zone, algae — such as Sea Lettuce, the brown Bubble Weed (*Phyllospora* sp), *Ecklonia*, the finely detailed *Cystophora* (found in Victoria and South Australia) and the giant, rubbery Southern Bull Kelp — must have secure holdfasts. Also among the marine flora will be numerous exquisite, pink-and-red, calcium-shelled algal species, along with yellow and mauve colonies of encrusting sponges and sea urchins. Rock lobsters scuttle about the lower levels of these "forests" of swaying seaweeds, while abalone, of which there are a number of species, settle on the boulders. At high tide the littoral zone is visited by foraging crustaceans and fishes from the deeper adjacent zones.

The zone of life below the broken, temperate waters of the reef reveals one of the most complex communities on Earth, biologically richer than most. Wrasse are the dominant fishes, the largest being the Blue Groper with Crimson-banded and Maori Wrasse being the most common. A metre above the reef floor, adult wrasse lay millions of sperm and eggs, which mature quickly into actively swimming, plankton-eating larvae capable of moving great distances with the currents. Some inevitably find suitable habitat, and after 20–50 days (at about 1 centimetre long) seek out a reef home. Fierce competition for space on the reef has led to incredible forms of camouflage and defence among wrasses and other vertebrate fishes, as well as among invertebrates such as isopods, crabs, worms, squids and octopuses.

Above, top to bottom: Children fossick for shells and small creatures in rockpools on North Stradbroke Island, Queensland; brittle stars are scavengers of the sea floor; male Crimson-banded Wrasses are found on rocky, kelp-covered reefs from eastern Victoria to southern Queensland; crabs are relatively versatile, ranging from reef to mangrove mud habitats.

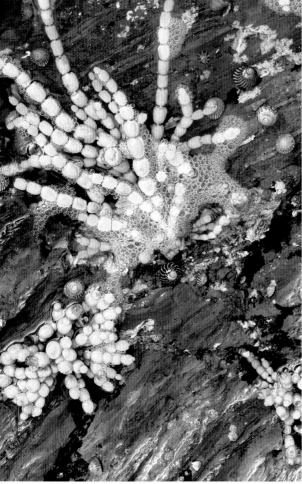

Flora of the Rocky Coasts, Islands and Reefs

Rocky shorelines are one of the toughest habitats in which organisms can live, being periodically flooded, exposed to the air and intense daylight, smashed by great waves and swept by rushing seawater. As sea levels constantly fluctuate, there is a vertical gradient in environmental conditions from the splash zone down to places below low tide. Survival of both plants and animals demands special adaptations to fit life's challenges, leading to a strict zonation of life forms. In southern Australian waters, more than 1150 species have been recorded in the algal flora, over 70% of which are unique to the region — creating one of the world's richest floral ecosystems.

Classic Plants: *Splash zone:* Conditions are too tough for most plants in this zone, but some green filamentous algae are found in freshwater to brackish drainage lines; some red and yellow lichens. *Rock pools:* Salinity changes dramatically, but Neptune's Necklace (*Hormosira banksii*); *Padina*; and Codium survive. *Intertidal zone:* Sea Lettuce (*Ulva lactuca*); *Enteromorpha* sp.; coralline algae; Bull Kelp. *Subtidal zone:* Leather Kelp (*Ecklonia radiata*); Southern Giant Kelp (*Macrocystis angustifolia*); Bubble Weed (*Phyllospora comosa*); *Cystophora* spp.; *Sargassum* spp.

Birds of the Rocky Coasts, Islands and Reefs

For birds that depend upon the sea for their food, rocky coasts have a number of benefits. They are adjacent to the birds' food supply, have frequent cliff-face nooks that are capped with densely growing tussocky grasses, matted plants such as Pigface, closed scrub or heath, as well as sometimes with perched dunes. These features — high ledges and caverns, broken rock, obscured ground surfaces and sandy soil for burrows — provide very secure places for nests. Offshore islands, such as North Solitary, Gabo, Lord Howe, Tasman and many other mainland islands off Queensland and northern Western Australia, are superb examples.

Classic Birds: Osprey; Lesser Frigatebird; boobies; gulls; terns; Storm Petrel and other petrels (Gould's is a classic on Cabbage Tree Island, NSW); Red-tailed Tropicbird (on Lord Howe Island); Little Penguin; visiting albatrosses; visiting White-bellied Sea-Eagles; Brahminy Kite; shearwaters and gannets; visiting cormorants, particularly Black-faced Cormorant, Great Black Cormorant and Pied Cormorant.

Above, clockwise from top left: Red Algae can endure reduced sunlight; Green Sea Algae, on the other hand, require plenty of sunlight; a species of green seaweed attaches firmly to a patch of hard corals. *Left, top to bottom:* Giant Kelp, one of the world's fastest-growing marine plants; Neptune's Necklace adorns a rocky shelf.

Invertebrates of the Rocky Coasts, Islands and Reefs

Due to continental drift over the past 20 million years, Australian tropical marine species have become mixed with the Indo-Pacific "species pool". Thus, only 10% of mollusc fauna remains endemic to our waters. On the other hand, the isolation of our long southern temperate coastline habitats for over 65 million years has created a remarkably high level of diversity — around 600 species of fish, 110 species of echinoderm and 189 species of ascidian. Some 90% of Australian molluscs are endemic. Just as the marine vegetation of the rocky coast is zoned according to environmental conditions, so too the invertebrate populations also occupy fairly strict zones.

Geography of the rocky coast is diverse, with cliffs, caverns, gorges, plains, deserts, dunes, areas of cyclonic winds and other calm places all bathed in circulating water. Life forms that evolved to fit this habitat and be sustained by it are bewilderingly varied. The phases of life embrace even greater diversity — from the egg, through the larval phase, to juvenile to adult. Sometimes these forms are anchored, sometimes free swimming or drifting. Populations of each phase fluctuate under environmental influence and by competition and predation. Incredibly fine detail of the geography ensures special spaces for all, albeit, in many instances, with a vast turnover in numbers. An abalone may release 10,000,000 eggs to have 100 (or fewer) survive to adulthood. But there is a place for all somewhere on the intricately carved rocky shoreline. The rigours of this environment, working over millions of generations, have filtered out inadequate forms. Those that remain live in one of five distinct zones: periwinkle zone; barnacle zone; galeolaria zone; cunjevoi zone; kelp zone.

Classic Invertebrates: *Periwinkle zone: Nodilittorina unifasciata*; various species of shore crab; Swift-footed Crab. *Barnacle zone:* Morula; *Nerita* shells; *Austrocochlea porcata*; *Siphonaria jeanae*; mussels. *Galeolaria zone:* limpets; chiton; Pacific Oysters; blue-ringed octopus; Red Bait Crab. *Cunjevoi zone:* Top shells; tritons; mitre shells; sea hares; nudibranchs; Lamp Shell; sea stars and sea urchins; sponges; hydroids; anemones; stony corals; soft corals; gorgonians; flatworms; feather worms; Mantis Shrimps; *Alpheus* shrimp; cleaner shrimp. *Kelp zone:* Abalone; Sponge-eating Cowries; volutes; *Octopus tetricus*; Southern Calamari; brittle stars; bryozoans; basket stars; sea whips; rock lobsters; hermit crabs; *Ozius* crab.

Above, clockwise from left: Sea stars come in an assortment of colours and patterns; weighing up to 15 kilograms, the Australian Giant Cuttlefish is the largest in the world; a shore crab shelters under a rocky overhang. *Right, top to bottom:* Tube Anemone; Pink Sea Whips move gracefully in the current.

Above, clockwise from top left: Reef fishes display some of the most flamboyant and varied colours of all marine life. Body shape and colour may change dramatically with sex, age and territory. Juvenile Eastern Smooth Boxfish are almost spherical in shape and completely yellow, adults (such as this one) have a rigid, box-like body shape covered in erratic, vaguely triangular spots; Banded Morwong are most common in Tasmanian waters; the Black-spotted Porcupinefish dwells on rocky and coral reefs around the world; Long-snouted Boarfish are native to Australia, inhabiting rocky reefs around the continent's south; a school of Butterfly Perch brings a flash of darting color to the rocky habitat; male Maori Wrasse — this species is also endemic to Australia.

Fishes of the Rocky Coasts and Reefs

Sea fishes are spectacularly coloured and have a remarkable variety of patterns. No other ecosystems compare with the marine production of such incredibly diverse large animals. This is probably because life began in the sea, so marine creatures have had vast periods to specialise their forms and habits to fit this testing environment. Conditions have been in a state of flux due to continents slowly drifting and changing location and consequently modifying the patterns of warm and cool ocean currents, the impact of winds on the coast and the tidal movements. Oceans are in a continuous state of change and organic survival depends upon the ability of living matter to evolve.

Living off plants, those primary producers of life, are the first line of animal consumers, the herbivorous fishes such as luderick or drummer. Then come a group of animals that feed directly on these consumers, usually with some plants thrown in; these might be flathead or bream. Feeding on these come more powerful carnivores, such as tuna or sharks. Most marine fishes have the complicated task of hunting for food while avoiding becoming a meal for other fishes.

The long evolution of marine life has allowed time for wonderful tricks of survival to develop — brilliant camouflage such as that of the Brown Morwong, living among kelp; the numerous multi-coloured fishes of the coral reef; counter-shading producing pale bellies that give no contrast against the light when seen from below; or a dark green-grey top to foil hunters from above; aggressive behaviour such as that of the tiny blenny; flashing vivid colours as in the blue-ringed octopus; sheer speed of reaction; poisonous spines as in the lionfish or stonefish and many more ruses. These attributes are also used in attack, to make the hunter more efficient. Predation is a great driving force in the evolution of diversity. The rocky coasts and reefs present the widest range of such superficial features.

Classic Fishes: Various leatherjackets; Convict Surgeonfish; parrotfishes; Eastern Blue Groper; Western Blue Groper; anemonefishes; wrasse, including Maori Wrasse; Port Jackson Shark; moray eels; luderick; rock cods; Red Gurnard; Red Cod; Rock Flathead; squirrelfishes; Eastern Wirrah; Old Wives; Tailor; Black Cod; seaperches; Snapper; Silver Bream; Silver Drummer; jewfishes; Silver Sweep; Eastern and Western Blackfish; Snubnose Drummer; morwongs; Stripey; kelpfishes.

Above, top to bottom: The endemic Black-banded Seaperch is usually found near caves and craggy overhangs on rocky reefs; Half-banded Seaperch grow to around 20 centimetres in length; Blotched Hawkfish use abstract colours to blend into the dappled rock environment; Painted Anglerfish resemble colourful sponges in soft-bottomed south coast areas. *Left:* The vividly attired Western Blue Devil is protected by law.

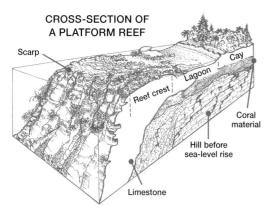

CROSS-SECTION OF A PLATFORM REEF

Scarp
Cay
Lagoon
Reef crest
Coral material
Hill before sea-level rise
Limestone

Above: When sea levels rose 10,000–6000 years ago, dry hills were submerged and eggs and larvae of coral polyps caught on reefs in these sunlit waters and colonised them. Waves broke on the exposed edges, sometimes smashing coral and throwing bits up onto the rim. This dead coral broke down to become coral sand that washed over the edge to form a veneer on the growing and rising reef.

Where Are They? *WA* — tropical coastal waters extending north from Geraldton. *Qld* — off Bundaberg. *NSW* — around Lord Howe Island.

What Do They Look Like? Reef and island outcrops on the continental shelf and islands and reefs of marine "hotspot" volcanic origin. Coral reefs are of the barrier, ribbon, fringing or platform types, constructed of nearly 500 reef-building corals of great form and colour diversity. These reefs, along with numerous "flat" coral cays, provide habitat for an incredible abundance of marine organisms of all kinds. Mainland-type islands range from hilly to mountainous, with numerous plant communities from grassland, shrubland, dry and wet sclerophyll woodland to forest, as well as pockets of rainforest.

Critical Conditions: Coral formations require clear, sunlit, warm waters for continuous maintenance and development. Mainland islands and reefs are built upon resistant rock, for example basalt/dolerite, granite, quartzite and slates. Violent cyclonic storms can make considerable modifications and increased pollution and global warming are destructive for marine organisms. Reefs are, however, particularly long-lived. Over the past 600 million years, corals have survived global crises such as geological uplifts and warping, drifting continents and extended climatic change.

What Are the Threats? Foreign materials entering these systems, such as oil, chemicals, herbicides, pesticides and human and industrial waste will be damaging, as will change in temperature due to industrial cooling water, landfill of estuaries and lagoons, destruction of mangrove systems, over-fishing, introduction of feral species and diseases.

Right: Russell Island and Normanby Island, part of the Frankland Island Group on the Great Barrier Reef, are outcrops of metamorphic rock from the Queensland coast's mountain range that became separated from the mainland at times of high sea level. Fringing reefs support a profusion of underwater life, while luxuriant rainforest on the islands provides shelter for numerous avian residents.

Tropical Coasts, Reefs, Cays and Islands

The island itself was high; we ascended the hill and when we were at the top saw plainly the Grand Reef still extending itself Parallel with the shore at about the distance of 3 leagues [15 km] from us or 8 [40 km] from the main; through it were several channels … A Reef such a one as I now speak of is a thing scarcely known in Europe or indeed anywhere but in these seas; it is a wall of Coral rock rising almost perpendicularly out of unfathomable ocean, always overflown at high water commonly 7 or 8 feet [c. 2 m], and generally bare at low water … the general trade wind blows directly upon it.

Joseph Banks, looking out from Lizard Island, 11–12 August 1770.

Banks, the scientist, and Cook, the navigator, discovered firsthand the problem of negotiating much of the tropical coast of northern Australia in a blunt-bowed, square rigger such as the *Endeavour*. The eastern Queensland coast in August is buffeted by the steady onshore South-East Trade Winds, making it an almost impossible task to navigate the maze of channels between the reefs. Australia's Great Barrier Reef, so named by that other great navigator, Matthew Flinders, is not a single reef. It is a broad continental shelf with scattered archipelagos of "mainland" islands and submerged hills, upon which, during the transgressions of the sea, have grown cappings and fringes of living coral reef. Along the edge of the shelf, growing on the rocky ridges of its rim, true barrier reefs have formed with the seaward edge dropping off the continental shelf into the "unfathomable" ocean. After his ship's hull was repaired following serious damage on Endeavour Reef off Cape Tribulation, Cook's temporary escape route through this "Grand Reef" was a length of shelf edge that had once been a valley. The water in this "gap", which he saw from Lizard Island, was too deep to sustain the sunlight-loving coral polyp animals.

REMARKABLE RELATIONSHIPS

Humankind has certainly risen to the challenge of constructing incredible feats of engineering, but can you imagine the following advertisement:

WANTED — engineering company to erect a breakwater around an area the size of the United Kingdom, in oceanic waters to depths of 145 metres. The wall will be 2000 kilometres long with much of it up to 1 kilometre thick. It must be cyclone resistant and self-repairing. In addition, the construction must provide self-supporting habitat for at least 1500 fish species, 4000 mollusc species, 6 species of turtle, 30 species of sea snake, and resting, nesting and feeding areas for 242 species of bird, as well as sanctuary for Dugong and whales.

No company would take on this task for any amount of cash! Yet such a structure — the astonishing Great Barrier Reef — was built by living organisms working as a multi-species, interdependent team. This team of highly capable engineers was mainly comprised of trillions of tiny, hollow-bodied animals — limestone-secreting coral polyps — and symbiotic algae nourished by countless trillions of free-floating plant and animal plankton, themselves dependent on warm, sunlit, oxygenated seawater. Such symbiosis occurs when two quite different organisms join together in one body for their common benefit. Over a billion years ago, green bacteria able to convert energy in sunlight to the manufacture of sugars from hydrogen, oxygen

The Oceanic Connection

Above, top to bottom: Green Island is a coral cay that creates an emerald haven of vegetation surrounded by the cerulean blue of the reef; the jagged ancient sandstone of Raft Point Bluff rises majestically from Doubtful Bay, along the Kimberley coast of Western Australia.

and carbon peacefully invaded algal cells and gained proteins from the algae. Payment for this service from the algae was made by way of surplus carbohydrate. This "marriage" gave rise to photosynthesising organisms, such as more-successful algae, as well as the green leaf.

About 600 million years ago, another union took place between photosynthesising algae and a 10-millimetre, soft, radially symmetrical polyp animal. The algae is believed to trigger off the secretion of limestone, forming a hollow, radially compartmental, lidless "box" in which the polyp's soft body is protected. At night, eight or so retractable, flexible arms project from this box to carry out nocturnal "netting" for drifting planktonic food. The algae provides a supply of carbohydrate (manufactured by photosynthesis) for its partner polyp, thus allowing the animal to live in tropical waters that are not rich in nutrients. Recompense is that the polyp provides the algae with nitrogen and phosphate fertilisers. However, there is a cost to all this: the coral polyp must live in clear, brightly sunlit waters. It lives a wonderfully prolific life in myriad forms and colours, but it remains trapped in this very limiting zone. So, many sensitive relationships and half a billion years bind together this complex underwater union of light, water clarity, chemical balance and temperature. Any rapid shift in these conditions, especially through human-induced changes such as agricultural and industrial pollution and atmospheric modification, can cause the death of this system over immense areas.

FINDING A NICHE

With such strict requirements for coral success, where then, in Australian waters, can reefs grow? Waters warm enough to support coral (20°C or more) lie north of about 30°S latitude, with some extension to Lord Howe Island (NSW) and the Houtman Abrolhos Islands (WA), where waters are warmed by south-flowing tropical currents. Shallow, well-lit waters are found either on the continental shelf, fringing the mainland and islands (such as Solitary Island, WA), flowing over drowned hills and mountains submerged by sea-level rise or, as in the case of Lord Howe Island, covering a volcano protruding from the deep ocean bed. However, tropical wet season flooding, which sweeps in quantities of freshwater and tonnes of mud, renders parts of these tropical areas unsuitable for coral.

At present sea levels, Australia's major coral kingdoms are the Great Barrier Reef; Flinders, Herald, Willis, Lihou, Caringa and Osprey Cays and Reefs in the Coral Sea; Lord Howe Island and older volcanic reefs north; Coral Bay (Cobourg Peninsula, NT) and offshore reefs away from Arnhem Land rivers; Ashmore and Cartier Reefs offshore from the Kimberly coast, as well as Ningaloo Reef and reefs around Dirk Hartog, Bernier, Dorre and Houtman Abrolhos Islands (WA). Most of these coral reefs are less than 8000 years old; at that time, sea level was 30 metres lower than at present. Even further back, to 18,000 years ago, sea levels were 120–140 metres lower. Thus today's reefs were constructed upon a foundation of older reef material that had succumbed to the drop in sea level.

There are other tropical coasts, reefs and islands around northern Australia where, due to muddy run-off and turbulent tides, corals do not survive. Huge areas of the Gulf of Carpentaria and parts of north-western Australia are smothered by mud. Much of the Darwin coastline, and of the Port Essington area of the Arnhem Land coast, is typical of tropical coasts worldwide, with brick-red cliffs sometimes underlain by white-bleached, soft sedimentary rock. One of the most spectacular coastline and island environments in the world is in Western Australia's Kimberley, where ancient red, brown and cream quartzite ranges plunge into the sea. This

Above: The lagoon-washed beach at Honeymoon Bay is dwarfed by 900 metre Mount Gower, an old volcano core built from multiple lava flows that formed Lord Howe Island in the Tasman Sea off the New South Wales Coast.

Best Examples: *Qld* — Great Barrier Reef Coral Cays (e.g. Heron, Capricorn Group, Lady Elliot, Green Island and Michaelmas Island), Redbill Reef and Bushy Cay off Mackay and North West Island in the Capricorn Group are perhaps the best cay examples, along with Lizard Island; mainland Islands (e.g. Whitsunday Group, Lizard Island, Hinchinbrook Island); various commercial Barrier Reef pontoons accessible from Townsville, Mission Beach, Cairns and Port Douglas. *NT* — Northern Australian reefs accessed from Gove and Seven Spirits Bay (Gurig Gunak Barlu National Park). *WA* — reefs accessed from Geraldton, Broome, Derby and Wyndham via boat tours and the Ningaloo Reef directly from Coral Bay, Ningaloo and Exmouth.

Sounds: Cacophony of island birds; clink of coral shingle; wind whipping through Casuarinas.

Smells: Salty; organic.

Sensations: Stinging tropical sun; warm saltwater.

flooded coastline comprises examples of every type of coastal and island landscape. Much more is written about this coast in the Tropical Estuaries, Mangroves and Mudflats chapter. For me, this is the most wondrous wilderness coast in existence.

RENEWING THE REEF

Reefs and their inhabitants balance precariously on a tightrope of environmental conditions, so how are these "underwater circuses" so readily repopulated after a change in balance? The answer lies in rampant reproduction. Coral polyps reproduce in two ways: budding off clones and sexual reproduction. Budding produces many of the wonderful branching corals. In a remarkable show of synchronisation, one or two nights each year (in November) living reef-building corals shed inestimable numbers of eggs and sperm into tropical waters. Fertilised eggs develop into free-swimming larvae, which ultimately find a surface where their development continues with a limestone "foot" adhering to the surface.

Some polyps, those without the algae, will grow only weakly, at about 10% of the speed of those with Zooxanthellae algae, and at great disadvantage. Other species of the 500-plus reef-building corals live deeper down on the edge of the abyss; these include the less light-dependent black, red or golden "precious" corals, which have few algae. With so many species, each with particular habitat requirements and in myriad forms and colour (staghorns, plates, brackets, mushrooms, brains, soft and more) there are almost an infinite number of coral possibilities. Habitat requirements tend to determine which species will share their environment in the different zones — zones such as the deepwater reef front; the violent littoral waterfront and top; the reef crest cemented by limestone-producing algal mats; the sheltered hind reef, lagoon areas and sandflats.

Stormy waves, the regular flooding and draining of lagoons and reef flats, and the diversity of coral all combine to create a veritable living fortress, honeycombed with tunnels, galleries, gardens, caverns, trenches and canyons of all magnitudes. During the expansion and reinvigoration of reef life as described above, the older, deeper, dead reef core becomes this fortress's dense, cemented foundation. But this stronghold is not impenetrable. Corals' porous limestone skeletons make the reef vulnerable to tunnelling, grinding animals and those (such as some worms) that use corrosive fluids to tunnel. When on the reef, stop and listen. Over the "shush" of the sea is an abrasive background sound — the various wrasse, surgeonfishes and other herbivores eating the reef, grinding it away with their chisel teeth in search of algae and pumping out their waste of pulverised coral as sand. All of the reef sands (around the grains of which algal cells still grow) have passed through the bodies of wrasse, bêche-de-mer (Holothurians) and other ocean "vacuum cleaners" before being swept higher onto the reef by wind and tide.

ANIMAL INHABITANTS

As in all long-term living systems, the reef's life is based on the energy building capacity of plants, upon which vegetarian grazers, such as some molluscs, crustaceans and wrasse, survive until eaten by predators. But, despite the importance of marine flora, in this submarine gallery the animals remain the most popular exhibits. Drifting along with the juvenile coral plankton are other larval

Left: An aerial view of Lady Musgrave Island, Queensland, shows the striated, underwater zones of the Great Barrier Reef. *Right:* Quartzite ranges sink to the sea where they are eroded by often-turbulent tides in the Kimberley region of Western Australia.

Above, top to bottom: Pandanus trees provide shelter for flocks of nesting Black Noddies on Australia's coral cays; stromatolites at Hamelin Pool, Western Australia are composed of sheets of sticky cyanobacteria, a very primitive form of life.

Plants of the Tropical Coasts, Reefs, Cays and Islands

On the sandy beaches, colonising plants such as convolvulus and Beach Spinifex act as binders but also shade the sand bed, and add humus that collects other organic algal flotsam. This rudimentary bank of "soil" attracts nesting sea birds, adding further seed and guano phosphate. The beach becomes stabilised and a succession of plants take advantage of the changing conditions, adding to this process.

Classic Plants: Encrusting algae; carbonate-producing green *Halimedia* algae and red algae; green grape-like *Caulerpa* sp.; brown *Turbinaria* sp.; brown *Padina* sp.; green Turtle Weed; green *Codium* sp. and other algal species; over 200 species of diatoms and many microscopic blue-green algae; kelp on mainland rocky shorelines; Dugong Weed or seagrass; Red Mangrove; dryland plants (as mentioned in text); plants of mainland and/or island communities.

plankton, as well as infant algae, echinoderms, worms, molluscs, crustaceans and fishes — all feeding off the current's drifting conveyor belt of living soup. Those who win this very dangerous game of early life will become the future populations of reef life. Each will settle into its appropriate home on the reef, near (as safely possible) to a food supply and to shelter.

To survive, the various animal species have adopted fantastic forms, colours, patterns and behavioural strategies. Some strategies are so successful they can even endanger the most threatening species of all — our own, *Homo sapiens*. But even our own hierarchy in the animal kingdom is diminished on the reef, where most human beings are reduced to simply gazing in awe at the spectacularly vivid Butterfly Cod, the triggerfish or leatherjacket, the brilliantly coloured crustaceans, the patterned and sculpted molluscs, the grotesquely poisonous Reef Stonefish, the dainty angelfish and the slinky, and generally docile, Conger Eels. At night, when the coral polyps expand their tiny colourful tentacles, the vibrancy of the reef explodes in a show more spectacular than any fireworks display.

CREATION OF A CORAL CAY

Wind and waves, it seems, are paradoxically both destroyers and creators of "islands". Over time, sand, strewn with the debris of coral clinker and massive broken lumps of coral, is pushed by wind or current to form a reef flat. Once heaped by wind and wash above the high-water mark, it forms the core of a coral cay (such as this example of an existing cay in the Capricorn Group). Along the tide line, flotsam begins to bind the sand, while rains dissolve the limestone sand and cement rubble and sand into a solid mass. Temporarily, a stability is reached.

However, inevitably, time passes and this core accumulates more and more sand. Its shores become a resting and nesting haven for thousands of birds, such as Crested and Sooty Terns, as well as migratory species. Travelling on the winds, birds or sea-borne drift, plant matter arrives — grasses, daisies, Beach Morning Glory and nightshade, all of which need plentiful light and little water. Over a number of seasons, they begin to succeed in this environment and become established, cooling and shading the surface and adding to the organic matter in this phosphate-rich (bird guano) environment.

Silvereyes and gulls feed on the succulent nightshade berries and spread the seeds across the low ridge. Current-borne Pigface is marooned onshore and warily takes root — yet another binder for the sandy soil. Ultimately, more species arrive and establish themselves in their favoured environment. About the exposed rim, in the droughty, saline environment, a few grass species, a daisy and Pigface, with a network of morning glory stems, mat an outer-zone community together. The floating fruit of Pandanus arrives by sea, and soon a number of Pandanus, several metres high, lean out on their prop roots from the matted sandy surface. Later, Argusia shrubs and Shore Oaks, loaded with a colony of Black Noddies, form a belt of vegetation around the tear-shaped island. In the centre, a dense forest of bright-green Pisonia trees grows: in the tallest is the heavy stick-nest of an Osprey.

At sunset, Sooty Terns become very active, diving into the "lagoon" on the sandflat, hunting small fishes. At dusk, hundreds of Wedge-tailed Shearwaters crash land near their nesting burrows and enrich the sandy ground with copious amounts of digested squid and fish. Once in their burrows, they begin a night-long cooing, a whining symphony of love. Less conspicuously, female Green and Loggerhead Turtles swim ashore to excavate a nest on the beach before steadily dropping around 80 shining "ping-pong ball" eggs into the nest's inner chamber.

Carefully placing damp sand over the eggs and firming it with their rear flippers, these turtle matriarchs then fill the hollow, scrabbling across it several times, before turning their sandy-teared heads back to sea. Their night's work is laborious and seemingly unrewarding — of that clutch, perhaps 3% of the hatchlings will survive the gauntlet of hungry sea birds, fishes and eels in their attempt to reach the ocean. At dawn, the noisy "yowlers" trundle up to the highest point of the island for take-off. They will spend the day flying far and wide across the ocean on their long, black swallow-shaped wings. This coral cay, brimming with life, took perhaps two centuries or more to reach its maturity as a cay — yet just one cyclonic evening could sweep the reef clean — such is the power of this dynamic planet.

Birds of the Tropical Coasts, Reefs, Cays and Islands

When a sandbank has become higher than high tide and storm levels, a beach becomes a haven for sea birds. Add vegetation and this complex community becomes suitable for a wider variety of birds. So, on the open beach one finds nests of Little Terns, Crested Terns, Caspian Terns and Bridled Terns. The Silver Gull is a principal predator of eggs and chicks. Above this very exposed site, along the higher shell and flotsam lines, will be Brown Boobies, oystercatchers and Beach Stone-curlews. In the grassy sandbanks are Hooded and Red-capped Plovers, more boobies and burrowing shearwaters. The shrubby woodland and forest edges provide higher nesting sites for herons, noddies and cormorants, while exposed rocks are the Osprey's prime nesting site.

Classic Birds: Noddies; Bridled, Roseate, Black-naped and Crested Terns; Silver Gull; Reef Heron; Sooty Oystercatcher; Buff-banded Rail; White-bellied Sea-Eagle; Osprey; Silvereyes; Golden-headed Cisticola; Sacred Kingfisher; Masked Booby; Red-footed Booby; Brown Booby; Great and Lesser Frigatebirds; Red-tailed Tropicbird; Wedge-tailed and Short-tailed Shearwaters; Australian Pelican; Ruddy Turnstone.

Above, top to bottom: Crested Terns congregate in noisy, congested colonies, squabbling for space on the cay's sandy surface; at sunset, terns take to the skies, dive-bombing to scoop up fish from below. *Right, top to bottom:* Bridled Terns form cacophonous colonies and the "ker-waka-wak" of their call seems ceaseless on these tropical islands; Red-tailed Tropicbirds nest on Lord Howe Island; a Masked Booby mother regurgitates digested fish for her hungry chick; Black Noddies make their homes on the islands of Queensland's Great Barrier Reef and along the Kimberley coast in Western Australia.

Reptiles of the Tropical Coasts, Reefs, Cays and Islands

In the warm open waters of the reef and in the reef lagoons, fish-eating sea snakes are common. These large venomous snakes separated from Elapid land snakes only quite recently and are able to live in the marine environment because of some remarkable adaptations: valves to stop water entering the nostrils; enlarged lungs allowing submergence for up to two hours; a paddle-shaped swimming tail; reduced, streamlined scales on the belly and salt excretory glands under the tongue. They are generally brilliantly marked, particularly the Yellow-bellied Sea Snake. The smaller ring-marked kraits spend much of their time on mangrove mudflats, where they digest their food and lay their eggs above high tide.

By far the most dangerous and largest reptile of the tropical coast is the Estuarine, or Saltwater, Crocodile. Australia has some of the world's largest populations of this powerful, prehistoric reptile, especially in places such as Kakadu, Arnhem Land and the Kimberley. It has been observed crossing Torres Strait and swims out to offshore islands, where it has been found up to 200 kilometres off the coast. Six species of marine turtle can also be seen in Australian waters, from the dinghy-sized Leatherback to the small Olive Ridley and the endemic Flatback. The Leatherback is seen as far south as Sydney Harbour and Broken Bay. Coral cays and mainland sandy tropical beaches are favoured nesting places. Predation by birds and fish appears to take more than 90% of hatchlings before adulthood is reached, but very little is known of the juvenile lives of sea turtles.

Classic Reptiles: Sea snakes (20 species); sea kraits; Green, Loggerhead, Hawksbill, Olive Ridley, Flatback and Leatherback Turtles; Estuarine Crocodiles.

Above, top to bottom: A female Green Turtle heads back to sea after laying eggs; Olive Ridley Turtles are endangered in Queensland; Loggerheads spend the entire year in warm reef waters; Hawksbills are distinguishable by a beak-like snout.

Above, top to bottom: Australia's tropical waters provide suitable habitat for the Olive Sea Snake, one of Australia's most common sea snake species. They are most plentiful around shallow coral reefs of around 20 metres depth, where they hunt for fishes, crabs and moray eels; the powerful, prehistoric-looking Estuarine (or Saltwater) Crocodile can easily swim long distances to offshore islands, where it preys on birds, mammals, fishes and turtles.

Mammals of the Tropical Coasts, Reefs, Cays and Islands

The tropical east coast and north-west coasts are favoured birthing and nursery areas for Humpback and Southern Right Whales, these being the most obvious sea mammals of Australian coasts. Their annual migrations take them back to Antarctic waters from September to November, where they again build stores of energy by consuming vast numbers of the small crustacean Krill. They will return to the tropical seas in June to July. Other Cetaceans are the much-loved and smaller dolphins, with the commonest being the Bottlenose Dolphin. Dolphins frolic along the continent's coasts throughout the year, consuming fishes and squid.

The other very large mammal, although rarely seen, is the herbivorous Dugong. This relative of the Manatee has its main feeding areas in the shallow sandy and mud areas where seagrasses grow. "sea cows" as they are sometimes known, graze in slow-moving herds on these pastures of the sea. The two major feeding areas are in the huge inlets of Hamelin Pool and Freycinet Reach at Shark Bay, Western Australia, where there are estimated to be between 7000 and 10,000 animals seasonally — probably the heaviest population left on the planet. Others are scattered around the northern coast as far as Moreton Bay in Queensland, with some 3500 living in a residual population around Torres Strait. The greatest threat to this species is drowning in trawling or fishing nets and collision with boat propellers. A small number are taken each year for traditional Indigenous purposes.

Classic Mammals: Bottlenose Dolphin; Striped Dolphin; Australian Sea-lion (WA); Dugong; Humpback Whales; Southern Right Whales.

Above, top to bottom: Bottlenose Dolphins frolic in the shallow waters of the tropics. Although they can travel as far as 1000 kilometres on open-ocean journeys, these friendly, intelligent mammals are usually seen close to the coast; Australian Sea-lions inhabit the warmer, reef-ringed Houtman Abrolhos Islands on Western Australia's coast as well as Seal Bay on Kangaroo Island in South Australia and isolated groups on Bass Strait islands. Populations are growing.

Above, top to bottom: Humpback Whales migrate north from Krill-rich Antarctic feeding grounds to breeding sites along Australia's east and west coasts; the endangered Dugong feeds on seagrass in the temperate waters of Australia's north.

Above, clockwise from top left: Blackspot Goatfish and Banded Goatfish; Sweetlips; Common Lionfish; adult Diana's Hogfish and cleanerfish; Crimson Soldierfish dwell in caves and crevices on Australian reefs where they grow up to 27 centimetres in length; anemonefish, such as the Brown Anemonefish, have an interesting commensal relationship with the stinging sea anemones that also make their homes on the reef. Anemonefish produce a body-covering of mucus that "tricks" the otherwise deadly anemone into believing the fish is a part of its own body, allowing the anemonefish to find shelter on the reef. In return for this shelter, anemonefish ensure that the sea anemone is likewise protected by chasing away other fishes that may peck at the anemone.

Fishes of the Tropical Coasts, Reefs and Cays

Is there a place on Earth where there are more forms, abstract patterns or colours than on the coral reef? Here, magical builders in the form of tiny coral polyps have found spaces and created spaces. In dying and being broken up by waves and currents, reefs have been cut into canyons, gutters, cliffs, caves, bouldery slopes, bommies, sandy beaches and flats — all are fringed by gardens of the most fantastic shapes and colours of living corals, sponges and diverse life forms. To survive here, fishes must evolve to fit particular places and roles in the community of life. Food supply, shelter and space with suitable "furniture" must be provided by the habitat.

Some fishes are vegetarians, others carnivores and still others recyclers. Speed will be necessary for some, distance for others and others require the ability to move deliberately and slowly. Colours need to fit the availability of light, and characteristics must attract partners or confuse and warn off competitors. In this complex jigsaw of marine life, there has been plenty of time for infinite strategies to be tried and tested. Unworkable survival strategies simply disappear with the user. A factor to remember is that many of the reef organisms have only part of their life histories on the actual reef. Barramundi, for instance, and Banana Prawns run major sections of their essential growth periods in the tidal freshwater of tropical rivers. Today there are at least 330 species of coral over 2900 individual reefs, and perhaps 2000 species of fish and thousands of invertebrate species on the Great Barrier Reef alone — a testament that these procedures of biodiversity are working.

Classic Fishes: Tuna; Barracuda; Bigeye Trevally; Golden Trevally; Gold-spotted Trevally; hawkfishes; anemonefishes; blennies; bannerfishes; Beaked Coralfish; seaperches; drummer; Sergeant Major; surgeonfishes; wrasses; Queensland Groper; Potato Cod; lionfishes; moray eels; damselfishes; cleanerfishes; Coral Cod; Moorish Idol; angelfishes; butterflyfishes; Coral Trout; Red Emperor; squirrelfishes; bannerfishes; scorpionfishes; stonefishes; batfishes; reef sharks and rays.

Above, top to bottom: A school of Moses Perch glides under a rocky overhang; the Longnose Butterflyfish pokes its thin, straw-like proboscis into the reef's crags and crevices to suck up food. *Right, top to bottom:* A school of Shortfin Batfish; Masked Bannerfish are a tropical species found only on reefs in Australia's northern seas.

CROSS-SECTION OF A CORAL POLYP

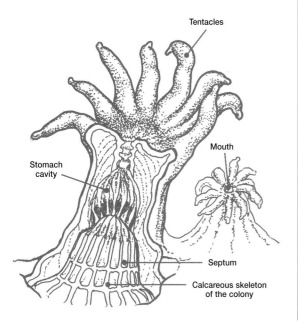

Tentacles

Mouth

Stomach cavity

Septum

Calcareous skeleton of the colony

Invertebrates of the Tropical Coasts, Reefs, Cays and Islands

The great diversity of conditions within the reef and island habitat has created even greater animal abundance, especially when it comes to invertebrates. Marine invertebrates — as with terrestrial invertebrates — play a critical role in nourishing land vertebrates. The marine food chain operates (as does any mature ecosystem) on a mixture of grazers, carnivores and decomposers. Many of the smaller animals, such as the Copepods, Seed Shrimps and Mysids, play an essential, linking role between decomposing kelp and larger beasts. These and many other planktonic animals live in vast swarms. Such is the importance of even the smallest creatures that these Euphausids are the major food supply for gigantic baleen whales. Research has shown many often-overlooked species of the invertebrate world have highly complex life histories — an important revelation for marine conservation. At one time in their lives, for example, mud crabs and Banana Prawns have planktonic phases, active swimming phases, and food needs dependent on healthy tropical rivers and estuaries. Management must preserve all of these locations, not just prime habitat for one life phase.

Classic Invertebrates: Staghorn, brain, plate, mushroom, *Diploaspera* sp., horse's tooth and needle coral; encrusting sponges; hydroids; anemones; Zoanthids; Black Corals; soft corals; sea fans; Gorgonians; sea whips; sea jellies; Box Jelly; basket stars; feather stars; brittle stars; Crown of Thorns Sea Star; Biscuit Sea Star; sea urchins; sand dollars; Heart Urchin; featherduster worms; fan worms, flatworms (*Callioplana* spp. and *Pseudoceros* sp.); segmented worms; nudibranchs such as Spanish Dancer; sea hares; chitons; blue-ringed octopus; squid; cuttlefish; abalone; tritons; limpets, top shells; turbans; trochus; screw shells; mud whelks; Violet Snails; cowries; helmet, murex, tulip, spindle and cone shells; dog whelks; mitres; volutes; bailers; spider shells; Arks; dog cockles; *Anadara* spp., mussels; Razor Clams; Chinamen's Fingernails; Pearl, Hammer, Rock, Spiny and Mud Oysters; scallops; pectens; file, trough, wedge and brooch shells; Thin-ribbed Cockle; Venus shells; Frilled Venus; Angels Wings; Teredo "worm"; lace corals; Holothurians; bêche-de-mer; various sea slugs; ascidians; sea squirts; Tunicates; barnacles; copepods; myriad water fleas; Mantis Shrimps; mysids; Opossum Shrimps; isopods; amphipods; Beach Hoppers; Krill; prawns; snapping shrimps, Western and Southern Rock Lobsters; Moreton Bay Bugs; Ghost Shrimps; hermit crabs; Swimmer Crabs; Pebble Crab (*Leucosia* sp.) Small Spider Crab of *Schizophrys* and *Hyastenas* spp.; Ghost and Fiddler Crabs; mud crabs.

Above, top to bottom: Scuba divers are immersed in underwater reef "gardens" where small, colourful fishes flit among corals (both alive and dead); reef walking, being careful to avoid causing damage to corals or reef inhabitants, is one of the best ways to learn about the abundance of marine life supported by reefs and cays. Note the vegetated cay in the distance beyond the beach. *Top left:* Sunshine Coral polyps.

Above left, top to bottom: Tube Worms are sometimes also known as Christmas Tree Worms due to their spiky, spiral appearance; sea anemone; Iljima's Sea Urchin; a Coral Crab adopts a defensive posture. *Above centre, top to bottom:* The Green Urn Sea Squirt is actually a colony of tiny ascidians; Pink Tube Sponges have no mouths or internal organs, instead plankton-rich water is filtered through their porous bodies by beating hair-like "flagella"; Lobed Soft Coral; the deadly Textile Cone Shell. *Above right, top to bottom:* Feather stars, attached here to boulder coral, position themselves to make the most of nutrient-rich currents; Linckia Sea Stars come in a variety of colours and body forms.

Above, top to bottom: Tweed Heads, NSW; The Broadwater, Gold Coast, Qld. Estuaries have always been attractive sites for human settlement, leading to resource-use conflicts between wildlife and humans. These areas are very susceptible to poisoning by chemical pollutants washed off the land.

Where Are They? From Moreton Bay (Qld) southwards around to Fremantle (WA), excluding the coast from Port Lincoln (SA) to Esperance (WA). Shark Bay (WA); Port Phillip and the Gippsland Lakes (Vic); Jervis Bay, Myall Lakes and Wallace Lake (NSW); Gulf St Vincent and Spencer Gulf (SA), and Port Davey, (Tas) are top areas for soft-bottom life.

What Do They Look Like? Samphire-covered mudflats edged with strips of mangrove where creeks and rivers meet the sea. In subtropical waters, the mangrove belt tends to be zoned according to species, the whole resembling a closed forest. Low diversity of plant species.

Critical Conditions: River mouths with tidal influence; a saline wedge moving up and down the lower river reaches according to freshwater flow. Sediment build-up by the river as it carries clay muds as well as sand. Waters free of non-natural pollutants.

Right: Mangroves fringe the foreshore of Moreton Bay, near Brisbane, Queensland, providing shelter and "nurseries" for many species of fish and marine invertebrates.

Temperate Estuaries, Mangroves and Mudflats

Because estuaries tend to be more productive than either the sea on one side or the freshwater drainage on the other, they function as the nursery and feeding grounds for a very large percentage of fish taken by commercial and amateur fishermen on our coasts.

Prawn and oyster production is almost entirely estuarine dependent. In addition, many species of local and migratory birds breed, rest and feed in estuarine areas.

Australian Marine Science Association's 'Guidelines for the Protection and Management of Estuaries and Estuarine Wetlands', *Australian Marine Science Bulletin*, Issue 60, October 1977.

Estuaries form when rivers arrive at their destination — where the river meets the sea. The river's role in the water cycle is completed here, although the water continues on its perpetual round trip, becoming seawater then evaporating and rising to form clouds in cooler air, travelling some distance, then becoming rain and once again entering the river system. On its riparian journey, the flowing river water becomes a transporter of salts, minerals, mud, sand, gravel and boulders, loosened from the surrounding country. The river channels these nutrients of the soil, much like a conveyor belt, but when it becomes blocked by tidal seawater in the estuary, it slows down and its transportation power is lessened. When this occurs, the light sandy and muddy sediment, which has travelled furthest, sinks; however, it has not yet become immobile. River and tidal currents nudge it into beds and banks of mud, behind which the shallow mudflats become exposed to air when the tide goes out twice daily. Seagrasses grow submerged in the shallows just below low tide. Mangroves, equipped with special "air-breathing" roots that enable them to grow even in tidal saltwater, colonise and hold the muddy tidal banks and flats. In cold southern waters (such as Corner Inlet, Victoria) only a single species of mangrove has this remarkable trait, but in the north the number increases and 36 species can survive the salty environment of Queensland's Cape York.

Some very deep estuaries were once old valleys, scored by deep rivers about 20,000 years ago when sea level was 120–140 metres lower than it is today. When sea level rose, sometime shortly before 6000 years ago, these deep 200-metre-plus gorges flooded, becoming estuaries such as Sydney Harbour. Over time, the settling mud and sand washed down the Parramatta River and its tributaries of Duck River, Middle Harbour Creek and Lane Cove River and almost filled the estuary, leaving it only 15–20 metres deep in places. In the quieter backwaters of Middle Harbour there are still basins of around 40 metres deep. This is also the case for the Hawkesbury, Port Hacking, Georges, Wagonga, Davey, Gordon–Franklin, and Derwent Rivers, as well as a number of others.

Of course all river valleys were flooded by the worldwide rise in sea level, but many had, geologically speaking, a low profile, with very broad valleys that formed extensive wide embayments, such as the Myall or Swan Rivers. Processes of long-shore drift, sweeping sand along, soon dammed off these valleys and left sandbars that linked the widely spaced headlands and recent islands, once part of the pre-sea-rise landscape. Tidal coastal lagoons, such as Lake Cootharaba, Wallis Lake, Myall Lakes, Lake Macquarie, Tuggerah Lakes, Gippsland Lakes, Lake Illawarra,

Above, top to bottom: Kate Kearny Entrance, Gippsland Lakes, Vic; eucalypts shade the banks of the Denmark River, WA; fishing boats bob on Macquarie Harbour, Strahan, Tas.

Best Examples: *Qld* — sites in Moreton Bay. *NSW* — Port Macquarie; Port Stephens; Hunter River; Hawkesbury River/Broken Bay/Brisbane Water; Homebush Bay Bicentennial Park; Towra Point Nature Reserve; Port Hacking; Clyde River. *Vic* — Mallacoota; Wingan Inlet; Gippsland Lakes. *Tas* — Derwent River/ Storm Bay; Macquarie Harbour and Gordon River. *SA* — St Kilda Mangrove Trail. *WA* — Frankland and Blackwood Rivers.

Sounds: Clacking Pistol Prawns; lapping waters.

Smells: Mud; decay; salt; the tinge of sulfur.

Sensations: Quiet but dynamic activity; mud between the toes; burning sun and cool breeze.

Brisbane Water, The Coorong, Wilson Inlet and Macquarie Harbour, were also formed this way. These lagoonal bodies of water, unlike true estuaries, are not as effectively ventilated by the tide, but are important places in their own right and more space will be devoted to exploring them later in this book.

EVOLUTION OF AN ESTUARY AND MUDFLATS

Let us discover the structure of the temperate estuary by allowing our minds to wander over an actual location. Many years ago, because of its extreme value as a study area, I proposed that the area we will visit — Towra Point, which runs out into Botany Bay Nature Reserve — and around which James Cook also wandered in 1770, should be set aside as a nature reserve, so significant are its geological and geographical features.

Many thousands of years ago, during low sea levels, the combined Cooks and Georges Rivers ran to sea south of a sandstone ridge (now Kurnell) north of Cronulla. With rising seas, this broad entrance was enclosed by a huge sandbank, now the remaining Cronulla dunes. The broad valley filled, forming the wide, shallow Botany Bay, and the water carved a new entrance over what had been a low, sandstone saddle in the Kurnell ridge. The rivers became independent streams spilling into the bay. Georges River, the larger stream, gathered (and still gathers) water and sand during floods from the sandstone country beyond Appin and mud from the rich shales around Campbelltown. These sediments were pushed down the river, settling in the serene waters of the lower flooded river estuary, where mangroves, samphire, Juncus Sedge and Swamp Oaks colonised the muddy backwater flats around Oatley, Oyster and Kogarah Bays.

Flooding continued to push sediments down the channel and into Botany Bay, where they settled against the sandbar that streamed out southwards from Kurnell, which was later to become Cronulla–Wanda Beach. When the mud had built to tidal levels and mudbanks appeared, gulls, terns and pelicans came to roost. The sediment continued to pile up. Summer north-easterly wind waves, generated on Botany Bay, winnowed the sand on the bayside to form a beach on the newly exposed Towra Point. This action helped shape the circular form of the entire bay. Winds heaped the beach sands into low dunes (now continually dry) fronting the bay. More sediment came sweeping down Georges River and followed the huge, slow eddy that had formed behind the point (now Pelican Point). Mud was gradually sifted from the heavier sand and the lighter mud settled at high tide on mudflats that were forming behind the bayside dunes. The structure of Towra Point was now in place and subsequent layers of sediment simply added veneers of sand and mud to the outer surfaces.

Flowing into the estuary, along with the water and sediment, was the river's rich harvest of seeds and other vegetation. Most perished in the saltwater, but some became part of the flotsam stranded on the beach. Salt-tolerant Couch Grass quickly became established, binding the dune faces. Tussocks of Parramatta Grass (*Sporobolas* sp.) knotted the dunes here and there, as did Coastal Spinifex, which was blown by southerly winds off the sea beach. Sydney Golden Wattle — the beach form that can withstand being buried by sand drift — added a layer of shade. Other floating fruit, seeds and cones washed up, including Coast Banksia, Shore Oaks and monotoca, the so-called Port Jackson Beech. The plumed seeds of Daisy and Blady Grass blew in and found a suitable seed bed. Soon after, birds arrived, and in their droppings came soft-fruited plant seeds, such as Ink Bush and Bush Tomato (*Solanum* sp.) The drier dune country was becoming stabilised

Above, clockwise from top left: The Murray River enters the sea out of its estuary, Lake Alexandrina, South Australia; Pinky Beach on Rottnest island, Western Australia; the mouth of Lake Merimbula, a coastal lagoon cut off by the sandspit beach connecting the headlands of Merimbula and Pambula, New South Wales; Patonga on the sandspit locking off Patonga Creek from the Hawkesbury River and Broken Bay, New South Wales; pockets of mangrove forest flourish on Victoria Point, Moreton Bay, Queensland; Point Nepean, a cuspate sandspit growing out from the eastern entrance point of Port Phillip, Victoria.

Flora of the Temperate Estuaries, Mangroves and Mudflats

In Australian waters there are nearly 40 plant species, from a number of families, that can be called mangroves. Mangroves, like all other flowering plants that occupy a saltwater habitat, face one major problem — their roots are submerged in water that has a higher concentration of salt than the fluids within their root cells. Stronger liquids draw weaker liquids through cell walls, meaning such plants would quickly lose their cellular water to the sea. Crazy as it might seem, these plants that live immersed in water suffer from a serious lack of water!

To combat this, saltmarsh and mangrove plants have strategies to reduce salt intake, slow down water loss and increase the excretion of salt. Salt is moved to the leaves, where it is excreted through pores or concentrated in old leaves about to be shed. To avoid dessication, these marine plants have waxy leaf coverings and very small (and fewer) stomates, or pores through which water is lost. Highly specialised root systems also enable these plants to survive in waterlogged mud. To move oxygen to the root system, they have an extensive network of cavities and spaces within roots that lie above the mud; this allows them to channel oxygen via hundreds of vertical "breathing roots" (pneumatophores) that branch upwards through the mud.

Classic Plants: *Zostera* seagrass; samphire (*Sarcocornia* spp.); mangroves (*Avicennia marina* and *Aegiceras corniculata*); Couch Grass; *Sporobolis* spp.; *Casuarina glauca*; *Juncus maritimus*; Bangalay; Coast Banksia; *Leptospermum* spp.; *Melaleuca* spp.; numerous algae.

under zones of vegetation. Superb Fairy-wrens found territories there, as did Brush Bronzewings, while Pheasant Coucals took up residence in the damper, dense ferny areas of the interdunes. Bangalay, or Swamp Eucalypts, ultimately entered these dry communities. Following them came marsupials: Swamp Wallabies, Long-nosed Bandicoots, Feathertail Gliders and ringtail possums all made the journey onto this "island" in the mud, joining the kingdom of Magpie Geese, Australian Pelicans, cormorants and teal.

However, by far the largest environments were the mudflats and isolated ponds lying behind the sandy beachfront. Plants that form communities in these saturated areas, which are covered with saltwater twice daily at high tide and much more deeply during spring, must be highly specialised. To thrive as part of these systems they must have seeds and other plant parts that are readily disseminated by water and which successfully take root when lodged in the right environment. Once established, special adaptations will help the seed continue to grow.

On Towra Point Peninsula, floating, partly-germinated seeds of the Grey Mangrove (*Avicennia marina*) became stranded on the edge of clay-rich mudbanks situated to the east and west of the north-east-facing sandy beach. At the same time, the lighter, floating River Mangrove (*Aegiceras corniculata*) was pushed by the high tide further out, onto the wide flats among the colonising, fleshy samphire plants (Glassworts) and algal mats. Grey Mangrove grows best on the edges of great mudflats, where there is active water movement. Ultimately, this growth created a strip of forest around 10 metres high and so dense that it is almost closed over above; the floor beneath bristles with pneumatophores and oyster-covered stems.

Ebbing tides draining off the samphire flats then cut narrow, deep, meandering channels through the *Avicennia* belt to deeper Botany Bay waters. The incoming tides sweep in masses of loose seagrass from shallow offshore beds and a mix of other flotsam that becomes caught up among the pneumatophores, building on the mud levels and providing, with leaf-fall, an intricate bed of shelter. In the soft, squishy mud hides an incredibly rich fauna of bacteria, micro-organisms and litter-feeding invertebrates such as worms, molluscs and crabs.

Local hollows and drainage channels within the mangroves and out on the samphire flat retain warm, intertidal water, where vast numbers of phyto- and zooplankton are nurtured, along with small predatory fishes and a suite of invertebrates. As the tide seeps into and through the mangrove belt, immature fishes and crustaceans return from their low tide shelter in adjacent seagrass to feed among the litter organisms. These are followed and hunted by animals further up the food chain, such as Silver Bream, Blackfish, Flat-tailed Mullet, flathead and whiting. The mullet feast on insects disturbed by the rising waters; the bream and whiting on aggregations of micro-crustaceans, and the Blackfish upon algae attached to the pneumatophores, tree trunks and channel banks.

High above, the White-bellied Sea-Eagle soars over its richest food source — a larder and resting place that is also known to migratory, seasonal fliers from the northern Pacific, such as Bar-tailed Godwit, Eastern Curlew, Greenshank, Marsh Sandpiper, Curlew Sandpiper, Red-necked Stint and Pacific Golden Plover. Also among these birds are the locals — Australian Pelicans, Black Swans, Chestnut Teal, Black Ducks, Rufous Night Herons, White-faced Herons, Eastern Reef Egrets, Great Egrets, Pied and Black Cormorants, and Azure and Sacred Kingfishers.

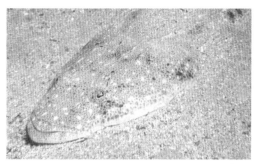
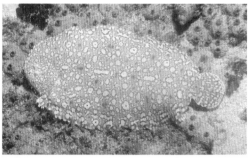

Fauna of the Temperate Estuaries, Mangroves and Mudflats

Estuaries are critical hotspots for fishes and crustaceans, as well as numerous birds — many annual migrants from as far away as China and Siberia. They are areas of international significance and are known to be some of the most productive living systems on the planet. Sediments and nutrients from inland catchments are dumped into these "sinks" by rivers, making them exceedingly nutrient-rich places where larval and juvenile marine species find a secure nursery in which to rapidly mature. The fertile muds and heavy leaf-fall from the mangroves hide a prodigious number of micro-organisms and invertebrates, which provide food for birds and marine organisms. Seagrass beds, too, support very high populations of micro-organisms.

Physical attributes of this habitat — deep, soft mud and sand, regular tidal inundation, often buried food and brightly lit and exposed surfaces — require numerous behavioural and physical adaptations for birds. Adaptations include specialised beak shapes and length; non-bogging, wading long toes and legs; and flight in dense flocks that are usually protectively coloured and patterned.

Classic Sealife: Sea jellies; herbivorous crabs such as the Semaphore Crab; King and School Prawns; Teredo "worms"; larval crustaceans; molluscs and fishes; Tun Shellfish; mud whelks; Sydney Cockle; Sydney Rock Oysters; Mud Oyster; barnacles (*Elminius covertus* and *Hexaminius* sp.); Predatory Whelk (*Lepsiells vinosa*); Periwinkle (*Bembicum auratum*); bream; Blackfish; whiting; flathead; mullet; Southern Conger Eel.

Classic Spiders and Insects: Leaf-curling Spiders; Golden Orb-weavers.

Classic Birds: Migratory waders; Great Egret; Little Egret; Eastern Reef Egret; White-faced Heron; White-necked Heron; Rufous Night Heron; Australian Pelican; Black Swan; Chestnut Teal; Black Duck; Australian White Ibis; Brahminy Kite; White-bellied Sea-Eagle; Swamp Harrier; Australian Spotted Crake; Bar-tailed Godwit; Azure and Sacred Kingfishers; Red-browed Finch; Grey and Rufous Fantails; Yellow-faced Honeyeater; Grass Owl; Pheasant Coucal.

Classic Mammals: Swamp Wallaby; Water-rat; ringtail possum; Feathertail Glider; Black Rat; Dugong.

Left, clockwise from top left: Australian Pelicans rest on a lagoon sandbank; the Dusky Flathead's colour suits its habitat, allowing it to lie in ambush until prey swims past; the Southern Peacock Sole is endemic to sandy coastal areas in southern Qld and NSW; the Frogfish's colours suit a rubble bed; Wavy Volute; the Port Jackson Shark is one of three Australian *Heterodontus* species that live among weed-covered rocks in or near estuaries; bristle worms are well-camouflaged for life among shelly rubble in shallow waters; a flock of godwits resting on a beach near Broome after spending low tide feeding on the mudflats to build up reserves of energy following their long migration from the Northern Hemisphere; Eel-tailed Catfish use their barbels as sensory organs when foraging on the bottom.

Above, top to bottom: Mangroves overhang the waters of Noah Creek in Daintree National Park, Queensland; the Red Mangrove (*Rhizophora* sp.).

Where Are They? Tropical coastlines with tidal influence from Carnarvon (WA) to Broad Sound (Qld).

What Do They Look Like? Broad, turbulent and muddy lower river reaches, frequently with deltaic islands and banks, usually with fringing belts of zoned mangrove forest that give way to forests of paperbarks in the fresh to brackish end of tidal limits. Behind the mangrove belt is often a hyper-saline, bare area that is broken in places by tidal creeks and gullies. Where conditions are less severe, samphire flats covered with low succulent species occur.

Critical Conditions: High solar radiation; warm waters; usually high tidal range; high and intense wet season rainfall.

What Are the Threats? Sedimentation and chemical pollution from inadequately managed inland farms; industrial development around ports; harbour dredging; rapid sea-level rises from global warming; timber exploitation of some tropical species.

Tropical Estuaries, Mangroves and Mudflats

May 12: … at eleven three quarter miles [c. 19 kilometres] over very bad travelling country, plains subject to much inundation, to a creek running into the river, with splendid water and feed; at twelve and a half miles [c. 20 kilometres] came to the river, with an immense sandspit opposite; appears to be within the influence of the sea, and is about 600 yards [c. 550 metres] wide, and dry half across. A number of pelicans up some distance; water either brackish a little, or with some other peculiarity about it. Started for apparently another bend in the river. One and three-quarter miles [c. 2.8 kilometres] saw a lagoon, on the left ahead; and, as the horses are tired, will bear for it and turn them out. Abundance of water and feed; lots of geese, ibis ducks and spoonbills. North three-quarters of a mile [c. 1 kilometre] from this is the river, about 500 yards [c. 460 metres] wide, treeless on the west bank, and cliffs about 20–30 feet [6–9 metres] high. All around an immense sweep; sandy beach opposite, within the influence of the sea; a rise and fall of four feet [1.2 metres] — and, at high water, a little brackish. Caught a few fish; the only thing we had for supper.

May 13: Started on a bearing of 330°, for a distant point like river timber, which turned out to be a small hill or ridge … a lagoon at its base. At 23 miles [35 kilometres] crossed a salty timberless creek; and then over a succession of salt swampy flats, with grassy plots intervening … at two miles [c. 3.2 kilometres] came to a mangrove creek; at two and a-quarter miles [c. 3.6 kilometres] the banks of the Albert River; salt arm, from half to three quarters of a mile [1 kilometre] broad; tide about five feet [1.5 metres].

John McKinlay, backtracking the missing Burke and Wills in the estuary of the Leichhardt River as it enters the Gulf of Carpentaria, in the late wet season of 1862.

McKinlay, a surveyor, trained on Sturt's expeditions to the interior before returning to Adelaide. One of Australia's less celebrated explorers, this Scot's successful expedition nevertheless emphasised the incredible incompetence of Burke. McKinlay was later made commandant of the attempt to settle the Northern Territory coast at Escape Cliffs, and experienced a near catastrophe on the boggy, wet-season estuarine plains of the Alligator Rivers (now in Kakadu National Park). He saved his party by killing his emaciated horses and using their wet, stretched hides to cover the frame of a punt made from saplings. This makeshift boat allowed him and his men to "sail" down the crocodile-infested East Alligator River estuary and across Van Diemen Gulf, pursued by "huge crocodiles" and sharks. Ludwig Leichhardt had also wandered around this country during the late dry season of 1845 and his descriptions of coastal plains are also well worth reading in any of the numerous facsimile editions of his journal.

As McKinlay's account attests, the scale of the estuarine and mangrove systems in the tropics is larger and more dynamic than that of their temperate, southern cousins. This is true for three main reasons. First, the wet season from December to late April brings intense rainfall, which scours out any loose sand and mud and transports it down the rivers, where it is sifted and deposited in the turbulent waters of the second factor — large to very large tidal movements along the coast, as much as 10–12 metres on the Kimberley coast and 5–6 metres at Kakadu. Sea level has remained around the present level here for the past 6000–8000 years, which has led to the development of the vast coastal plains, as well as a tidal

Fauna of the Tropical Estuaries, Mangroves and Mudflats

These ecosystems have evolved in a fertile but diverse and rapidly changing environment. A heavy annual fall of mangrove litter sustains an incredibly rich fauna of micro-organisms that in turn nourish countless larvae of crustaceans and vertebrates that drift into the mangrove areas and mudflats during tidal changes. Estuarine conditions are critical nurseries for vast numbers of fish species and invertebrate marine life; among these is the largest predator of all, the Estuarine Crocodile, along with smaller avian predators, kingfishers, Ospreys and White-bellied Sea-Eagles. So rich are these ecosystems that these pages can only skim the diversity of life found there.

Classic Invertebrates: Box Jellies; mud whelks (*Terebralia palustris; Telescopium* sp.); Giant Whelk; cerith shells; Mangrove Worm; mud crab; Banana Prawn; Fiddler Crab; Mud Lobster; hermit crabs.

Classic Fishes: Barramundi; Mangrove Jack; various stingrays; Shovel-nosed Ray; Long Tom; Estuary Cod; Javelin Fish; Moses Perch; Threadfin Salmon.

Classic Birds: Intermediate Egret; Great Egret; Reef Heron; White-bellied Sea-Eagle; Osprey; Brahminy Kite; Brown Booby; Rufous Night Heron; Jabiru; Chestnut Rail; Red-headed Honeyeater; Rufous-banded Honeyeater; Black Butcherbird; Yellow White-eyes; Orange-footed Scrubfowl; Chestnut Rail.

Classic Reptiles: Estuarine Crocodile; Mangrove Monitor; White-bellied Mangrove Snake; Carpet Python; Northern Brown Tree Snake.

Classic Mammals: Little Red Flying-fox; Black Flying-fox; Northern Brushtail Possum; False Water-rat.

Flora of the Tropical Estuaries, Mangroves and Mudflats

To grow in these salty areas mangroves must be specifically adapted. Each species, of which Australia has many, has strategies, such as an ability to concentrate salt in the leaves, block the entry of salt into the roots, provide breathing roots that stand above the saturated muds, provide stilt, buttress and prop roots, lock canopies together to create a closed forest community, or weave a network of roots to stabilise the mud bank. Behind the mangroves, a belt of low succulent samphire plants often grows.

Classic Plants: *Zostera* seagrass; samphire (*Sarcocornia* sp.); mangroves (*Avicennia marina* and *Aegiceras corniculata*); Couch Grass; *Sporobolis* sp. *Casuarina glauca*; *Juncus maritimus*; Bangalay; Coast Banksia; *Leptospermum* sp.; *Melaleuca* sp.; algae.

Left, clockwise from top left: Rufous Night Herons forage in the mudflat and mangrove habitat; Australia has four species of mud crab that for years were believed to be the same species; Figbird; Estuarine Crocodile; Wandering Whistling-Ducks; bristle worm; Mudskipper; White-faced Heron; Little Red Flying-foxes form noisy colonies around tropical estuaries.

Above, top to bottom: Byfield National Park, Queensland; Hinchinbrook Island, Queensland; estuaries on the Kimberley coast, Western Australia, at high tide. *Right:* The exposed roots of mangroves at low tide on Cape Tribulation.

Best Examples: *WA* — Kimberley estuaries. *NT* — Victoria River; Daly River; Alligator Rivers; Kakadu. *Qld* — MacArthur Ranges; Karumba; Weipa; Endeavour River; Hinchinbrook Channel; Bowling Green Bay; Cape Hillsborough National Park; Broad Sound; Curtis Island.

Sounds: Muffled movements; mysterious clacking.

Smells: Salt mingling with mud.

Sensations: Close, sweaty humidity.

influence running back up the Alligator Rivers for 90 kilometres to Kakadu. The third factor is the high water temperature of 24–35°C. Run-off has been increased by the burning-off of the tropical catchments in the mid to late dry season (July to November). Most of the soils of these coastal estuarine flats and tidal verges are heavy clays, broken by low sand ridges that mark the positions of old shorelines. Occasionally, these ridges are punctuated by shelly cheniers — ridges of shelly material pushed into place by cyclonic storm surges. More open soils nourish trees and shrubs such as the Kapok (*Bombax ceiba*). Behind the mangrove belt, the hyper-saline clay flats are exposed to extreme sunlight, leading to frequent large, scalded areas, sometimes puffy from the salt. In damper areas, flooded by spring high tides and/or freshwater seepage from the inland, large areas of samphire grow. Perhaps the best description of a tropical mangrove swamp was written by Alfred Searcy, a Collector of Customs in Darwin, writing in 1909 of the experiences of a friend, Aeneas Gunn (of *We of the Never Never* fame):

The place seemed to be the very heart of the huge solitude in which we were situated [Roper River]. Overhead there was a dark, closely knitted canopy of leaves. Only here and there a patch of ineffably blue sky. Through the apertures the sun shot vertical shafts of golden light that counterfeited gilded pillars, except where their masses were broken by contact with the trunks and limbs of the trees. It was like a weird, uncanny underworld, a vast, shapeless vault, whose roof was supported by gnarled and knotted trunks, carved with fantastic devices by the processes of Nature. Slender flying buttresses vaulted away from the trunks [Red Mangroves] in a long series of elliptical arches. The whole scheme of design of the jungle might have been that of an unimaginable mediaeval cathedral, conceived in a nightmare and executed in a delirium … The atmosphere was stifling, and permeated with a hot, miasmic vapour. The silence was intense, and broken only by faint sounds of something moving, the gasping of shellfish that lay in the mud or clung to the roots and trunks of the mangroves. So still was it that one could almost hear the moisture exuding from the ooze. I could hear a crack, the sound of a branch pushed aside. Nothing was visible, here was no distance, no vista, no perspective, only knotted and twisted trunks, a tangle of boughs and branches and roots and branches and boughs; above, a roof of leaden leaves; underfoot, a slushy noisome ooze of decaying leaves, roots, shells and mud.

Such evocative imagery transports me to the swamps of Kakadu or the Kimberley, and especially to Channel Island in Darwin Harbour and its wonderful mangrove forests — the cyclone shock absorbers of the tropical coast. Yet they are much more than that: after rainforests and coral reefs they are the most productive ecosystems on Earth! The life stories of the Banana Prawn, mud crab, Barramundi and Estuarine Crocodile best demonstrate the fecundity of these habitats.

In the warm, living mud of the mangrove forests, often hidden between 18–36 tree species, a plethora of plant and animal species are locked together in very complex food webs. Offshore in the warm sea, Banana Prawns, an important player in this ecosystem, are being spawned. These crustaceans pass through a number of larval phases in the plankton before the mobile, immature prawns make their way to the fertile, algae-producing estuaries. Despite the mangroves' shelter, they become prey for Mangrove Jacks, voracious juvenile Barramundi and many other fishes. With the onset of the Wet, freshwater dilutes the saltwater in the estuary, which triggers a move back towards the coast for the 24-centimetre adult Banana Prawns, which go to lay their eggs in their sea spawning grounds.

The wet season also heralds another species' reproductive cycle. Adult Barramundi, usually from 4 to 7 years old, begin spawning in the estuaries during an incoming tide. Females produce more than a million eggs that are swept in among the mangroves and hatch within 24 hours. In this rich, estuarine environment, the young "Barra" rapidly increase in size before taking up temporary residence in wetlands on the floodplain. Towards the end of the dry season, when flooded depressions become too warm and begin to dry up, the year-old, carnivorous fish head upriver as far as they can go to feed on insects, crustaceans and smaller fishes. They will grow there for several years, reaching sexual maturity after three years, when these Barramundi, all males at this point, swim back to the sea spawning areas where they will fertilise drifting eggs. At about six years, and more than a metre long, these males undergo a sex change, becoming females and producing millions of eggs. Sustaining populations of Barramundi demands strict regulation of size limits and protection of the entire river habitat that supports their life cycle, from the upper freshwater reaches to the cradling wetlands and mangrove-lined estuarine forests to the near offshore waters. In terrestrial ecosystems, humans generally harvest the bottom end of the food chain (farming and consuming vegetation and herbivores) … in the case of Barramundi we are harvesting the top carnivore, and in this instance the large females. Harvesting these big female fish must severely impact the population.

Mud crabs, too, have active offshore larval phases during juvenile life. Their larvae join the plankton and then move onto the protecting mangrove mudbanks and flats, where abundant food allows them to grow into beasts of up to 20 centimetres across the carapace with snapping fore-claws that can crack an oar! Living representatives of dinosaurs, in the shape of Estuarine (Saltwater) Crocodiles, also inhabit these murky waters and mangrove and paperbark-fringed areas are central to their survival. As the world's largest crocodile species, the Estuarine Crocodile grows up to 7 metres long and finds its core habitat in the wetlands around tropical estuaries from Broome to Mackay (although it can also live in freshwater and can spend considerable periods on offshore islands). "Salties", as they are colloquially known, breed in the wet season, when they rake together a nesting mound of swamp vegetation, mud and soil in which to lay 30–70 eggs. Females are ferociously maternal. The mother defends the nest for three months until the young hatch then she uses her impressive, gaping jaws to gently carry the hatchlings (whose sex has been determined by the nest temperature) to the estuarine edge. Dense mangrove or paperbark roots provide food and shelter for the hungry young, who swim on first contact with water. About three months later, the infant crocodiles swim off to fend for themselves, taking their chances over predaceous fish, reptiles, Ospreys, White-bellied Sea-Eagles and larger crocodiles. These are just a few examples of the specialised animals whose existence depends on highly productive tropical estuarine habits.

Above: Buttressed tree roots on the edge of a mangrove forest, Cape Tribulation, Queensland.

Above: The active, growing sandbar at the northern end of Nambucca Heads beach, New South Wales, continuously builds up, hindering the flow of the Nambucca River. Except for during short periods of severe drought, it will never entirely succeed in blocking the river's flow, which is too strong. *Right:* New River Lagoon formed below Precipitous Bluff in Southwest National Park, Tasmania, when this bay-mouth sandbar finally closed the estuary of New River. The beach dune has been overtaken by a scrub of tea-tree, paperbarks, acacias and eucalypts. The great Southern Ocean waves crash into Prion Bay and salinate the estuary, defeating even the heavy rainfall that this country experiences. At the peak of those rains and floods, however, the sand barrier will be temporarily breached, allowing lagoonal and ocean waters to mix.

Where Are They? Wherever there is a coastline, rising and falling sea levels, a supply of sediment (usually of coarse sand) and transporting ocean currents, they will appear at different stages of formation, including the island phase, the sandspit–beach phase, the locking-off phase, the infill phase and the plain phase.

What Do They Look Like? Coastal lagoons with extensive shoreline shallows and mid-lake sand, mudflats and islands; sometimes long, sinuous river deltas of mud snaking out from inland shores. Low ephemeral swampy country covered by sedges and wet heath with shorelines of She-Oaks or Broad-leafed Paperbarks. Sequences of low, old barrier dunes that frequently run parallel with and adjoin the outer barrier.

Critical Conditions: A regime of open and closed ventilation to the sea; saltwater and freshwater mixing; fire sequence and mosaic across the wetlands and wet heath shrublands; for wildlife, the sequence of coastal wetlands and lagoons along the coast is critical.

What Are the Threats? Chemical pollution of hinterland streams by fertilisers, herbicides, pesticides, industrial and human wastes.

Temperate Coastal Lagoons and Wetlands

The river is navigable for vessels of fifty or sixty tons, to a distance of thirty-four miles [56 kilometres] from its bar, the water being of a good depth, except at Shark and Pelican Islands, where sand flats extend across the river, which can be passed by vessels only at high water. The reaches of the river are long and straight, averaging about a quarter of mile [400 metres] in width, and flanked on both sides by huge walls of dense brush. These borders of alluvial brushland on the banks of the river, are generally half a mile or a mile wide [1–2 kilometres], and are then backed by extensive swamps of many thousands of acres in extent, whose verdant sea, of high waving reeds and sedge, stretches away to the base of the distant forest ranges. There are several lagoons in these swamps, and stagnant water is very generally diffused over their surface. Their soil is very good in some parts. The continuous brush renders the aspect of the lower part of the MacLeay very monotonous; green islands covered with palms, now and then vary the uniform sameness of the reaches of the river, not to speak of the air of cheerfulness imparted to the scene, by the large flocks of aquatic birds, of wonderful variety, all busily engaged, and fish leaping out of the water in every direction, renders an excursion on the waters of the MacLeay pleasant enough.

Clement Hodgkinson, Government Land Surveyor, gives a description of the MacLeay River flats in 1845.

Coastal lagoons are common around the Australian coast, with highest concentrations along the south-east coastline and in north-east Tasmania. The area Hodgkinson describes is that of the bare Clybucca paddocks to the west of the Pacific Highway (NSW), which were covered by a huge coastal lagoon 4000 years ago. If only there were areas of such "monotonous" scenery available to us today! Unfortunately, such lagoons and their surrounding floodplains are now rarely to be found in their natural condition, after having largely been drained for agriculture.

THE EVOLUTION OF A COASTAL LAGOON

Cape Hawke Lookout, just south of Forster in New South Wales, provides not only an incredible panorama over Wallis Lake and stretches of coastline from Seal Rocks to Crowdy Head, but also an excellent example of how such habitats are formed. Six thousand years ago this "lookout" was perched atop an island among an archipelago of islands and long peninsulas. At that time, the sea had just reached its present level. Aborigines, who had for centuries sustained themselves on the plants and wildlife of the old coastal plain, had been driven inland by the rising seas. The sea rising across the sand-covered (from previous sea-level fluctuations) broad continental shelf, moved sand inshore, dragging along with it more sand that had washed out to sea from the rivers. As the current swirled and eddied around the then islands (now Black Head, Bennetts Head, Cape Hawke, Charlotte Head and Seal Rocks), some of the heavier sand sank to the bottom. Slowly, this sand piled up on the quieter, lee side of the islands and streamed out in long tongues or spits. Gradually, the sweeping spit, or sandbar, connected each island to the next in the chain. Wide embayments behind the islands were cut off, becoming the coastal lagoons of Smith and Wallis Lakes. These lakes represent the two types of coastal lagoon: seasonally closed and permanently open.

Smith Lake, because of its small catchment, is often closed to the sea, whereas Wallis, because of its much greater catchment and size, remains continuously tidal. Both lagoons have quite different water quality. Lagoon entrances are most often at the quieter end of the beach, behind the protection of a headland. Most coastal lagoons in New South Wales are at the southern ends of their barriers, because, year-round, the dominant waves are driven by south-easterly winds. Long-shore drift, a sand-sweeping local beach current driven by these wind-generated waves, soon fills any channel opened at the northern ends.

Sometime in the future, if sea levels remain as at present, these coastal lagoons will disappear under sand and mud washed in from the surrounding catchments. They will first become wetlands, growing dense vegetation, but will eventually become dry enough to form a broad, alluvial plain, such as the one behind the Gippsland Lakes in Victoria. The disappearance of these coastal lagoons is a long-term natural process of global change; we may slow the rate of this change, but we can never stop the process from occurring. Change, in nature, is ever-present.

MYALL LAKES — A SPECIAL STORY

Two large and similar systems are the Myall Lakes in central New South Wales and the Gippsland Lakes of Victoria. The Myall system, just south of Wallis Lake, is an archetypal example of this environment, and I have explored it at length as bushwalker, boater, botanist, tourist, environmental activist and wildlife management consultant.

The geological stability of this coast has weathered numerous fluctuations in sea level. At low sea levels, this shelf region became a coastal plain. Across this plain were scattered many high, isolated hills and mountains that were linked to the radial ridges running down from the highlands of Barrington Tops. Seal Rocks and the knot of high hills that form the present-day Treachery Head were the most outstanding and played a significant role in shaping the Myall Lakes. In the past, a number of high sea levels raised sandbars and barriers between many of the rocky hills that today form the low, parallel ridges and marshy swales (approximately 1 metre high) on the lagoon side of today's coastal barrier of high dunes. These sandbars link Treachery Head to Big Gibber before sweeping out in the refracted, quieter waters behind Broughton Island, past Dark Point and then in a giant arc around to Yacaaba Head (the northern entrance to Port Stephens) — nearly 50 kilometres of wonderful, north-east-extending beaches that are perfectly at right angles to the onshore, dune-shaping, south-easterly wind. Massive dunes have built behind Seal Rocks as sand accumulates at this northern end. In the gradual building and rebuilding of these barriers over numerous sea-level changes, the heavy mineral sands of rutile, illmenite and zircon were winnowed out into old strandline deposits, causing the mining-versus-nature environmental battles of the fifties, sixties and seventies. Disturbance and destruction of the stabilising dune vegetation, usually by fire, is evident in the vast blowouts and older, now-vegetated, transgressive hollows, which are rimmed by sharp dunes that have covered many kilometres in overriding the previous dune system.

That 50 kilometre long sand barrier dammed off the ends of five parallel valleys — the two largest being the Myall River and Boolambayte Creek, both draining waters from a high, wet catchment. The dammed valleys filled with water then drained south-westwards, behind the dune system, through an everglades-like swamp before finally emptying into Port Stephens. The top and largest lagoon, located a long way from tidal ventilation, was Myall Lake. It passes through the narrows at

Violet Hill into U-shaped Boolambayte Lake, through another narrows at Bombah Point and into the Bombah Broadwater, then down the meandering, sandy Myall River to the estuary of Port Stephens. The Broadwater, actually part of the Myall River valley, is the only lagoon that remains vaguely tidal, and the one that receives the largest input of freshwater. Aquatic organisms of this system, therefore, occupy a very unusual environment. In the deeper Myall Lake, a brackish layer forms over salty depths. The middle lagoon, Boolambayte, has mixed waters, while the shallow Broadwater — before the introduction of power boats at least — was strongly stratified, with a freshwater system perched on top of a marine one. Once, one could catch marine flathead, whiting, Blackfish and bream on a sinkered line, and bass and other freshwater species near the surface — but that has changed now, with the water being mixed. The shallows are a haven for Black Swans, Australian Pelicans, cormorants, egrets, teals and Black Ducks. Although lagoon

Above, top to bottom: The seaside town of Merimbula, NSW, is sandwiched between Merimbula and Back Lakes; Tweed River nestled behind the shelter of Fingal Head, NSW. *Right:* Noosa River, above Lake Cootharaba, Qld.

Best Examples: *Vic* — Lake King, Gippsland Lakes; Marlo; Wingan Inlet; Mallacoota. *NSW* — Tuross Lake; Lake Illawarra; Marley Lagoon; Lake Macquarie; Port Stephens; Smith Lake; Myall Lakes; Wallis Lake; Watson Taylors Lake. *Qld* — Pumicestone Passage; Noosa River and Lake Cootharaba. *WA* — Blackwood estuary; Swan River. *SA* — The Coorong; American River on Kangaroo Island. *Tas* — Logan Lagoon; Sellars Lagoon; Cameron Inlet on Flinders Island; Musselroe Lagoon; Bowlers Lagoon; Ansons Bay; Bay of Fires Lagoon; Moulting Lagoon.

Sounds: Lapping waves; shrill honeyeaters.

Smells: Dead waterweed; tea-tree.

Sensations: Vibrant, teeming life.

waters are rarely turbid, they are always stained a translucent brown by organic seepage and tannins. Wind–wave action across the broad, shallow lagoons allows for ample oxygenation, although the uptake of oxygen can be restricted in summer when water temperature rises.

The "February dark" is a time of great interest in the Myall Lakes lagoon system. During spring tides following the full moon, millions of school prawns (that first arrived there as very active larvae after a long journey from the sea via Port Stephens) leave the rich seagrass beds and sandflats of the Broadwater where they have spent a year feeding and growing. Masses of them move out with the high tides that flood back down the Myall River. Where the Myall River makes its channel south, out of the Broadwater, a unique fishing village has sprung up. Tamboy has been built on a slight rise among the Cabbage Tree Palms and Swamp Mahoganys, and it is here that fishermen take the gamble as to whether it is the right night to stretch their nets across the river. Once the prawns' exodus begins, a catch of 10–15 tonnes is not unusual! Prawns surviving this artificial barrier swim on down the river to their spawning grounds in the sea. Supporting this food chain are the seagrass beds of the shallow lagoons. Seagrass beds maintain a diverse, miniature world of flora and fauna that includes grasses, algae, plant and animal plankton and invertebrates, and feeds crustaceans, fishes and birds.

Surface waters across the lagoon system and swamps are at worst brackish. They are often littered with organic matter that falls from the magnificent Broad-leafed Paperbarks, Swamp Oaks and, in the saturated swamps south of the Broadwater, Cabbage Tree Palms, that line their shores. These give way to dry heath and dry sclerophyll woodland and forest on the less watered dunes, while a complex mosaic of wet and dry heath covers the moors of the ancient, inner-barrier country. River and Grey Mangroves grow where the tide strengthens near Tea Gardens and Port Stephens, and Corrie Island Nature Reserve, part of the Myall River delta, is a mangrove system that rewards exploration.

Between the water and wetland in the shallow "dead end" bays of the lagoons are extensive reed beds and sedgeland comprised of tangled sedges, ferns, *Gahnia*, small *Melaleuca* species and Dog Rose. Unfortunately for this flora, and in part because of it, these coastal lagoons are ephemeral: both the vegetation and settling silt will gradually fill the beds. Measurements at Lake Macquarie, the Shoalhaven and in the Hunter River show that fine mud sedimentation is taking place from 0.5 to 5.5 millimetres per year. So, the lagoons become wetlands, then saturated plain and then coastal plain with a build-up of wonderful, if acidic, soil.

PROTECTING TEMPERATE COASTAL LAGOONS AND WETLANDS

In 1788, Europeans first settled Port Jackson after 200 years or more of adverse reports from explorations carried out by Dutch, Spanish, French and English navigators. Areas of this land were said to be uninhabitable, populated only by the "miserablest people on Earth" (in the words of William Dampier). For a further 25 years, these early settlers were hemmed in by the sandstone barrier of the Blue Mountains. Ultimately, intrepid explorers battled their way across this barrier and others followed to establish settlements. Human efforts were, however, always pitted against a difficult adversary: the Australian environment. It seemed that the eastern coastal lands, the south-east, Tasmania and the south-west were the likely places for Europeans to make their homes — and 90% of our population consequently settled along this rim. Here we concentrated our industry and our leisure. Ever more intense development occurred. Space became tighter as our affluent, relatively small population sought bigger or more home sites and as recreational requirements increased. Much of the best coastal lands became unproductive; swallowed up by the urban jungle. In the early 1960s, coastal wetlands in New South Wales lost 60% of their area in five years due to flood-mitigation works. Mining also changed the shape of coastal dune country. In order to stabilise it, the highly aggressive Bitou Bush from South Africa was planted, destroying endemic vegetation and rendering much of the coast inaccessible.

With the 1970s came the beginnings of a new idea: that by learning to understand the natural ecological processes we might actually find ways to support them and repair the damaging impact of our own activities. To do this, we had to retain samples of diverse habitat — keeping them as banks of biological diversity, from which we might later draw the capital to invest in a happier future for the environment. Hence, our national parks and nature reserves, systems of the last vestiges of untouched habitat, are crucial to a positive future for all animal species.

Above: The pristine Hastings River, in New South Wales, as seen by surveyor Clement Hodgkinson in 1845. Lagoons and wetlands that sustained Indigenous Australians for many thousands of years are threatened not only by inevitable environmental factors, but also by the modern desire for "water views". Pollution caused by development along waterfronts, wetlands and lagoons may affect species that once flourished in this habitat.

Above, top to bottom: Gold Coast suburbs have built up the great sandspit from South Stradbroke Island to Coolangatta, Qld; the sandspit locking off Lake Illawarra and Tom Thumb Lagoon is now an urban/industrial area, Port Kembla, NSW; Lakes Entrance and the Gippsland Lakes, Vic.

Above, top to bottom: New South Wales Christmas Bell (*Blandifordia nobilis*) with a white form, Myall Lakes, NSW; Geraldton Wax, a member of the myrtle family, occurs only in South-West Western Australia. It can survive extended dry periods, making it suitable for colonising temporary lagoons.

Flora of the Temperate Coastal Lagoons and Wetlands

Plants living in water are partially supported by the water, but water levels in wetlands are not as regular as seawater and at times may even dry out, determining what plants can grow where. Some species, such as Spike Rushes and sedges, have bodies of air within their stout stems and leaves to help them support themselves occasionally and provide air when submerged. Waterlilies float, preferring stable water levels in sheltered ponds. Others, living in running water, are strap-like, while still others crowd the surface with short, adventitious roots to absorb nutrients from the water. When a pond is over-fertilised from contaminated run-off it can become so eutrophic and densely packed with these "floaters" that light is shut out, killing underlying plant matter and the animals that depend on it for their survival.

Classic Plants: *Lagoon — Zostera* seagrass; Australian Lilaeopsis; Watercress (fresh); Watershield; Waterbuttons; Jointed Twigrush; Spike Rush; Tall Spike Rush; Lepironia; Marsh Club Rush; Common Reed (fresh); Seawrack; Ribbonweed; *Posidonia australis*; Sago Pondweed; Clasped Pondweed; Sea Tassel (*Ruppia*); River Mangrove; Grey Mangrove. *Wetland:* Tassel Sedge; Saw Sedge (*Gahnia*); Spiny Rush; Tussock Rush; Sea Rush (*Juncus maritimus*); Streaked Arrow Grass; Nardoo Fern; Water Primrose; Slender Knotweed; Coastal She-oak; *Callistemon* spp.; Swamp Paperbark; Scented Paperbark; Prickly-leaved Paperbark; Woolly Tea-tree; Christmas Bell.

Fauna of the Temperate Coastal Lagoons and Wetlands

A complete micro-ecosystem dwells in the shelter of the vegetation of temperal coastal lagoons and on the pond bottom and among the detritus of wetlands. Many wetland plants carry numerous epiphytes and provide surfaces for grazing invertebrates, such as snails. Insects such as mayflies, caddisflies, dragonflies, stoneflies and mosquitoes have aquatic juvenile phases that feed on the epiphytes and/or on other animal larvae. This is the world of micro-organisms, worms and insects such as the water-scorpion and those arachnids that have entire aquatic life histories. Small and nursery fishes, amphibian vertebrates, turtles, freshwater snakes, the Platypus and water-rats also occupy this watery wonderland. Larger lagoon and wetland animals feast on a diet of crustaceans such as crayfishes and shrimps.

Water-level changes, according to cyclic flooding phases, are critical in understanding the movements and breeding behaviour of waterfowl, which are highly dependent on the food supplies provided by pond and lagoon life. Aquatic organisms proliferate according to the state of flooding, and this causes corresponding waves in the populations of predatory wildlife. Some ducks feed only on invertebrates produced at given water levels and specific levels trigger the breeding habits of different species of waterfowl. Non-seasonal reproduction that occurs across Australia's unpredictable aridlands also determines the mass movement of waterfowl. Rain in the aridlands instigates a series of randomised movements. In this regard, too, the lower Murray–Darling River system and its pre-settlement flood regime were critical. Reduce the number and depth of floods by damming rivers and the impact can be disastrous for the wildlife of this continent.

Classic Birds: Little Wattlebird; Lewin's Honeyeater; Yellow-faced Honeyeater; Tawny-crowned Honeyeater; New Holland Honeyeater; Scarlet Honeyeater; Pheasant Coucal; Superb Fairy-wren; Variegated Fairy-wren; Southern Emu-wren; Ground Parrot; White-browed Scrubwren; Red-browed Finch; Nankeen Kestrel; Swamp Harrier; Whipbird; Black Swan; Australian Pelican; various cormorants; teals; Black Duck; Musk Duck; White-bellied Sea-Eagle; Osprey; Whistling Kite; Silver Gull; Crested Tern.

Classic Reptiles: Red-bellied Black Snake; tiger snakes; Diamond and Carpet Pythons; Eastern Water Skink; Sun Skink; Rocket, Haswell's and Wallum Froglets; Eastern Banjo Frog; Common Eastern Froglet.

Classic Invertebrates: Numerous worms; yabbies; amphipods; insects such as damselflies, dragonflies, beetles, flies, mosquitoes, weevils, crickets and cockroaches; centipedes; wolf, large-jawed and spiny spiders; leeches.

Above: Australia's graceful Black Swan, seen here with dusky cygnets in tow, occupies much of Australia but is most common around extensive wetlands and freshwater lagoons. Such environments cater for this swan's herbivorous diet of waterweeds and provide reeds, sticks and grasses for shelter and nest building.

Above, clockwise from top left: Eastern Pygmy-possums are nocturnal nectarivores that feast on the sweet nectar of Banksia blossoms; monitor lizards, commonly known as goannas, often stand their ground around wetlands or lagoons in order to bluff larger predators, however they soon flee to the safety of surrounding paperbark trees if truly threatened; shallow lagoons provide a source of freshwater and the possibility of food for hungry dingoes, especially on Fraser Island in Queensland, and as seen here in the Nadgee Nature Reserve, NSW; Spotted Marsh Frog; flatheads find suitable shelter by partly covering themselves in sand and waiting on the bottom for prey to swim overhead.

Above: Underwater "pastures" of seagrass, such as those just west of Point Hicks in Victoria, provide both shelter and nourishment. Dugongs, the only remaining herbivorous mammals, rely on seagrass as their sole form of sustenance.

Where Are They? *WA* — Shark Bay; Rottnest Island; Cockburn Sound; Princess Royal Harbour; Oyster Harbour. *NT* — Gulf of Carpentaria near the Sir Edward Pellew Group. *Qld* — Gulf of Carpentaria near the Mornington Island Group; Torres Strait; inner Great Barrier Reef waters; Hinchinbrook Channel; Broad Sound; Hervey Bay; Moreton Bay. *NSW* — Clarence River estuary; Lake Macquarie; Tuggerah Lakes; Botany Bay. *Vic* — Gippsland Lakes; Western Port Bay. *Tas* — Pittwater; Norfolk Bay. *SA* — Spencer Gulf; Gulf St Vincent; American Bay on Kangaroo Island.

What Do They Look Like? Shallow, sandy or muddy bottomed saltwater areas with brown or greenish-brown grass-covered floor containing patches of open ground. Some grasses are very narrow leafed, others are more straplike. Some leaves may be extensively covered with algae and micro-fauna. Seagrass may be exposed at spring low tides.

Critical Conditions: Marine shallows to about 15 metres deep; clear water where plenty of sunlight can penetrate; currents and tidal change causing little turbidity; relatively small tidal change.

What Are the Threats? Chemical, oil and waste disposal in water; pollution and urban developments; careless anchoring; increased sediment from run-off.

Right: Temperate waters around Maria Island, Tasmania, support a wealth of fish and invertebrate species. During the Ice Age, the island was once two separate land masses. With rising sea levels they have been joined by spits of silica sand deposited in the "quieter" waters between the two ends.

Soft Bottoms and Seagrass Meadows

Vast areas of Australia's continental shelf are covered with a mosaic of mud, sand and gravels — the so-called soft bottoms. These materials are produced by the local erosion of country rock or shifted distances by water movement that is generated by wind–wave action, long-shore or cross-shore drift, or strong ocean currents. How far these soil particles travel is directly affected by the depth of the seawater; hence soft-bottom development is strongly influenced by the rise and fall of sea levels. Movement of the sea bed causes continuous abrasion, which reduces the particles and sifts similar-sized grains into individual beds. Components of soft bottoms are usually of two kinds: those with a silica base, arising from the erosion of sandstone or granite, and those of calcium carbonate derived from generations of pulverised marine shell. Clay muds, leached from the weathering of rock such as granite and shale, usually settle close to estuaries where they mix (flocculate) with seawater, while sand remains mobile. These soft-bottom areas of the shelf stretch from a few metres to 200 metres in depth.

SCAVENGERS OF THE SOFT BOTTOM

In the world's oceans, light availability, ground fertility, stability, water temperature and chemical composition of the water have a dramatic impact on the communities that can survive in any given place. In the most brightly lit clear waters photosynthesising plants flourish. In places where depth reduces light penetration, few large plant species can grow. To counteract this lack of marine flora, food chains in darker waters are based around dense populations of micro-algae, on which phytoplankton and diatoms forage. The open sea bed is therefore covered with a combination of living and dead micro-organisms — a smorgasbord for detritus feeders.

In the exposed environment of open sea bed, larger animals such as worms, sea pens, bivalve molluscs (scallops and Mud Oysters) and other invertebrates spend at least part of their lives hidden beneath the surface, avoiding sea stars and carnivorous Sand Octopuses, Helmet Shells and Stargazers. Hollow-bodied, filter-feeding Holothurians (such as sea cucumbers) traverse the surface, passing huge quantities of sediment through their guts but digesting only small amounts. Unappealing as it sounds to us, much of the more nutritious food for these detritus-feeding animals is old faecal material that is inhabited by bacteria, fungi and protozoans. Further up the chain are crustaceans and fishes, such as the well-camouflaged flounder, which make a meal of filter feeders.

Of these systems, the muddy bottom is the most productive. Comparatively, sandy sediment can account for as little as 1% of the muddy bottom production. But this microscopic abundance can, paradoxically, lead to reduced species diversity. A population eruption of bacteria and "decomposer" micro-organisms can expend virtually all available oxygen, making the sea bed temporarily uninhabitable for larger organisms. Some animals, such as Ghost Shrimps, capitalise on this fact by having lifestyles that inhibit other life — they eject so much sediment from their burrows that they clog the filtering apparatus of filter feeders. The challenge

Above, top to bottom: Seagrass blankets a shallow sea bed in Cape Le Grand National Park, Western Australia; all manner of ruse is adopted to allow species to go unnoticed in their submarine environment — the Rough Flutemouth employs the tactic of resembling the reedy, thin shape of seagrass.

Best Examples: *WA —* Shark Bay from Denham to Monkey Mia. *Qld —* Hinchinbrook Channel out of Cardwell; Moreton Bay; Brisbane River. *NSW —* Port Hacking; Sydney Harbour; Wallis and Myall Lakes from Forster to Bulahdelah. *SA —* Gulf St Vincent.

Sounds: Clacking of Pistol Prawns at low tide.

Smells: Marine muddy smell.

Sensations: The squelch of soft mud underfoot, often with mysterious lumps in it.

Flora of the Soft Bottoms and Seagrass Meadows

Seagrasses have remarkably long life spans. Research in the Baltic Sea shows that some *Zostera* seagrass, which expanded from a single plant, is over 1000 years old! Despite this longevity, damaged seagrass can also take a long time to regenerate. *Posidonia* beds in Spencer Gulf still show unrestored tracks of vehicles made in the 1910s, while seismic blasts in Jervis Bay of 1940s vintage are still clear of growth and show no apparent recolonisation. Considering the high productivity of this living system, every opportunity should be taken to protect the seagrass meadows.

Classic Plants: *Zostera* spp.; *Posidonia* spp.; *Amphibolis* spp.; *Syringodium* spp.; *Halodule* spp.; *Cymodocea* spp.; *Halophila* spp.; numerous algae.

---

of oxygen availability is rarely prolonged, sea bed currents usually rapidly clean out the system. Research suggests that the majority of the worms, molluscs and nematodes that dwell in the mud of the soft bottom die of starvation, old age or physical disturbance, rather than oxygen loss. Their deaths continue the perpetual recycling of the submarine world, as their carcasses are scavenged by invertebrates.

PASTURES OF THE SEA

Life in the well-lit seagrass meadows is in stark contrast with that of the darker, soft-bottom sea bed. Seagrass, the floral foundation for life in this habitat, is actually a flowering angiosperm and a relative of land plants. Australian waters are a hotspot of seagrass diversity. Of the 60 species worldwide, one-third live in temperate Australian waters and 14 are endemic. There are a number of genera, but they are all very similar because all of these formerly terrestrial organisms had to adapt to an underwater world and solve the problems of living with an "atmosphere" of liquid water rather than gases. The strap-like or grassy leaves are supported by the waters, so they do not have to be very stiff, allowing them to drift and flow with the tidal currents, perfectly bathed in the oxygenated ocean.

In Western Australian waters, *Posidonia* genus, with eight of the nine worldwide species represented, is the most common. *Posidonia* shed their leaves every two months to avoid the leave's crucial photosynthetic surface becoming covered by rapidly growing foreign growths, such as epiphytic algae (particularly calcareous types). Most of this plant's bulk (50 to 90%) is buried in the form of a vigorous, anchoring rhizome, with leaves and roots shooting out from nodes. Being immersed in water, the leaves do not require gas-exchange pores known as stomates. Instead, they have evolved a very thin cuticle, or skin, through which the plant cells can directly exchange gases from seawater to use in photosynthesis; this also allows the cells to absorb nutrients from the water.

Underwater reproduction, without the distribution of pollen by the birds and the bees, poses quite a challenge. Most seagrasses produce very large pollen grains; indeed, one of them produces the largest of any plant. *Posidonia*'s floral spikes are held well above the sea floor, while other species' pollen floats to the surface. Eventually, one way or another, water currents disperse the pollen and cross-pollination — even at a distance — is achieved. Most dispersal is by seed, vegetative growth from the rhizomes aside. In one *Posidonia* species, a seed is retained until it has germinated, upon which stage it resembles a grappling hook and is liberated to flow in the currents until it becomes entrapped in anchoring seagrasses. Here it begins to grow vigorously, sometimes even smothering its "anchor". On death, leaves fall to the sea floor or are washed ashore to form great banks wherever they lodge. Recyclable material is then consumed by detritus feeders and decomposers. An astonishing level of mineral residue is also found.

A SOJOURN ON A SEAGRASS MEADOW

For our brief journey through this habitat, let us visit an area of World-Heritage biodiversity significance, and one I know and love well — Shark Bay in Western Australia. The seagrass beds of Shark Bay are the largest natural submerged meadows in the world, extending some 4000 square kilometres. This massive body of marine flora nourishes the largest population of Dugong on the planet, some 10,000. The dominant seagrass species here are *Amphibolis antarctica* (85%), *Posidonia australis*, *Syringodium isoetifolium* and *Halodule uninervis*, which combined achieve a biomass of up to 2 kilograms dry weight per square metre,

Above, clockwise from top left: Coastline of Cape York, Qld, shows how the low area behind the beach and its dune has been filled with sediment from the hills and overtaken with vegetation; Bowen Island in Jervis Bay National Park, NSW; Granite Island, offshore from Victor Harbor, SA, shelters the shore behind from the southerly swell, allowing sand to accumulate in the quieter water and seagrass meadows to develop in the well-lit shallow water; long-shore currents have dragged white granite sands to link the island to the shoreline in King George Sound, Albany, WA; Point Nepean, at the mouth of Port Phillip Bay, Vic; some of the largest and richest seagrass meadows in Australian waters are off Monkey Mia, WA, which attracts some of the highest Dugong populations in the world.

with a maximum daily production of 17 grams dry weight per day! Limited phosphate requires very efficient recycling by the environmental system in which these grasses live. *Amphibolis* has erect stems up to 2 metres long, with a canopy of 4500 leaf clusters per square metre — imagine the phenomenal support this provides for the known 66 algal epiphyte and 40 animal epiphyte species. The seagrasses, and their associated epiphytes, create food and cover in waters down to about 13 metres for animals ranging from Dugong, snapper, whiting, lobsters, prawns, Pearl Oysters and countless larval animals. Shark Bay (and Queensland's Moreton Bay for that matter) straddle tropical and temperate conditions, which contributes to their immense diversity by enriching them with a wonderful mix of temperate and tropical species.

The density of vegetation covering the sea bed retards the flow of current, causing a more rapid accretion of sediment than is usual over open areas. When the many calcareous epiphytes attached to the seagrasses die, large amounts of calcium carbonate are also deposited on the sea floor below — a build-up of sediment of geological proportion. Such calcium carbonate accumulation was a major cause of the development of the Faure Sill, the huge bank that blocks significant tidal flow into Hamelin Pool to provide the hyper-saline warm water required for the growth of the stromatolites. Lharidon Bight, with its vast shell beds and Shell Beach of *Fragum erugatum*, also owes the life of its bivalves to this same partial barrier to tidal flow. Of the 218 species of bivalve shellfish recorded for Shark Bay, 49% are at the limit of their range. Of Shark Bay's tropical species, 46% range no further south, while 57% of temperate species go no further north. These facts bestow the area with great biological importance. We can learn much by studying the limiting environmental factors for the species living at habitat borderlines.

Apart from Tiger Sharks, and the gentle, gigantic Whale Sharks, the most remarkable Shark Bay animal is the distinctive Dugong. These shallow-water dwellers are the world's only herbivorous marine mammal and possess downward-facing, pig-like snouts and broad, flexible mouths to graze the seagrasses of the underwater meadows. As vegetarians living on low-nutrition seagrasses, they have large stomachs and long intestines suitable for digesting large volumes of food — an efficient physiological feature that enables these "sea cows" to weigh up to 500 kilograms and grow to 3 metres long.

Like Humpback Whales and dolphins (which also frequent the Western Australian coast) and all marine mammals, Dugongs are air breathers that must surface regularly to breathe. They lack a dorsal fin; instead, steering is accomplished by manoeuvrable front flipper "legs", which are also used to prop them on the sea floor while feeding and to "clasp" while mating. A powerful tail, like that of a dolphin, propels them through the water. Where populations are high, as at Shark Bay, Dugongs seasonally gather in large herds of 100–200 animals. A low reproductive rate (females first mate at about ten years of age and raise a single infant at each birthing period), loss of habitat, drowning in prawn nets and fatal injury by boat propellers, threatens their population levels. Without greater conservation efforts, the future for this magnificent mammal, which should by rights enjoy a lifespan comparable to that of humans, could be catastrophic.

Left: Gregarious Bottlenose Dolphins are regular visitors to the shallow, food-rich waters of Shark Bay. *Right, top to bottom:* A heavy skeleton overlaid with a thick "padding" of blubber helps the Dugong sink to the sea floor to graze, although it must return to the surface to breathe; Tiger Sharks are predaceous overlords of the realm; Southern Right Whales, such as this mother with calf, are at the northern limits of their range in Shark Bay.

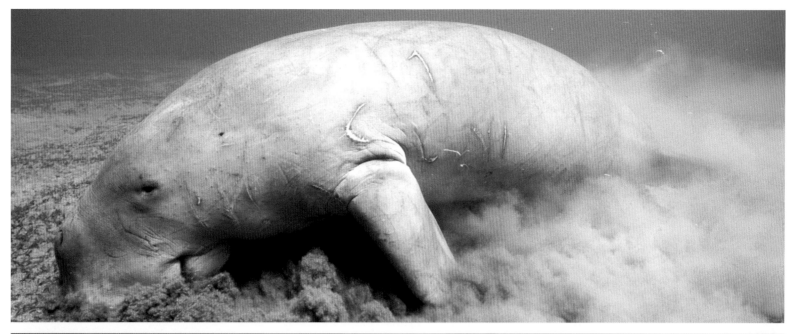

Above: Prickly-skinned echinoderms known as sea stars (or, less correctly, starfish) traverse the soft bottoms on hundreds of "sucker-like" tube feet.

Sealife of the Soft Bottoms and Seagrass Meadows

Subtidal soft-bottom habitats of mud, sand or gravel are more widely distributed than any other. They occur above the continental slope and represent old shorelines at periods of low sea levels. Exposure during low sea level "reworks" surface materials, sorting them by wind and water into three grades of sediment and topping them, during high sea level, with sediment comprised mainly of stratified fine clays and mud or, nearer to the coast, coarser sediment. Larger organisms live on or close to the surface; smaller ones, such as bivalves and worms, can dig with less use of energy. Even smaller organisms live in the pore spaces between and around the grains.

Classic Sealife: Plankton of sea jellies; crustaceans and fishes; cockles; Pearl Oyster; Saucer Scallop; clams; *Pecten modestus*; *Solemnya* spp.; *Botula vagina; Modiolus philippinarum*; *Pinna bicolor; Gomphina undulosa*; Cerith Creeper; Mulberry Whelk; amphipods; *Alpheus edwardsii* (a Snapping Prawn); *Alpheus novaezealandiae*; Ghost Shrimp; Grease-back Prawn; rock lobsters; Sponge Crab; spider crabs (*Halicarcinus* spp. and *Naxia aurita*); Blue Swimmer Crab and other *Portunus* spp.; hermit crabs; sea cucumbers; sea squirts; free-swimming anemone; urchins and polychaete worm larvae; Rock Flathead; *Nephtys* sp.; grunter; silver biddy; Old Wives; cardinalfish; whiting; Bridled Leatherjacket; Threadfin Bream (*Pentapodus vitta*); Sea Trumpeter; Yellow-eye Mullet; False Scorpionfish (*Centrogenys vaigiensis*); Silver Bream; Tongue Sole and flounder; at least three sea snakes, including the Shark Bay Sea Snake (*Aipysurus pooleorum*); Australian Sea-lions; Dugong; Bottlenose Dolphins.

Classic Birds: Herons; egrets; cormorants.

Seagrass — a Habitat Building Block

Some 60 flowering species conduct their life cycles below water level and Australia is the centre of their diversity, with fourteen found nowhere else. Strong tidal currents demand strap-like leaf shapes that flow with the current. Water also provides buoyancy and lift for flexible plants. Continually bathed in water, plant cells are enclosed in a fine membranous cuticle through which nutrient and gas exchange takes place directly from the water. Root systems develop from nodes along an underground stem or rhizome, functioning as anchors in the soft floor. Pollination presents another problem, because the usual methods cannot work. Pollen grains in seagrasses are very large; prior to shedding them into the water, mechanisms lift the flower heads high in the water column.

The environmental conditions are rigorous not only for the plants, but also for animals. In growing on the shallow, largely unstable sea bed, the grasses provide a rough texture that creates an anchor for a great many other smaller plants and animals. These, then, are the basis for complex food webs that support a plethora of larger life, such as Western Crayfish, Snapper, Old Wife, Dugong, Australian Sea-lions, a number of leatherjacket species, octopuses, Garfish and Black Swans. Most of these animals do not consume the seagrass itself, but rely on the epiphytic algae, bacteria, fungi and protozoa resident on the seagrass or any of the dependent organisms. So, from a habitat point of view, seagrass stabilises the entire system, provides habitat furniture, shelters animals from predators or from excessive sunlight and facilitates the "special space" quality required by organisms in carrying out their life functions. The system as a whole, but particularly the bulk of the grass, ultimately forms stable organic strata that assists in buffering the impact of storms.

Above and inset: Sand Octopuses belong to the class Cephalopoda (from the Greek meaning "head-and-foot animal") — the most intelligent, highly evolved class of invertebrates. Well-developed nervous systems and attached sacs called chromatopores allow them to quickly change colour for camouflage, mating or defence purposes.

Above left, top to bottom: Soft bottoms and seagrass habitats have both inspired marvellous attempts at concealment — the Eastern Stargazer remains stationary, using the eyes on top of its head to watch for food from above; Sand Flathead; Common Stingaree; not all sea stars have five arms — they may have as many as 40, each with a remarkable ability to regenerate. *Centre, top to bottom:* A sea anemone perches on a scallop; Hinge-beaked Shrimps are well-hidden in this habitat; Crested Weedfish pass themselves off as weed to avoid predation; seahorses scour the seagrass for shrimps. *Right, top to bottom:* Sea pens, named for their resemblance to feather quills, can grow several metres tall; the Eastern Spiny Gurnard employs a false eye-spot to make it appear more threatening; sea urchin; sea hares, a type of sea slug, glide across the sea floor where they feed on seaweeds and seagrasses.

Forests

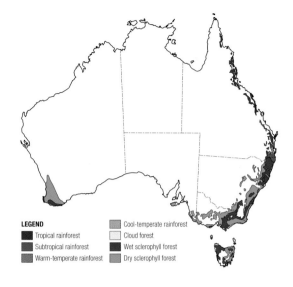

LEGEND

LEGEND

■	Tropical rainforest	▨	Cool-temperate rainforest
■	Subtropical rainforest	□	Cloud forest
▨	Warm-temperate rainforest	■	Wet sclerophyll forest
		▨	Dry sclerophyll forest

Above: Australia is blessed with some of the most pristine forest habitats in the world, including the World-Heritage-listed Central Eastern Rainforest Reserves and the Tasmanian Wilderness. The vegetation map above shows the distribution of Australian forest habitats.

Previous pages: Dense forest blankets the slopes of Mount Cloudmaker in Kanangra–Boyd National Park, New South Wales.

Above: The Superb Lyrebird is an accomplished mimic that inhabits the dense forests of coastal south-east Australia. *Right:* Mountain Ash forest at Healesville, Victoria.

Sclerophyll Forests

Some places, where the trees are fewer and at a lower altitude, the timber is much larger in diameter, averaging from 6–10 feet [2–3 metres] and frequently trees to 15 feet [4.5 metres] in diameter are met with on alluvial flats near the river. These trees average about ten per acre [25 per hectare]; their size sometimes is enormous. Many of the trees that have fallen through decay and by bushfires measure 350 feet [108 metres], with girth in proportion. In one instance I measured with the tape line one huge specimen that lay prostrate across a tributary of the Watts River [Healesville] and found it to be 435 feet [134 metres] from its roots to the top of its trunk. At 5 feet [1.7 metres] from the ground it measures 18 feet [5.5 metres] in diameter. At the extreme end where it has broken in its fall, it is 3 feet [1 metre] in diameter, This tree has been much burnt by fire, and I fully believe that before it fell it must have been more than 500 feet [154 metres] high. As it now lies it forms a complete bridge across a deep ravine.

Report by Surveyor William Ferguson to Victorian State Forests Assistant Commissioner, Clement Hodgkinson, in 1872.

This remarkable tree, perhaps the highest ever measured by humans anywhere, apparently wasn't all that remarkable when the great wet sclerophyll forests of Mountain Ash were first plundered by pioneering Victorian settlers.

When Melbourne was settled, Australia contained some of the tallest trees on Earth! Four or five generations ago, in the wet southern gullies of the Great Divide to the east and north-east of Melbourne, lived trees that measured more than 150 metres high (500 feet by William Ferguson's measurement). These were the great Mountain Ash of Victoria, known as Swamp Gums in Tasmania (*Eucalyptus regnans*). Throughout the great gold rush of 1851, the wonderful free-splitting straight grain of these tall hardwoods proved perfect for fulfilling the urgent need for millions of roofing shingles and fence palings. By the 1870s, a combination of clearing for the establishment of farms, as well as natural and lit fires and timber-getting had destroyed these giants. Worse still, they have now disappeared from the human imagination, therefore limiting our expectations. These forests were the ultimate wet sclerophyll ecosystems.

THE EVOLUTION OF AUSTRALIAN FORESTS

Foreigners are usually impressed by how different Australian vegetation is from that of the Northern Hemisphere, particularly the forests. Yet they see similarities in many of the smaller plant species to those of South Africa and some plants from South America. Why is that so? The answer is simply that these similarities have real evolutionary connections.

Some 135 million years ago, these continents were joined with the Antarctic to form the supercontinent of Gondwana, and plant life was passing through one of its great revolutions. Flowering plants, the angiosperms, were evolving. The more "primitive" plants were spore- and cone-bearers — gymnosperms, such as ferns and pines. Northern Hemisphere continents, dominated by conifers, were much further away from these centres of flowering plant development.

Green Fire

Plants are the great food producers for animals, which either directly consume plant matter (flowers, nectar, leaves, fruit, seeds, sap or wood) or eat other animals further down the food chain, which in turn have eaten and grown on plants.

Plants have chlorophyll, the "green fire" that, by the plant's magical processes, can use the sun's energy to convert lifeless chemical elements from the soil and the air (dissolved in water) into living tissue.

Chloroplasts, derived from ancient bacteria in plant leaves, are the miraculous link between the animate and inanimate worlds of this planet — they enable plants to create the living from the lifeless in an ongoing cycle of death to life, to death to life. The ingredients are soil minerals, atmospheric gases, water and sunlight. The sun's warmth keeps water liquid and governs the processes of life. Trees, as giant plants, need plenty of these ingredients.

Approximately 50 million years ago, once Australia had completely broken free from Gondwana, the evolution of endemic Australian flora (and fauna for that matter) began in earnest. There were, of course, long-distance immigrants, notably those species borne by air or water. Migration became more common as Australia rafted closer to Asia and the distance and difficulty was lessened. Australia has always been open to adventurous travellers seeking supportive environmental conditions on this continent; some adventurous Australian species likewise travelled overseas.

Around about the time Australia became a separate continent, the best known Australian family, Myrtaceae, came to be. Thirty million years later, the genus *Eucalyptus* appeared, and soon after, when the continent was close enough to the Indonesian archipelago for tropical invaders to arrive, *Acacia* made its appearance.

The vegetation map on page 100 shows the location of Australian forests. Before we proceed, here are thoughts to ponder. Where are the Wet Tropics? Where is the High Country? Where are the richest soils? Where is the dry country? Where is the cool country?

Now study the map and work out why the different forests are where they are. The names of the forest types used here will help: dry sclerophyll forest, wet sclerophyll forest, wet tropical rainforest, subtropical rainforest, warm- and cool-temperate rainforests, cloud forest, monsoon and dry rainforest, and dry rainforest.

Let's visit the dry sclerophyll forests first.

Above: The 500 metre Tahune Forest Air Walk, over the Huon River, Tasmania, takes visitors high into the canopy of tall Tasmanian Blue Gum, Swamp Gum and Messmate forest.

Above: Dense tropical rainforest surrounding Lake Eacham, Atherton Tableland, Queensland, can best be observed from the circular walking track or from a boat. *Below:* Adventurers rest on granite boulders after the rainforest walk up the Mossman River, Queensland.

Above, top to bottom: Mountain Ash forest in Yarra Ranges National Park, Victoria; the Tahune Air Walk rising above the forest understorey in Huon Valley, Tasmania.

40 m

Emergent forest
trees have trunks longer
than the depth of the canopy.

Where Are They? Places with low soil-moisture retention require moderate rainfall to sustain these forests. These conditions are found in New South Wales around the Hunter Valley, the Mid-Clarence Valley, the western edge of the New England region and the Ulan–Tuena area. In Victoria, they exist around Lake Eildon, near Maryborough, in the Pyrenees area, south of Colac, and in the Black Range State Park area. Dry sclerophyll habitat also grows north-east of Launceston (Tas), on west Kangaroo Island (SA), and in South-West Western Australia from Mount Barker to Perth, excluding the Karri–Tingle forests.

What Do They Look Like? These 25–35 metre high forests of fairly even height have moderately dense canopies that frequently link. The dry to damp forest floor is covered with grasses and shrubs.

Critical Conditions: Undulating to hilly well-drained country, generally within the 450–650 millimetre rainfall area, with cool winters and warm to hot summers. Soils are usually grey-brown and brown podzolic with an acid reaction and are free of lime and strongly leached.

Dry Sclerophyll Forests

2 December, 1642 … an abundance of excellent timber, and a gently sloping watercourse in a barren valley … they had seen two trees about 2 or 2.5 fathoms [c. 4 metres] in thickness, measuring from 60 to 65 feet [22 metres] from the ground to the lowermost branches … That on the ground they had observed certain footprints of animals, not unlike those of a tiger's claws; they also brought on board … a small quantity of gum of a seemingly very fine quality, which had exuded from the trees. [They reported] That the land is pretty generally covered with trees, standing so far apart that they allow a passage everywhere, and a lookout to a great distance, so that when landing our men could always get sight of natives or wild beasts unhindered by dense shrubbery or underwood … in the interior they had in several places observed numerous trees which had deep holes burnt into them … the surrounding soil having become as hard as flint through the action of the fire. We now and then saw clouds of dense smoke rising up from the land.

Abel Janszoon Tasman's *Journal of the Discovery of Van Diemen's Land and New Zealand* in 1642.

This is the very first description of sclerophyll forest. The giant trees were probably Messmate (*Eucalyptus obliqua*) growing on the east coast of Tasmania. The bay shore on which the crew had landed was Frederick Hendrick Bay, on the Forestier Peninsula — an area where wet and dry sclerophyll forests overlap. The comment on fire explains why the understorey was so clear of shrubbery.

Eucalypt trees (gums, bloodwoods, ironbarks, stringybarks, peppermints, box, ash and mallee) have thick, leathery leaves, usually with waxy coatings and oil glands — features that evolved to enable these plants to conserve water. They are sclerophyllous (from the Greek *sclero* meaning hard and *phyllon*, leaf). Dry sclerophyll forest, then, is a community of tall, closely growing trees that are mostly eucalypts. There are more than 700 species and subspecies in the genus *Eucalyptus* in Australia. Because these trees grow close together and almost interlock up top, bright sunlight reaches the top of the canopy and much less filters through to the forest below (even though eucalypt leaves generally hang edgeways to the light). The trunks of forest trees are usually much longer than the depth of the forest canopy. Where the woodland trees have hemispherical canopies, most forest trees have a flat, wedge-shaped crown. These tall forests with floors covered with sclerophyllous shrubs, such as acacias and peas, develop on drier ridges and droughtier soils than wet sclerophyll forests, which have dense, wet ferny floors.

Dry sclerophyll forests produce a large mass of living material, so they require an accessible nutrient supply and moderate soil moisture. The dry forests of tall trees are perhaps best represented by the Jarrah of Western Australia, but by far the largest communities of dry sclerophyll forest are found in the south-east Australian region. This community has adapted to make efficient use of nutrients and available water, particularly the Spotted Gum–Narrow-leafed Ironbark community of the Hunter Valley. Mature natural forests include trees of different ages, from juvenile to 300–400-year-old senile trees in "old-growth forests".

Left: Dry sclerophyll forest, as in this section of Brisbane Forest Park, Queensland, has a very rich sclerophyllous understorey of plants, such as acacias (wattles), grass-trees, bush peas, grasses and boronias. *Right:* This majestic stand of eucalypts west of Batemans Bay depicts classic dry sclerophyll forest made up of valuable Spotted Gum (*Eucalyptus maculata*), with a cycad (*Macrozamia* sp.) and Blady Grass (*Imperata cylindrica*) understorey.

EFFECTIVE ADAPTATIONS OF GUM TREES

Australian forests and woodlands are said to be evergreen. However, they do lose leaves throughout the year. In tropical Australia the climate is described as having two seasons, the Wet and the Dry, coinciding with the working of the monsoon. Each year, drought occurs in the north. To survive, trees must reduce water loss by cutting evapo-transpiration from their leaves. Tropical trees are well adapted to this regime; as the air and soil dry out, they begin to drop their leaves. By August, drought worsens until humidity increases in November, when, as a signal that the Wet is on its way, the miracle of fresh growth begins.

Four plant mechanisms protect the eucalypt tree from death by defoliation, whether it be by insect attack, fire or drought. Two of these are different kinds of buds that lie where the leaf stem (petiole) is attached to the twig — one looks like a tiny bud and lies in the angle of the leaf axil; the other is unformed bud material in the same area. As the original leaf grows, the axillary bud begins its growth. In this way, a dense canopy can develop very rapidly. If the living leaves are removed, the tree system reacts immediately because the power supply of the plant has been shut down. Reserve energy, in the form of sugar stores, takes over. Hormones are released and rapidly flow in the sap to the remaining axillary areas, setting the second types of bud material growing. Within a week or two, fully formed buds appear. Fresh young leaves begin to develop, meaning that, suddenly, the sun's energy supply has been reignited!

If ever there is a time when an insect attack is likely it is after a fire, when there is a vast stock of fresh, succulent leaves. After the big Nadgee (NSW) fire in 1972, a series of insect plagues arose, which for many trees caused the complete loss of the new leaves. Ultimately, this surge of opportunistic vegetarians resulted in subsequent increases in predatory populations of other organisms (mainly other insects and birds) in the very diverse natural system. The trialling, testing and adaptation of gum trees in competitive Australian environments has shown the eucalypt to be such an effective plant that when grown overseas, away from its competitive environment, it quickly develops an incredibly heavy canopy and experiences very rapid growth, producing softer, weaker timber.

There are times after very intense fire, which "cooks" those upper buds, or after the upper tree has been destroyed by storm, when two other adaptations come into play to produce photosynthesising surfaces. These are the dormant buds of the trunk and branches (epicormic) and of the underground, woody root stock (lignotuber); both types have origins in the unused bud material of the leaf petioles from the very first seedling tree leaf. It has been estimated that there are about 7000 epicormic buds available within an undamaged mature eucalypt. Only when the canopy leaves and buds have been shut down do the hormones trigger growth of some of the epicormic buds.

Some species, particularly the mallees, have developed greater use of the underground buds and avoided the development of epicormic shoots. The various uses of these four bud systems, particularly of the lignotubers, by different eucalypt species tells us much about the environments in which the species are found. These systems are used most frequently in areas where fire or severe drought is most likely.

Left, top to bottom: Vertically hanging eucalypt leaves protect the leaf surface from the intense sunlight. The exposed edge grows larger cells and produces the typical sickle shape; epicormic shoots grow from buds buried beneath the thick, insulating, corky bark of the bloodwood eucalypt sapling. This bud growth is triggered by hormones, which are set flowing by the tree after the leaves of the canopy have been scorched or lost.

Clockwise from top left: Dry season grassfire burns through dry sclerophyll forest on Cape York, Queensland; the bunched, grass-like leaves of this grass-tree in Stirling Range National Park, Western Australia, are rich in flammable resins that virtually explode once alight — buds within the cool centre of the tip are not affected and very quickly shoot in a long flower spike, sometimes causing the plant to be called a "kangaroo-tail" plant; banksia, hakeas and other woody-fruited plants of the Proteaceae family have seeds protected from fire by thick, woody capsules — when roasted by fire or drought, these capsules open to release their seeds onto a cool ash bed before the next rain; tree ferns, bracken and Blady Grass rapidly reshoot after fire because the buds are either below ground or protected by the robust trunk of the fern — the manager of this fire near Bombala, New South Wales, called it a "cool" fire because it did not burn out the canopy.

Above: Spring is wonderful in these forests as the wattles burst with gold and bush peas speckle the understorey. *Below:* In the south-west, some dry forests of Karri produce a larkspur haze above the green of bracken ferns, particularly in autumn after a shower. *Right:* After rain, the vegetation in this dry forest near Pemberton, WA, responds with vigorous growth.

AUSTRALIA'S TYPICAL "BUSH" HABITAT

Dry sclerophyll forests and woodlands are probably the nearest communities to the "bush" in its Australian context. The word comes from the Dutch *bosch*, which was used to describe the natural country of South Africa and which British author Anthony Trollope defined for Australia as "the gum-tree forest". Dry sclerophyll forest and dry sclerophyll woodland communities occupy a niche midway between desert and rainforest, the two driest and wettest terrestrial communities.

Looking at the map records of drought over Australia in the last century, only 34 years had average (or better) humid years. For the other 66 years, drought affected the greater part of the Australian continent. Drought is normal in Australia, where rainfall is apparently largely accidental. Of course, particular locations had worse or better conditions than the average. Two or three years of successive drought following a couple of years of above-average rainfall is not unusual and leads to ideal conditions for wildfire.

A few times a century, ideal conditions for extreme wildfire occur over a very large area. Species in the genus *Eucalyptus*, as the dominant tree cover between the semi-arid and humid areas of the continent, have had to become adapted to regular drought and catastrophic wildfire. These adaptations make this genus extremely valuable in a world that appears to be drying out: they protect the trees from death caused by loss of leaf cover — their source of cell energy — but they also protect the tree from animals, mainly insects, that defoliate trees.

Although a variety of floral species comprise the sclerophyll forest, the eucalypt is the main character. So widespread are eucalypts that most Australian kids have heard of Snugglepot and Cuddlepie, the gumnut babies created by celebrated children's author May Gibbs. The peaked caps the gumnut babies wear are the little caps, called operculums, worn by the bush gumnuts to protect the budding flower beneath. The French botanist who gave eucalypts their generic name borrowed from the Greek *eu* (well) and *kalyptos* (covered) to create the name that describes this defining characteristic of these hard-headed little gumnuts.

Post-fire studies conducted in the Nadgee Nature Reserve (NSW) found that parasitic mistletoes, one of the great thieves of eucalypt nutrients as well as potential tree killers, were killed by crown wildfires. Months after the fire more than 90% of the remaining tree branches were mistletoe-free. In this sense, even though the wildfire caused much damage, it also acted as a "cleaning" agent.

What is Sclerophyll Forest?

The word sclerophyll, however difficult it might seem to spell, is an extremely significant word for understanding Australian plant communities because it describes some of the most important elements of Australian flora, including eucalypts, tea-trees, banksias, grevilleas, wattles and Epacrids.

Sclerophyll is derived from the Greek *sclero* (hard), and *phyllon* (leaf). So sclerophyllous plants have hard leaves. Why would important Australian plant groups have hard leaves? The reason goes back to the soil's history, with help from the climate.

Any place in which plants grow has a range of plant species that fit those growing conditions. The environmental conditions in Australia, like those of Africa, are quite different from other continents. The land surface is ancient, not having been recently swept by massive volcanic flows, glaciers or other rapid landscape-changing forces. So the soils have been slowly drained of their nutrients, which create food for plants, and particularly of phosphorous.

Unlike that of other continents, Australian flora was largely isolated on this island continent until about 25 million years ago, when Asian plants began to migrate successfully. Long isolation, low-phosphate soils and increasing aridity, meant that those plants able to build hard leaves with much lignin (a material impairing the loss of water) were the best survivors. They were aided along the way by also having, embedded in their leaves, cells that produced coatings of waxes and oils. Thus the families Myrtaceae and Proteaceae succeeded where many softer, less rigid leaf producers could not. The leathery leaves of the eucalypts and acacias certainly won out in Australia. There is, however, a downside. These sclerophyllous, wax-coated plants are also highly flammable. Australia's searing hot bushfires are infamous. To survive this hazard, these plants had to develop further strategies of survival, which will be discovered later.

Best Examples: *Qld* — Brisbane Forest Park. *NSW* — Gibraltar Range, Coolah Tops and Wollemi National Parks; Kanangra–Boyd, Blue Mountains and Morton National Parks; Deua National Park; Yarrangobilly–Talbingo and Sawpit Creek sections of Kosciuszko National Park; South East Forest National Park. *ACT* — Namadgi National Park. *Vic* — Alpine National Park (lower sections); Mount Buffalo National Park; Croajingolong National Park; Grampians National Park. *Tas* — Douglas Apsley National Park; Scottsdale. *WA* — John Forrest National Park; Wandoo Conservation Park; Dryandra Nature Reserve; Tuart Forest National Park; Porongurup and Stirling Range National Parks.

Sounds: Wind in the treetops; bellbirds; parrots.

Smells: Eucalyptus.

Sensations: Feel insignificant and humbled by these incredible forests.

Above, top to bottom: Stirling Range, Western Australia; Three Sisters, Blue Mountains, New South Wales; A view through sclerophyll forest from Wivenhoe Outlook, Queensland. Here, in Brisbane Forest Park, the soils are deeper and there is generally good rainfall, so there are adequate supplies of nutrients to support such large plants. However, global warming is dramatically altering the landscape and bringing widespread drought to much of South-East Queensland.

Above, left and right: Mighty Mountain Ash trees, the world's tallest flowering plants, tower over large tree ferns that thrive on the floor of sclerophyll forest in Yarra Ranges National Park, Victoria. These tall timbers provide refuge for a multitude of wildlife, including the endangered Leadbeater's Possum.

Flora of the Dry Sclerophyll Forests

Dry sclerophyll eucalypt canopies let sunlight through to the forest floor, so numerous smaller sclerophyllous plants, shrubs and grasses can grow there. The environment these plants occupy is even drier than the tree layer, so they must have very water-efficient growth strategies. These strategies include leaves protected against water loss; rapid take-up of available groundwater by the roots; small, stem-clasping leaves; and a capacity to store water.

Acacias, banksias (and others of the Proteaceae family) and heath-like plants are particularly well suited to the living conditions in dry sclerophyll forests. They frequently form a dense, prickly understorey, as in the Silvertop Ash forests of the continent's south-east, the stringybark forests of Glenrowan (Vic), and the Pilliga forest (NSW). West of Batemans Bay (NSW), and verging on wet sclerophyll forests, are unusual great Spotted Gum forests with an understorey of cycads. Eucalypts of all bark types — gums, ashes, bloodwoods, stringybarks, peppermints and ironbarks — are present in this environment.

Classic Plants: Spotted Gum; White Gum; Blackbutt; Mulga Ironbark; White Mahogany; Pink Bloodwood; Silvertop Ash; Red Stringybark; Messmate; peppermints; Manna Gum; Tasmanian Blue Gum; Jarrah; Marri; Tuart; Pink Summer Calytrix; Swan River Myrtle; Old Man Banksia; *Dryandra* spp.; Silver, Cootamundra, Sunshine, Spreading, Knife-leaf and Prickly Moses Wattles; Prickly Hakea; Forest Woody Pear; Sword-leaf, Hickory, Deane's and Gosford Wattles; hopbushes; *Pultenaea* spp.; *Stypandra* spp.; *Dianella laevis*; Basket Grass (*Lomandra longifolia*); *Stipa* spp.; False Sarsaparilla; Pink Heath; grass-trees; Drumsticks; Cherry Ballart; Handsome Flat Pea; Grey Everlasting; Bitter Pea; Prickly Bitter Pea; *Daviesia* spp.; Yellow-eyed Flame Pea; Golden Glory Pea; spider orchids; Blue China Orchid; Wedding Bush; Bitter Pea; Bush Pea (*Pultenaea* spp.); Hyacinth Orchid (*Dipodium roseum*); Geebung (*Persoonia salicina*); Pine-leaf Geebung (*Persoonia pinifolius*); Gymea Lily (*Doryanthes excelsa*); Pink Five-corners (*Styphelia tubiflora*); Austral Indigo (*Indigofera australis*); Spike Wattle (*Acacia oxycedrus*); Myrtle Wattle (*Acacia myrtifolia*); Queensland Silver Wattle (*Acacia podalyriifolia*); Wax-lip Orchid (*Glossodia major*); Grey Spider Flower (*Grevillea buxifolia*); Silky Grevillea (*Grevillea sericea*); Sydney Boronia (*Boronia ledifolia*); *Crowea saligna*.

Above: A Sugar Glider feeds on gum tree nectar. *Left, top to bottom: Hovea speciosa;* Hairpin Banksia; the Handsome Flame Pea grows on the floor of the dry forests on a foundation of Sydney sandstone; False Sarsaparilla (*Hardenbergia violacea*), also known as Native Wisteria, scrambles vigorously over the ground-cover plants.

Clockwise from top: Woodlands in the Bunya Mountains in Queensland are covered with typical dry sclerophyll forest with numerous grass-trees in the understorey; Curled-tongue Shell Orchids sneak into the dry forests along creek lines, where the soil may be deeper, damper and better shaded by scrub; Pink Heath is the floral emblem of Victoria; Flannel Flowers bloom en masse in the sandstone forests of Warrumbungle National Park, Blue Mountains National Park and other sandy coastal country, particularly if the forest has been disturbed; Epacrids, such as this Native Fuschia Heath, share numerous communities from the dry sclerophyll forests to woodlands, heathlands and even wetland edges; Cootamundra Wattle, as with many other *Acacia* species, flowers prolifically in dry forests of eastern Australia, such as in the Temora and Pilliga (NSW), and Ballarat (Vic), areas.

Classic Mammals: Eastern Grey Kangaroo; Western Grey Kangaroo; Swamp Wallaby; Wallaroo; Whiptail Wallaby; Rufus Rat-kangaroo; Tammar Wallaby; Tasmanian Devil; Eastern Quoll; Western Quoll; Spotted-tailed Quoll; Dingo; Brush-tailed Phascogale; Red-tailed Phascogale; Yellow-footed and Dusky Antechinus; Common Dunnart; White-footed Dunnart; Numbat; Short-nosed Bandicoot; Long-nosed Bandicoot; Common Wombat; Koala; brushtail possums; Yellow-bellied Glider; Greater Glider; Eastern Pygmy-possum; Western Pygmy-possum; Honey Possum; Potoroo; Tasmanian Pademelon; Red Flying-fox; Lesser Long-eared Bat; Chocolate Bat; White-striped Mastiff-bat; Gould's Wattled Bat; Southern Forest Bat; Bush Rat.

Above, top to bottom: The Koala inhabits both dry and wet sclerophyll forests; Common Brushtail Possum.

Above, clockwise from top left: Whiptail Wallabies; Yellow-bellied Glider; Eastern Grey Kangaroo; Common Wombat.

Mammals of the Dry Sclerophyll Forests

The dry forests and woodlands are the real Australian bush and the continent's most characteristic bushland animals call it home, including the Whiptail Wallaby of the central east, the ubiquitous Common Brushtail Possum, the Common Wombat and the Eastern Grey Kangaroo. In the south-west is the Western Grey Kangaroo, as well as many wallabies, the Common Wallaroo (or Common Wallaroo), possums and a number of gliders, along with predatory quolls. Numerous small mammals scramble about the trunks, branches and canopy of these forest trees, or forage among the leaf litter. Some of the most ferocious small dasyurid mammal predators are common, preying primarily on invertebrate fauna.

Like all rich and sustaining habitats, these forests contain food, water, shelter and specialised space for each species to carry out a fulfilling social and sexual life. They are multi-storeyed habitats, from the floor litter and logs and the grassy understorey to the tree structures and the tree-top "boarding houses". Human habitat destruction aside, fire too has the capacity to greatly simplify resources and thereby reduce habitat, population and species diversity.

Above, clockwise from top left: Helmeted Honeyeater; Scaly-breasted Lorikeet; Pied Butcherbird; Superb Fairy-wren.

Reptiles of Dry Sclerophyll Forests

Marauders of the forest floor are the monitors, which scrounge a living from invertebrates, small mammals and smaller reptiles as well as any luckless ground-nesting birds. Eggs are a delicacy and monitors will often climb into forest trees in search of nesting animals there.

Classic Reptiles: Marbled, Stone, Bynoe's, Lesueur's, Southern Leaf-tailed and Barking Geckoes; Tree Dtella; Jacky Lizard; Bearded Dragon; Gould's, Lace and Rosenberg's Monitor; Tree Skink; *Ctenotus* spp.; Dwarf Skink; Blotched Blue-tongue Lizard; Diamond Python; Brown Tree Snake; Green Tree Snake; Common Death Adder; Yellow-faced and Collared Whipsnake; White-lipped Snake; Red-naped Snake; Pale-headed Snake; Broad-headed Snake; Black Tiger, Island Tiger and Eastern Tiger Snakes; Red-bellied Black Snake; Eastern and Western Brown Snakes; Bandy Bandy.

Above, top and bottom: Monitor lizards and taipans are both roaming predators of dry sclerophyll forests.

Birds of the Dry Sclerophyll Forests

Birds that occupy woodlands also live, to a lesser or greater degree, in the dry forest, largely because this community thins out to become woodland. Birds have the great advantage of being able to bridge gaps in habitats, so the spacing of trees provides few problems and indeed some advantages for birds wishing to protect susceptible young from predation. Flight also means that the forest or woodland home can be isolated from food or water sources. The forest may only be one essential part of a bird's habitat. Thus the Pied Butcherbird may nest in a forest tree but may also forage across grassland for small lizards or mice. The Scaly-breasted Lorikeet makes the forests of the east coast its habitat, settling for a period to nest in a hollow before living the life of a wanderer, following the seasonal flowering of forest trees. For the Superb Fairy-wren, a tight little grass nest near ground level may well be the centre of the world. However, as the wren's brood grows, the whole family (conveniently camouflaged by non-breeding brown plumage) scatters about the brownish, grassy ground storey on its hunt for insects. The Helmeted Honeyeater, an endangered subspecies of the Yellow-tufted Honeyeater, is threatened by loss of habitat due to clearing and the impact of the advancing threat of human activity. A species has no greater threat than the destruction or modification of its habitat.

Classic Birds: Parrots and cockatoos; Bell Miner; Wedge-tailed Eagle; Little Eagle; Square-tailed Kite; Black-shouldered Kite; Pacific Baza; Grey Goshawk; Brown Goshawk; Common Bronzewing; Wonga Pigeon; Powerful Owl; Channel-billed Cuckoo; Sulphur-crested Cockatoo; Short and Long-billed Black-Cockatoos; Purple-crowned Lorikeet; Regent Parrot; Western Rosella; Red-capped Parrot; Shining Bronze-Cuckoo; Southern Boobook; Barn Owl; Rainbow Bee-eater; Splendid Fairy-wren; Painted Button-quail; Dollarbird; Spotted and Forty-spotted Pardalotes; Yellow and Buff-rumped Thornbills; Black-headed Honeyeater; Flame and Scarlet Robin; Western Yellow-Robins; Crested Shrike-tit; Rufous Whistler; Mistletoebird; Restless Flycatcher; White-winged Triller; Olive-backed Oriole.

Boarding Houses of the Sclerophyll Forests

Wet sclerophyll forests are sometimes referred to as "tall open forests", in contrast to the closed forests that are rainforests. Eucalypts, the dominant trees of the open forests, have been called "Nature's boarding houses" in that they provide excellent shelters for arboreal animals.

Long before trees die, the processes of death have begun. Fungi locate airways up the old, dead cores of trees and spread up these, consuming and decomposing core wood material as the tree grows upwards and leaving a hardwood outer casing inside the growing cambium layer of cells beneath the bark. A pipe develops, which, when it reaches the lower, older branches that also have dead heartwood, allows the fungal community to move into those places. The strength of cellulose is the factor determining the length of these lateral branches. In wet forests where there is considerable tree height, usually above 50 metres, branches rarely exceed 15 metres because, as the heartwood begins to decay, branches fall during strong winds. The jagged hollows of the stump are ready-made shelters for arboreal nesting birds, bats, possums, gliders, reptiles, spiders, insects and numerous other beasts.

Cockatoos and parrots tear away and remodel these hollowed-out "apartments", making a comfortably shaped lining out of chips and soft, rotting wood tissue. Meanwhile, other animals take up squatter's rights in the grounded branches. The senile trees of old-growth forests, some 300–400 years old in the case of eucalypts, make the most important contribution to the tall open forest — both from the point of view of total and diverse production as well as wildlife habitat.

However, the sclerophyllous leaves of eucalypts are toxic when young, which presents difficulties for haven-seeking animals residing in the trees' wonderful "boarding house" hollows. If they wished to feed off the trees, arboreal species had to develop specialised chewing and digestive features and habits. Consequently, Koalas developed exceptionally long, 2 metre caecums (similar to the human appendix) to help break down the gumleaf by extra fermentation. Possums, other frequent inhabitants of these forests, developed the habit of feeding their own faeces, containing partially broken down leaf, to their babies. This behaviour also transplanted helpful adult stomach bacteria into the baby's immature belly. Other arboreal animals, such as the Yellow-bellied Glider, sip a tree's sap directly by chewing holes through the bark into the tree's vascular system, while the Sugar Glider sips the nectar of flowers as well as nibbling them. These behavioural techniques bypass the problems presented by the tough sclerophyll leaves.

Above: A genetic mutation causes the rare, golden colouration of this brushtail possum, but these animals don't survive long in the wild. *Left, top and bottom:* Sugar Gliders live in tree-hollow nests and forage at night for nectar.

Above, clockwise from top left: The Blue-winged Kookaburra nests and rests on branches and in tree hollows across Australia's north; arriving in spring after wintering on northern islands, the Dollarbird searches out a nesting hollows in trees around the edge of the wet forests; hollows high in the trees make the perfect haven from predation; a Crimson Rosella at the entrance to its nest; newly hatched Blue-winged Kookaburras; juvenile Blue-winged Kookaburras.

60–75 m (150m until 1850)

Where Are They? In temperate and subtropical hilly country with average rainfall of more than 900 millimetres a year and with a January mean temperature greater than 30°C and a July mean of less than 5°C.

What Do They Look Like? Tall, dense eucalypt forests with open, almost continuous canopies, with a layer of lower trees filling the space between the trunks of the dominant trees. There will be a lush floor of bright green ferns, many of them tree ferns. In subtropical conditions there may be some palms in the understorey.

Critical Conditions: Require moisture, temperature and drainage, but with a heavy blanket of cycling, moisture-sustaining soil and organic material. Soils are podzolic and moderately fertile with a deep and damp organic horizon.

Wet Sclerophyll Forests

The thick high scrub was entwined with strong vines. At last we had to take it in turns to cut away the vines and scrub, to allow our horses to proceed, and one of the party always had a compass in his hand. Sometimes we came upon an immense tree that had fallen down across our course, perhaps five or six feet [2 metres] in diameter and a hundred yards [91.5 metres] long. Here we had to cut our way around the tree with our tomahawks; at night we had to tie our horses up, and allow them to eat the leaves of the scrub, the only food that they could procure. Scarcely a day passed but we were drenched with rain — our clothes were very wet. Our black man had to procure us a monkey, or sloth [Koala] every day, to supply us with animal food … he used to climb up quietly and kill one. The flesh is very tough, still we were glad to eat it; sometimes he would produce for us an opossum or bandicoot. These were considered a delicacy.

William Brodribb, explorer and pastoralist, following up Count Strzelecki in Gippsland, March 1841.

Brodribb's account describes the structure of a temperate wet sclerophyll forest very effectively: tall trees, low light, much moisture, vines, mid-storey trees, dense ferny understorey and deep, damp litter. It also describes Koalas in the trees, ringtail possums in the mid-storey and bandicoots in the litter.

With interlocking branches reaching for the sunlight, the forest canopy of leaves locks in high humidity and diminishes the light. In these conditions, a mid-storey of shorter trees with very efficient light-collecting leaves flourishes; this further reduces the light and creates an environment in which tree ferns, King Ferns and vines proliferate on the ground storey. These were the kinds of tangled barriers that made travelling on horseback impossible and forced Strzelecki to take 22 days to cover just 75 kilometres! Supporting this huge volume of living matter is rainfall greater than 900 millimetres per year and a great depth of damp, rotting organic litter. Beneath that lies deeply weathered organic soil.

Above, left to right: A fern-covered floor, deep, damp litter, a heavy understorey and rocketing eucalypts in the Brindabella Range, New South Wales, typify wet sclerophyll forest; River Red Gums depend entirely on the flow of rivers. These, on the Murray River floodplain near Barmah, Victoria, require flooding to encourage germination, usually along drift lines where seed accumulates. *Left:* Driving through wet sclerophyll forest on Fraser Island, Queensland. *Right:* Giants in any forest, these Karri are in the D'Entrecasteaux National Park, Western Australia.

Above: Tall, straight ash, Monkey Gums and Messmate, with interlocked canopies, comprise the wet sclerophyll forests of Walpole–Nornalup National Park, Western Australia.

Above: A Laughing Kookaburra, the largest of the kingfishers, finds a perch in the morning sun. The kookaburra's raucous laughter often heralds a morning chorus of songbirds in the wet forests.

LISTENING TO FOREST LIFE

Human beings are accustomed to using sight to understand the nature of things, but there was a time when sound, too, was important to our survival. These forests with their wonderful Mountain and Alpine Ash, and Shining Blue, Flooded and Monkey Gum trunks rocketing upwards through banks of tree ferns, can contain traps for bushwalkers and campers. Five-metre, smoothly dry spears sticking into the ground are lesser lateral branches, designed to break cleanly across a couple of centimetres of short cells (a brittle zone) when the branch is superseded by its parent's growth. Falling from 50 metres they will cut clean through a tent — or a skull for that matter! A keen sense of sound may be the key to survival.

A few months back I was reminded not of the dangers but of the delights of the auditory sense while camping in one of my favorite places, the wet forests of the South East Forest National Park in New South Wales. Following are my notes:

Dawn in August — canopies of Messmate, Brown Barrel, Ribbon Gum, River White Gum, Monkey Gum, Shining Gum and Swamp Gums are swimming in a sea of mist. Beyond them, the morning star pales against a rose sky. The air is chill, and on the forest floor, a flow of faint rustlings follow the path of a Yellow-footed Antechinus, the tiny tiger of the damp litter. There are other chirps, whistles and grindings, almost inaudible, made by the diminutive folk of the ferny gully. A series of muffled thumps and a dry raspy rattle of Gahnia leaves pushed aside cue a Swamp Wallaby warily approaching the water.

A soft bump, a series of scratchings by a moss-covered log, then a rising, gauzy cloud of shimmering silver feathers, vibrating excitedly above an earthy mound, heralds the first clear, ringing notes of a male lyrebird's dance to the dawn. The bush along the Monaro escarpment is waking. Australia's day-shy Sugar Gliders and Yellow-bellied Gliders, along with Long-footed Potoroos, retire to the safety of their nest hollows, high in the forest or deep among the tussocks. Powerful Owls lock their talons onto a high limb, for they, too, are creatures of the night.

The morning chorus gathers. High up on the exposed limb of a Monkey Gum, a pair of sunlit kookaburras welcome the rising warmth in competitive mirth.

Above: Damp litter of the forest floor produces a rich harvest of worms, insect larvae and other invertebrates for the Superb Lyrebird. While females busily forage, the males entertain with a medley of their neighbours' songs.

Friendly Grey Fantails chatter as they feed on insects coming to flight off creek-side ferns. A solo Golden Whistler echoes through the forest, while Shining Bronze-Cuckoos harmonise with their own conversation pieces. A shower of Red-browed Finches drop onto the inside grassy creek bank. The opposite, undercut bank hides a half-circular burrow of a Platypus among soft water fern fronds. Long streamers of hanging dry bark, the ribbons of the Ribbon Gum, rattle as White-throated Treecreepers chip away with searching beaks.

In a creek-side melaleuca, an Eastern Yellow Robin squats low on eggs in an exquisite wineglass of a nest of fine bark, hair and lichen. Like a shower of hugely raucous snowflakes, Sulphur-crested Cockatoos tumble and career from the highland woodlands across the scarp and into the forest below, leaving a couple of sentinels on watch in the sunlight above. Later, with the warming day, they will return to rejoin their mates, to preen, loaf and chortle among themselves. Far off, down the valley in a lerp-infested stand of Ribbon Gum and Brown Barrel, the clear, almost continuous call of Bellbirds drifts on the breeze.

There are many more animals of the forest communicating for food, fear, territory and reproduction. Give your eyes a spell for a while, or at least use eyes and ears — if not all the senses — to "feel" the life with which we share our planet.

Above: Forest-canopy walks give the visitor a unique view of the wet sclerophyll forest. Here the view is of Mountain Ash in the Mount Donna Buang Rainforest Gallery Walk, east of Melbourne, Victoria.

Above: Flooded Gums reach for the sky near Booloumba Creek in Conondale National Park, north of Brisbane, Queensland.

Above: Few human-designed columns rival the beauty of columns of Mountain Ash in Tarra-Bulga National Park, Victoria.

Best Examples: *NSW* — Mt Lindesay–Woodenbong; upper Clarence Valley; Guy Fawkes River; Comboyne area; Gloucester–Barrington–Karuah Rivers headwaters; Barrington Tops National Park; Mount Coricudgy; Mount Wilson; Bulahdelah; Macquarie Pass; Upper Clyde River; Monga; South East Forest National Park. *Vic* — Coopracambra State Park; Errinundra National Park; Mount Nunniong; Erica–Walhalla; Yarra Ranges and Dandenong National Parks; Otways area. *Tas* — Ben Lomond, Upper Huon Valley; Russell Falls area; north-west Tasmania. *WA* — Upper Forth River; Scott National Park; Tree Top Walk and Walpole–Nornalup National Park.

Sounds: Lyrebirds in winter; currawongs.

Smells: Damp earth and mulch.

Sensations: Cool dankness.

FORMATION OF THE WET SCLEROPHYLL FORESTS

Wet sclerophyll forest occurs along the ranges of the east coast, as well as in Tasmania and south Western Australia — the wetter areas of Australia. These areas are particularly found in the valleys and floodplains of the coastal river systems, many of which have been cleared for farming. Moisture, however, is not the only criteria for the location of wet sclerophyll forest. Soil fertility is important because these eucalypts contain the largest flowering plants on Earth and until quite recently boasted the tallest trees by far, exceeding the Giant Sequoia of California by at least 30 metres. Such large organisms require many soil nutrients — and the water to make them available.

The wet sclerophyll forest is a complex living system. Competition by many species is intense. While eucalypts may tower over other forest trees, young gums must battle for sunlight with pioneering rainforest species. Once gums reach the sunlight above, their competition is with other eucalypts and sometimes the Turpentine; the race for dominance remains intense. The cramped space prompts narrow crowns and close-growing trees.

Australia's coastal plain is relatively narrow, and if the country rock of the ranges behind is composed of granites, basalts or shales (all of which contain many nutrients) the drainage system will be fertile; if composed of sandstones and quartzites, it will be infertile. All of the wetter coastal areas, however, will have developed over time heavy litter-producing vegetation. In the moist environment, this wetness establishes thick beds of fertile mulch, covered by mosses, ferns and other understorey plants. Such an understorey attracts a mass of invertebrate and other animal life, which further helps in the turnover of litter nutrients that become rich plant foods.

Above: Beech forest rises above the tree ferns that line a cool creek in Tasmania. Lush gullies and pockets of moist green ferns set amid wet sclerophyll forest are extremely common in Tasmania.

Above, top to bottom: Tingle trees in The Valley of the Giants, Walpole–Nornalup National Park, South-West Western Australia; this wet sclerophyll forest of Tasmania's Recherche Bay hides early nineteenth-century gardens created by French navigators.

Classic Plants: Mountain Ash (Swamp Gum); Alpine Ash; Mountain Gum; Flooded Gum; Messmate; Blue Gum; Sydney Blue Gum; Blackbutt; Manna Gum; Shining Gum; Mountain Grey Gum; Karri; Yellow, Red and Rate's Tingles; Marri; Jarrah; She-oak; Turpentine; Tasmanian Blackwood; Silver Wattle; Sticky Wattle; Tree Hovea; Karri Hazel; Bird Orchid; Southern Sassafras; Mint Bush; Blanket Leaf; Musk Daisy Bush; Hazel Pomaderris; most *Pittosporum* spp.; Mountain Correa; Stinkwood; Muttonwood; Soft Water Fern; Fishbone Fern; Slender Tree Fern; Soft Tree Fern; Coral Fern; King Fern; Batswing Fern; Filmy Ferns; Tender Bracken; Bristle Fern; numerous fungi.

Above, top to bottom: The Tasmanian Waratah (*Telopea truncata*) is found at 600–1200 metres altitude in mountain forests; in warm-temperate wet forests, the King Orchid (*Dendrobium speciosum*) grows on dead tree trunks and rocks.

Frogs and Reptiles of the Wet Sclerophyll Forests

Classic Frogs and Reptiles: Bleating Tree-frog; Peron's Tree-frog; Green Tree-frog; Great Barred Frog; Common Eastern Froglet; tiger snakes; Common Death Adder; Broad-headed Snake; Rainforest Crowned Snake; Diamond Python; Highland Forest Skink; Eastern Blue-tongue; *Ctenotus* skinks; Land Mullet; Rainbow Skink; Lace Monitor; Eastern Bearded Dragon; Burton's Snake-lizard; Common Scaly-foot.

Above, top to bottom: Diamond Pythons are widely distributed but delight in the wet forests, where they prey on small mammals, amphibians and birds; Bleating Tree-frogs are small (4 centimetes long), breed after summer storms and get their name from their long, wavering, bleating call.

WET SCLEROPHYLL FORESTS AS ANIMAL HABITAT

This is a multi-storeyed habitat. Its top is the high forest canopy that, despite its low plant diversity, produces a high volume of leaves. Below that is the branch level, where many hollows and comfortable forks close down to a mid-storey of clear air between tall trunks rising from an understorey of frequently dense-growing shrubs and grasses. The ground storey is very sheltered from the sun and wind, and so remains damp and comprises a deep litter layer over moist mineral soil. Consider, then, which animals might occupy this moisture-laden territory.

Top-storey fauna must be flyers or climbers: Koalas, brushtail possums, fruit bats and birds. The clear mid-storey allows gliders and phalangers to move between trees, although they are also great climbers. All of these arboreal animals will devour nectar, flowers, leaves and fruit products of the canopy and utilise hollows and forks as "furniture" or shelter. Birds, meanwhile, chip away at invertebrates that have taken up residence on leaves and beneath bark. Height above ground level provides protection from many predators, but is no foil for strongly climbing monitors and birds of prey, such as falcons, goshawks, eagles and large owls.

The ground storey, with its diversity of food producers and its dense shelter, provides for numerous small herbivores that consume fruit, seeds, leaves and fungi in the damp litter. Many invertebrates live by tunnelling and foraging in the litter; these provide a food source for both vertebrates (antechinuses, frogs, skinks, lyrebirds and pigeons) and predatory invertebrates (centipedes, scorpions, ants and spiders). This whole system is a dynamically balanced natural environment.

Above: A Scarlet Robin remains alert for small insects.

Birds of the Wet Sclerophyll Forests

Classic Birds: Albert's Lyrebird; Satin Bowerbird; Regent Bowerbird; Torresian Crow; Pied Currawong; Grey Currawong; Grey Butcherbird; Australian Hobby; Figbird; Olive-backed Oriole; Black-faced Cuckoo-shrike; Trillers; Rufous and Grey Fantails; Leaden Flycatcher; Grey Shrike-thrush; Golden Whistler; Eastern and Western Yellow Robin; Eastern Spinebill; White-naped and White-eared Honeyeaters; White-browed Scrubwren; Striated and Spotted Pardalotes; Red-browed and White-throated Treecreepers; Noisy Pitta; Sacred and Forest Kingfishers; Sooty Owl; Masked Owl; Southern Boobook; Powerful Owl; Australian Owlet-nightjar; Common Koel; Channel-billed Cuckoo; Shining Bronze-Cuckoo; Brush Cuckoo; Fan-tailed Cuckoo; Crimson Rosella; Australian King-Parrot; Purple-crowned Lorikeet; Regent Parrot; Western Rosella; Red-capped Parrot; Rainbow Lorikeet; Laughing Kookaburra; Blue-winged Kookaburra; Splendid Fairy-wren; Red-winged Fairy-wren; White-browed Scrubwren; Western Gerygone; Western Thornbill; New Holland Honeyeater; Scarlet Robin; Golden Whistler; Black-faced Cuckoo-shrike; Paradise Riflebird; Gang-gang Cockatoo; Long-billed Black-Cockatoo; Wonga Pigeon; Common Bronzewing.

Mammals of the Wet Sclerophyll Forests

Classic Mammals: Koala; Greater Glider; Yellow-bellied Glider; Sugar Glider; Feathertail Glider; Mountain Brushtail Possum; Common Brushtail Possum; Common Ringtail Possum; Dingo; Bush Rat; Lesser Long-eared Bat (Tas); Long-eared Bat; Forest Bats; Chocolate Wattled Bat; Grey-headed Flying-fox; Long-nosed Flying-fox; antechinuses; Eastern and Western Quolls; Spotted-tailed Quoll; Brush-tailed Phascogale; dunnarts; Tasmanian Devil; Long-nosed and Long-footed Potoroos; Swamp Wallaby; Red-legged Pademelon; Red-bellied and Red-necked Pademelons; Parma Wallaby; Whiptail Wallaby; Red-necked Wallaby; Quokka; Short-beaked Echidna; Platypuses in the streams.

Above, clockwise from top left: The Long-footed Potoroo, the smallest of the macropods, feeds mainly on fungi growing in the damp litter of wet forests of Australia's south-east corner. Its numbers are quite low; Koalas were once widespread in dry and wet forests and woodlands, but now find their most agreeable habitats in the wet sclerophyll forest; Red-necked Pademelons dwell on forest edges close to grassed areas; the fierce Tasmanian Devil, once found on the mainland and depicted in Aboriginal art, is now restricted to the Tasmanian forests; Greater Gliders, Australia's largest possums, dine on eucalypt leaves.

Above, top to bottom: Christmas Beetles are scarabs that emerge from their underground larval stage in mid-summer to congregate in large numbers on wet sclerophyll trees; spiny leaf insects and phasmids periodically build populations up to plague proportions, doing considerable damage to wet forests by defoliating trees; one of the many land snail species that graze the forest floor, particularly in the evening after rain.

Invertebrates of the Wet Sclerophyll Forests

Classic Invertebrates: Red-triangle Slug; forest snails; amphipods; slaters; pill bugs; leeches; Leaf-curling Spider; Golden Orb-weaver; huntsmans; Sydney Funnel-web; trapdoor spiders; centipedes; millipedes; wasps; termites; Christmas Beetle; Stag Beetle; Cicada; phasmids; leaf-hoppers; earwigs; cockroaches; earthworms.

Rainforests

The relic rainforests strewn across the Australian continent has within a few years become a classic landscape for scientific research and aesthetic appreciation. It links us in our imagination with the stupendous ecological scenarios of the past. Many of the community types and habitats link us with similar types and habitats in tropical and temperate regions elsewhere. Thus despite cultural differences, here are the rudiments of a common ecological language as the result of shared natural resources and of shared human options for the future in a contracting world.

Dr Len Webb at the University of New England Summer School on Wildlife Conservation, 1966.

Rainforests are the hothouses of the plant world. They experience environmental conditions that are as near perfect for plant life as possible: bright sunshine to provide energy, rapid recycling of soil nutrients to provide nourishment, and warm wetness to maximise chemical reactions in the building of organic matter. Competition is extreme in such a rich environment and as many opportunities as are offered are quickly accepted by a myriad of plant and dependent animal species. Of course, over the billions of years that life has been evolving on this planet there has been time for many species of plants and animals to adapt to environments of all quality, hence there are communities in deserts, the oceans and on the alps. In fact, it is very difficult to find an environment where life is absent! However, as in most things, some rainforests are more perfect than others. The lowland tropical rainforest environment of the Daintree is richer than the subtropical rainforest at the foot of Mount Warning — although that is preferable to the warm-temperate conditions at Dorrigo — which are still better than those of the cool-temperate Barrington Tops, the Otways and Tasmania, or the highly seasonal monsoon areas of northern Australia.

Above: Cape Tribulation in Daintree National Park, Queensland, where the rainforest meets the azure waters of the reef. *Left:* Palms, such as these Fan Palms in lowland tropical rainforest near Cape Tribulation, play a significant role in the structure of subtropical and tropical rainforest ecosystems. They supply birds and bats with a diet of fruit, and their leaves, both dead and alive, provide important shelter.

Above: The buttressed roots of a Strangler Fig tangle over the forest floor in Mossman Gorge, within the Wet Tropics World Heritage Area, Queensland.

Left, top to bottom: Warm-temperate rainforest is resplendent with Coachwoods, tree ferns and palms in the Maiala section of Brisbane Forest Park, Queensland; tree ferns nestle beside a flowing creek in Melba Gully State Park, Victoria; cool-temperate rainforest nourishes Myrtle Beech, Richea and Sassafras in Mount Field National Park, Tasmania.

There is an intriguing variety of rainforests in Australia, even if they comprise just one-quarter of a percent of the planet's known rainforest resources. The intrigue is created because they represent a mix of primitive, isolated Gondwana stock. These remnants of ancient times were protected from the chill of the cooling planet by being rafted towards the equator on a continent adrift for over fifty million years. During this epic journey, the body of Australia was dehydrated but the Gondwanan relics survived in moist, warm pockets tucked into the eastern slopes of the Great Dividing Range in north-east Queensland. When the continental plate (of which New Guinea is part) had drifted close enough to Indonesia, some plant and animal species were finally able to cohabit. Some species from the rich, modern rainforests of South-East Asia were able to bridge the oceanic gap, being borne to these shores by birds, wind or waves. Yet many of the primitive species remained unchanged — that mix, although such a small percentage of rainforest worldwide, is nevertheless priceless in a world sense. Australia is an immense landmass, with a latitude stretching from 10° to 44° south. The sheer scale of this country — coupled with the geologically diverse mountain ranges of the eastern seaboard, which produce broad temperature, high rainfall and moist soil — allows for a wonderful diversity of plant environments. The 1200 or more rainforest tree species have either thrived or perished across these varied environments, creating our many rainforest types, from south-west Tasmania to Cape York and the Kimberley.

A major consequence of aeons of isolation and continental drift, combined with the desiccation of the interior, was that some of the primitive rainforest plants adapted to arid conditions. Two of Australia's most successful plant families, Myrtaceae (eucalypts, tea-trees and bottlebrushes) and Proteaceae (waratahs, needlebushes, banksias and so on) evolved in these harsh habitats; both have existed long enough to sustain themselves from the alpine tree line to sea level across this vast continent.

Above: In mountainous rainforest areas one is never far from a cascade. Here, Crystal Shower Falls in Dorrigo National Park, New South Wales, shows how water collected on a volcanic plateau tumbles off the edge to carve valleys and deep plunge pools as it heads towards the sea. *Left:* Humidity is maintained by misty spray from the falling water of Chalahn Falls, secreted in a subtropical rainforest gully in Lamington National Park, Queensland.

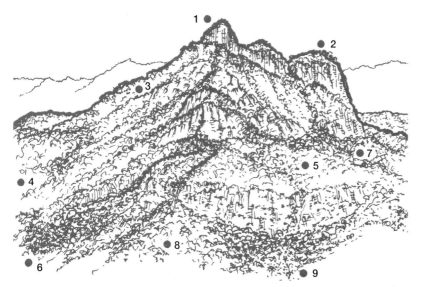

Mount Warning is all that remains of the core of the giant Tweed Volcano, which spewed out lava that hardened to form the McPherson and Richmond Ranges and Fingal Point. The lava's slow erosion and breakdown has left a craggy range with many great rock exposures, shallow soil pockets, steep well-drained slopes, gullies and areas of deeply weathered rock. Such a mosaic of surfaces is colonised by a complementing mosaic of vegetation, producing a very diverse range of habitats, shown with corresponding numbered habitats in the line drawing at left.

1. Shallow, dry soil on rocky top ground is Casuarina scrub.

2. This is deeper soil but is still droughty; on top is dry sclerophyll woodland.

3. Broken surface with good soil pockets; on the coolest south side is stunted warm-temperate rainforest.

4. & 5. Deep gullies, hot, wet and with good soil depth: subtropical rainforest.

6. & 7. The deepest soils in hot, humid valley areas verging on tropical rainforest.

8. Dry-ridge sclerophyll forest.

9. The heaviest rainforest growth is in this humid north-east valley.

Where Are they? Between Townsville and Cape York, Queensland, with the richest examples bounded by the Tully River, Great Dividing Range and Cooktown.

What Do They Look Like? Heavy forest with numerous tree species of varying height. Low light beneath the canopy and many vines and epiphytes. The edge of the forest is very dense, but inside a relatively clear floor is covered with thick, damp, decomposing litter. There are many plank buttresses on larger, taller trees.

Critical Conditions: Annual rainfall above 2000 millimetres per year (higher on granite, lower on basalt); humid atmosphere; no frosts; temperature of 20°C–35°C; high percentage of the area's nutrients are in active circulation in the standing crop.

Above: The walking track up the Tully River in Tropical North Queensland passes through majestic wet tropical rainforest.

Wet Tropical Rainforests

Rainforest is the single most important biological resource we hold in trust for Australia's future.

Professor Michael Archer in *Conserving Australia's Rainforests*, Aila Keto and Keith Scott, 1995.

The World-Heritage-listed Wet Tropics rainforests from Mackay to Cape York are Australia's richest and most biologically diverse, with around 1160 tree species. All are within 200 kilometres of the ocean. Rainforests to the west and south of this area progressively lose species and become less complex, with as few as 80 flowering species in Tasmania. Some individual rainforest species, such as the figs (*Ficus* spp.), have tiny, very specialised residual populations that are reminders of wetter times, hidden deep in the semi-arid and arid interior. The lushest, most magnificent and diverse area of tropical rainforest covers about 7500 square kilometres between Ingham and Cooktown. This is the heart of the 894,000 hectare Wet Tropics World Heritage Area, inscribed in 1988 for its "outstanding natural universal values" and for being an example of "superlative natural phenomena". This primitive rainforest is largely pristine, undamaged by human interference or natural catastrophe. Its intactness means it operates almost as a huge interdependent organism, parts of which are ancient. One Macintyre's Boxwood tree is 80 centimetres in diameter and aged at least 3500 years old!

NATURE OF THE RAINFOREST

Wet Tropics rainforests are such uniquely located and productive habitats that some 1164 genera of vascular plants have been recorded, including 13 of the 19 angiosperm families, the most primitive families of flowering plants worldwide. Two of these families are found nowhere else. No less than 50 species in the most primitive families are endemic to the Wet Tropics, but overall at least 700 plant species are unique to this place. Of the more than 400 Australian fern species, 240 are found here, with about 40 endemic to the region. To this impressive list we can add 90 species of orchid, with 40 of these being endemic. This abundance of flora has meant names such as Daintree, Cape Tribulation, Mossman Gorge, Downey Creek and Tully Gorge are rightfully imbedded in environmental history and these areas are to be protected as wet tropical rainforest wonders of the world.

From the lowlands, almost from sea level, to the top of Mount Bartle Frere there is a considerable range in temperature, humidity and soil type, expressed by various mixes of rainforest plant species. The area experiences 60% of its precipitation in just four months (December to March) with rainfall peaking on Mount Bartle Frere at around 10,000 millimetres. The average is about 2800 millimetres, which is near the optimum level for rainforest. Thus, graduations of habitat occur — the lowlands are very wet; the foothills, wet; the uplands, cloudy and wet; the highlands, moist; the peaks, extremely wet and cloudy; and the western aspects in rain shadow. The most luxuriant forests are in lowland rainforest. Imagine the forest as a multi-storeyed block of apartments. The penthouses are the tall emergent trees, such as Flooded Gum, Queensland Maple, Candle Nut, Kauri Pines and figs, which lift above the main canopy. These emergents have very large

Right: Coachwoods in Wooroonooran National Park in the Wet Tropics, Qld, carry heavy loads of epiphytes.

Best Examples: *Qld* — Palmerston Highway; Lake Barrine tour and around the lake's 5 kilometre walking track; Josephine Falls in Wooroonooran National Park; beneath the 7.5 kilometre Skyrail from Kuranda to Cairns; Wongabel State Forest with its 2.4 kilometre Botanical Walk with 190 identified trees; Mossman Gorge walking track; Cape Tribulation; Alexandra Lookout; Marrdja Boardwalk into lowland rainforest.

Sounds: Patter of fruit falling on the leafy floor; the gentle, low cooing of pigeons.

Smells: Damp fungi; spicy leaves.

Sensations: Humidity.

Above: Brightly coloured fruit from the Blue Quandong (*Eleocarpus augustifolius*) litters the floor of wet subtropical rainforest. The fruit is a favourite of the Wompoo Fruit-Dove, Southern Cassowary and Musky Rat-kangaroo.

supporting root buttresses to withstand extra wind buffeting above the general canopy. Numerous minor levels in the canopy give these trees a heavy load of fern and flowering epiphytes, as well as a tangle of woody vines and rattan palm. Usually, less than 5% of diffuse sunlight reaches the wet tropical rainforest floor. Consequently, the floor is often quite open, with most plants that have trunks lifting their large, light-seeking leaves far above. Where streams break the darkness or swampy, poorly drained ground makes up the forest floor, palms, such as the elegant Bangalow and Fan Palms may become dominant. Both tree size and leaf size diminish as one ascends higher into the ranges.

FRUITS OF THE FOREST

Many rainforest trees produce succulent fruits, some of which are borne directly along the trunk and branches, a process known as cauliflory. Often these fruits have brilliantly coloured flesh covering a hard kernel. The green gloom of the rainforest is punctuated by flashes of colour in the stunning purple-blue of the Blue Quandong; the apricot, vile-smelling fruit of the primitive *Austrobaileya* vine; the cream of Lemon Aspen; the vermilion of Lacewing Vine and Alexandra Palm; and the shining black Variegated Grape. All of the 33 wonderful *Syzygium* Satinashes add to the rainforest's palette. These species comprise just a fraction of the "fruits of the forest", all brilliantly painted in the eponymous book by William T. Cooper.

All of this vibrant colour is not mere decoration, it has a clear purpose. It is a highly effective attractant for animal seed-dispersal agents in this fruity "supermarket". Agents come in many forms, from forest birds to rats, possums, tree-kangaroos, Musky Rat-kangaroos, fruit bats and Southern Cassowaries.

Above, left to right: Satinash flowers and fruits directly from the branch or trunk, a process known as cauliflory and an indicator of a number of rainforest species in the Wet Tropics, Queensland; epiphytic plants trail over other rainforest flora, using tree trunks, limbs and stumps as support in their quest for light and living space.

Above left, top to bottom: An abundance of fruit, with fruiting fig species being some of the most prolific, draws a diversity of birds and fruit-eating mammals to the rainforest "supermarket" — Red Silkwood (*Palaquium galoctoxylum*); Cream Mahogany (*Chisocheton longistipitatus*); Australian Nutmeg (*Myristica insipida*); Variegated Fig (*Ficus variegata*). *Above centre, top to bottom:* Variegated Fig (*Ficus variegata*); Variegated Fig (*Ficus variegata*); Pandanus (*Pandanus gemmifer*); Fig (*Ficus* sp.). *Above right, top to bottom:* Cluster Fig (*Ficus racemosa*); Native Raspberry (*Rubus probus*); fig (*Ficus* sp.); fruits are often produced in dense clusters but later drop to the forest floor and roll or are spread by faunal rainforest inhabitants or washed in streams to new niches, where they struggle their way upwards to the light.

ANIMALS OF THE RAINFOREST ARBOUR

The sanctuary provided by the rainforest, along with its floral wealth, proves irresistible for a vast number of faunal species. Here, tree-top "furniture" protects canopy dwellers. Trunks and limbs provide masses of epiphytic cover as heavy as any grassland or heath. Cavernous tree hollows and thousands of easy vine routes simplify travel between forest canopy and floor. Soft, damp, deep litter or boulder-strewn floors with deep moss and fern beds, as well as numerous waterways from rocky rapids to quiet ponds, entice all manner of creatures. Given these multifarious habitats, the list of animals that dwell in this damp green wonderland is understandably impressive.

Wet tropical rainforests are home to the richest fauna in the country. Included are at least 666 species of vertebrates, made up of 89 mammal, 370 bird, at least 47 frog and 160 reptile species. About 160 of these are dependent on the rainforest habitats, and because Cape York at lower sea levels was once a "highway" from New Guinea, many of the species are shared with that island. The faunal importance of the Wet Tropics is emphasised by the fact that no less than 58 species of vertebrates are found only in this region. They include 9 mammal, 13 bird, 20 frog and 16 reptile species.

Of the mammals, the Musky Rat-kangaroo is of special interest. It is the smallest macropod, at just 25 centimetres high, and appears to be the most primitive of the kangaroos, showing a tree-living possum ancestry. Both species of tree-kangaroo, Lumholtz's and Bennett's, are found here. The region also has the highest representation of Dasyurids (quolls, antechinuses and dunnarts) with nine species found in the region, along with five of Australia's six ringtail possums, including the Herbert River Ringtail and Daintree River Ringtail Possums in the upland areas.

The bird species are a spectacular group, divided into those that favour the lowlands and those that tend to inhabit the upland areas. Few utilise the entire rainforest area. The largest representative is the heavyweight, 2 metre tall Southern Cassowary, with its "armour-plated" casque-crowned head and powerful legs perfect for crashing through the dense forest. Huge nesting mounds of fermenting vegetation signify the presence of incubator birds, such as the Orange-footed Scrubfowl and the Brush-turkey. No less elaborate are the massive, twin-tower structures (up to 3 metres tall and a metre apart) of the upland Golden Bowerbird, specifically designed to impress his olive-brown mate. Another lowland rainforest inhabitant, the White-rumped Swiftlet (sometimes called the Grey Swiftlet), is one of the few birds in the world to use echolocation for navigation. Rivalling the incredible spectrum of forest fruits is the magnificent, iridescent Victoria's Riflebird and the nectar-seeking lorikeets, including the Rainbow, Scaly-breasted and Little Lorikeets, the small Fig-Parrots, screeching Australian King-Parrots, the Eclectus Parrot and Wompoo Fruit-Dove.

This kaleidoscope of living colour is only enhanced by the sinuous emerald brilliance of the Green Python, with its golden dorsal spots, and by the many species of frog, such as the Orange-eyed Tree-frog, White-lipped Tree-frog and Ornate Burrowing-frog.

Left: The lustrous, lime-coloured Green Python resides in wet tropical rainforest in Cape Tribulation National Park, Queensland. *Right:* Small (5–8 kilogram) Lumholtz's Tree-kangaroo is superbly adapted to moving about sloping, broad tree limbs and trunks in highland rainforests between Mount Spurgeon and the Cardwell Range. It is a solitary animal, but populations can be quite dense in residual forest. Its forelimbs are large and strongly muscled, while its hindlimbs can move independently — a feature unique among macropods. The tail is long and somewhat prehensile.

Flora of the Rainforest

Where rainforest meets a river or a clearing it becomes much denser, packed with species that require more light. Here are vines such as the Native Raspberry and Lawyer Vine, armed with thorns to assist their scrambling. Most flowers and fruit grow high up in the canopy, but the brilliant ripe fruits (many poisonous to humans) fall to the forest floor. Exquisite fungi, in the process of breaking down fallen vegetation, grow on the floor, while delicate-looking sundews (which obtain their nitrogen by trapping marauding insects on their leaf hairs) shelter in damp pockets.

Classic Plants: Alexandra, Fan and Black Palms; Kapok; White, Strangler, Watkin's and Curtain Figs; Johnstone River, Bumpy and Grey Satinash; Blue Quandong; Johnson's Quandong; Native Bleeding Heart; Brown Pine; Kauri Pine; Hope's Cycad; Ivory Curl Tree; Stockwellia; Northern Silky Oak; Black Bean; Flame Tree; Shepherd's Ironwood; Flooded Gum; Red Carabeen; Umbrella Tree; Brown Tuckeroo; Powder Puff; lilly pillies; Boonjee Tulip Oak; Native Lasiandra; cunjevoi; Scrub Breadfruit; native peppers; gingers; Wild Raspberry; Lawyer Vine, or Wait-a-While; Pothos Vine; Brown Kurrajong; Celerywood; White Basswood; Gympie Stinging Tree; Slender and Scaly Tree Ferns; Basket Ferns; Elkhorn; Bird's Nest Fern; King, Flat Fork, Ribbon and Umbrella Ferns; Golden, Oak, Blue China and Cooktown Orchids; Beach Calophyllum; fungi.

Above, top to bottom: Butterflies are prolific in the Wet Tropics — this collection is in the Daintree Rainforest Discovery Centre; masses of cunjevoi grow in wet hollows on the forest floor.

One must not overlook the invertebrates, so important in all living systems and so abundant in the Wet Tropics. Are there any more ethereal creatures than butterflies — the Cairns Birdwing or the shimmering, cobalt-blue Ulysses? And what could be more grotesquely fascinating than the iridescent Mueller's Stag Beetle?

It is simply not possible for the written word to do justice, especially in so few lines, to the spectacular array of rainforest life in the Wet Tropics. There is only one way to truly experience it, and that is to give yourself plenty of time, equip yourself with a set of reliable field guides (particularly for plants, birds, reptiles and amphibians), carry up-to-date maps, a notebook, raincoat, insect repellent and a camera and take a long, observant bushwalk in the forest. If you have the luxury of a local informed guide, your experience will be greatly enhanced. To really familiarise yourself with the majesty of the wet tropical rainforest, you should make return visits in different seasons, only by being there can you truly appreciate the wonder of this incredible environment.

Above: Daintree Rainforest Discovery Centre. *Right:* The diverse flora on a wet tropical rainforest floor is showcased by this environment in the Daintree Rainforest Discovery Centre. The tall, slender trees are partially supported by the rest of the canopy. Cyclonic winds can do damage if they break into such tight systems.

Classic Birds: Cassowary; Orange-footed Scrubfowl; Brush-turkey; Satin, Golden and Tooth-billed Bowerbirds; Rose-crowned, Topknot and Pied Imperial-Pigeons; Figbird; Noisy Pitta; Victoria's Riflebird; Spotted Catbird; Australian King-Parrot; Red-cheeked Parrot; Palm Cockatoo; Double-eyed Fig-Parrot; Eclectus Parrot; boobook; Rufous Owl; Northern Logrunner; Spectacled Monarch; Rufous Fantail; Golden Whistler; Grey-headed Robin; Pale-yellow Robin; Lovely Fairy-wren; Chowchilla; Bower's Shrike-thrush; Macleay's Honeyeater; Bridled Honeyeater; Yellow-bellied Sunbird; Eastern Whipbird; Grey Goshawk; Buff-breasted Paradise-Kingfisher.

Above, top to bottom: Wet tropical rainforest is filled with the call of the Spotted Catbird; the Southern Cassowary is able to excavate much litter in search of food and can push its way through almost impenetrable scrub and vine-matted thickets.

WET TROPICAL RAINFORESTS AS ANIMAL HABITAT

Wet tropical rainforest habitat has more layers than eucalypt forest. There is a dense, interlinked upper canopy of extreme species diversity and productivity, particularly in flowers, fruits and leaves. Some very tall species, such as figs, break right through to become immense emergents. Tying many of the individuals together and connecting them to the ground are networks of vines or lianes. Larger trees carry huge loads of epiphytes and are "gardens of life", where climbers such as ants, other invertebrates, reptiles, frogs and birds can nest — this is a very special micro-habitat within the larger system. Light and wind conditions below the canopy are subdued and control what may grow beneath. Below this primary canopy, palms form a storey and usually outpace the young trees,which are impaired by the lack of light. Below the palms and young trees are numerous smaller climbers, such as rattans, Lawyer Vine, peppers, Walking-stick Palms and shrubs. Tree ferns may overtop this ground layer. Most of the lower-layer plants are awaiting a storm to open up the light. All the while, collecting on the floor is a considerable depth of the combined litter fall from plants and animals. The moist, warm conditions maintain a high rate of fermentation — a feature used by the Brush-turkey in building its incubator nest. There is also a constant release of nutrients from this mulch. Moisture and nutrients are in abundance, so only shallow roots are needed; instead, trees grow huge plank buttresses and props to assist their standing. If we think of all of the rainforest nutrient as a bank account, we find that more than half the capital is in the living forest itself. Human use of rainforest tends to destroy that 60% of infrastructure in one attack!

Each tree leans on its surrounding neighbours, providing access for fruit-eating and predatory climbers — lizards, invertebrates, small mammals, possums, frogs and even tree-kangaroos — to reach from the ground to all parts of the canopy.

Above: Boyd's Forest Dragon is something of an icon for the wet tropical rainforest of Tropical North Queensland.

Classic Frogs and Reptiles: Green-eyed Tree-frog; Red Tree-frog; Northern Barred Frog; Lesueur's Frog; Robust Frog; Dwarf Tree-frog; Orange-eyed Tree-frog; Dainty Tree-frog and White-lipped Tree-frog; Red-throated Rainbow Skink; Spiny Skink; Pink-tongued Skink; Chameleon Gecko; Red-sided Skink; Lace Monitor; Boyd's Forest Dragon; Brown and Green Tree Snakes; Carpet Python; Scrub Python; Green Python.

Above, top to bottom: Common Spotted Cuscus; Striped Possum.

Classic Mammals: Musky Rat-kangaroo; Lumholtz's Tree-kangaroo; Red-legged Pademelon; Herbert River Ringtail Possum; Lemuroid Ringtail Possum; Green Ringtail Possum; Striped Possum; Fawn-footed Melomys; Giant White-tailed Rat; Yellow-footed Antechinus; Spotted-tailed Quoll; Tube-nosed Bat; Diadem Bat; Ghost Bat; Spectacled Flying-fox; Little Red Flying-fox; Black Flying-fox; Blossom Bat.

Classic Spiders and Insects: Cairns Birdwing, Ulysses, Orchard, White Nymph, Australian Rustic Red Lacewing, Green Spotted Triangle, Union Jack and Cruiser Butterflies; Hercules, Yellow Emperor and Blue-banded Moths; Stag, Mueller's Stag, Rhinoceros, Green Leaf, Jewel and Pink-spotted Longicorn Beetles; King Cricket; Spiny Long-horned Grasshopper; White-kneed Weta; mantids; stick insects; katydids; the world's largest dragonfly (*Petaleura ingentissima*); numerous bugs; Jumping Spider; Golden Orb-weaver; Spined Spider; *Cataxia* and *Homogona* trapdoor spiders.

Above, top to bottom: Killer of the insect world, the Praying Mantis; one of Australia's most spectacular butterflies, the Ulysses Butterfly delights in the sunlight above the canopy but also in small forest clearings. Adults are attracted by the pink flowers of the *Melicope elleryana*, laying eggs on the leaves.

Subtropical Rainforests

The face of the mountain is also studded with very large fine timber ... but there is more cedar ... also vast quantities of the cabbage palm and fern trees growing, the former being very beautiful and of great height. I had one noble [red] cedar measured, which measured 21 feet [6.3 metres] in circumference and 120 feet [38 metres] in height. The part of it which measured 21 feet in circumference was ten feet [3 metres] from the root of it, and continued to be of the same size for 60 feet [19 metres] above the ground.

Governor Lachlan Macquarie, describing the rainforest on Illawarra coal-measure shales, 16 February 1822.

Most perceptions of rainforest are those described in the earlier section of wet tropical rainforest — a lush, deep green verdure of many species of buttressed trees carrying loads of epiphytes, vines and an interlocking heavy canopy. However, from these areas of dense, rich rainforest, supporting environmental conditions taper off southwards and westwards, with conditions becoming cooler southwards and drier westwards. Down the continent's south-east, merging with tropical rainforests from outliers near Gladstone, run forests ranging from subtropical to cool-temperate beech myrtle forests, such as those of Tasmania. Along this range, richer soils on volcanic aspects provide refuges of denser forest, creating pockets of subtropical rainforest quite a distance from the tropics; these are the coal-measure shales that Macquarie described, tucked below the very wet sandstone escarpment of the Illawarra and in the deep southern and eastern valleys of the 1555 metre, wet Barrington Tops.

Where Are They? Subtropical rainforests are confined to coastal lowlands and adjacent highlands, rarely extending more than 150 kilometres from the coast. They are discontinuous, being usually limited to soils of floodplain, shale and volcanic origin that receive few frosts, if any, and rainfall greater than 750 millimetres on aspects sheltered from desiccating westerly winds.

What Do They Look Like? Dense tall forest of mixed tree species with deep green, "soft" fleshy leaves (that can absorb moisture from humidity and mist) on upper branches that frequently interlock to produce a closed canopy. There is a deep, full shade at ground level. Light is also intercepted by layers of smaller trees below the main canopy. There may be some large trees that rise above the canopy. Many trees will be buttressed in the warmest areas of the region. Vines and palms will be present.

Critical Conditions: Completeness of the community, retaining temperature and moisture; active recycling of litter.

Above: A stand of Bangalow Palms growing in a wet area in Eungella National Park, Queensland. *Left:* Flowering Bangalow Palm in Brisbane Forest Park, Queensland. *Right:* Typical subtropical rainforest species, such as lilly pillies and palms, growing in a wet gully on Mount Glorious, Queensland.

Best Examples: *Qld* — Brisbane Forest Park; Cunninghams Gap; Lamington National Park. *NSW* — Mount Warning; Victoria Park Nature Reserve; Border Ranges, Richmond Range, and Nightcap National Parks; Broken Head Nature Reserve; Iluka Nature Reserve; Dorrigo National Park; New England National Park; Oxley Wild Rivers National Park; Barrington/Gloucester Tops National Parks; Minnamurra Falls; Morton and Macquarie Pass National Parks.

Sounds: Lyrebirds; Wonga Pigeons.

Smells: Damp soil; aromatic plants.

Sensations: The snare of thorny tangled vines; moist green fertility.

Above: Coomera Falls, north of Mount Warning in Lamington National Park (Qld), cuts through a slot in rock that was once the great volcanic flow of the Tweed Volcano.

Above: Pockets of rainforest occur along Wanggoolba Creek on Fraser Island, Queensland, and among some wet litter-enriched swales between the giant dunes. Ancient tree ferns and Bangalow Palms also thrive in these warm, moist enclaves.

If there is a true centre of subtropical rainforest, then it lies around the Tweed Volcano, Mount Warning, and its network of subsidiary vents. Volcanic activity here some 24–21 million years ago produced the mountainous landscape of the New South Wales–Queensland Border Ranges, Richmond Range and the Big Scrub area. Of the 160,000 hectares of once-pristine Big Scrub, just 18 hectares remain. Perhaps the closest image of the lowland rainforests that once existed here lies in the irreplaceable Stotts Island Nature Reserve, protected by the Richmond River and clouds of mosquitoes. Other superb examples of subtropical rainforest lie within the Springbrook, Lamington, Main Range, Cunninghams Gap, Nightcap and Maiala (Brisbane Forest Park) National Parks. Government Surveyor Clement Hodgkinson in the 1830s saw these wonderful pristine systems. Shortly after, when the settlers who followed ringbarked and burned the rainforests, they destroyed about 80% of that land's fertility in one fell swoop! There is no better description of this process than that given in Arthur Groom's *One Mountain After Another*, which provides a good history of Lamington National Park.

Further south, forest becomes slightly cooler on the Dorrigo volcanic flow and its eastern slopes, as well as in the Bellinger River valleys, rising to Point Lookout (at 1566 metres in New England National Park) and over into the Upper Macleay River. This extends into cooler warm-temperate rainforest and, at Point Lookout, into the cool-temperate rainforest dominated by Antarctic Beech, similar to the forests of McPherson Range and Barrington Tops and Gloucester National Parks.

The most inland, driest examples are in the high, damp, south-east facing valley heads of the Mount Kaputar National Park in New South Wales. Similarly, there are small southerly pockets of rainforest in gullies of the Liverpool Range. South of these outliers are a number of pockets scattered across the Sydney sandstones in volcanic necks or diatremes. Soils enriched by volcanic material compensate for

Above: Buttresses of a giant Strangler Fig on Tamborine Mountain, north of Lamington National Park, Qld. *Below:* One of the rainforest trails on the plateau in Eungella National Park, Qld, makes a wonderful bird and plant walk.

Above, top to bottom: Mount Lindsay, on the Qld–NSW border, has Australia's widest range of rainforest types; Kondalilla Falls, Qld; Bunya Mountains National Park, Qld.

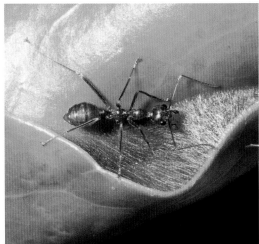

Above, top to bottom: A forest leech rises from the leaf litter; the tenacious Green Tree Ant; Lamington Blue Crayfish.

Spiders and Insects of the Subtropical Rainforests

These forests host an abundance of invertebrates adapted to various plants and secretive shelters. Some, such as the striking Golden Orb-weavers and the Green Tree Ant, weave large protective shelters in leaves hanging high in the trees, but the base of this ecosystem, as far as insect populations are concerned, is the deep, damp floor of leaf litter.

Classic Invertebrates: Forest snails; Red-triangle Slug; amphipods; crayfishes; Golden Orb-weavers; Large-jawed Spider; Ant-mimicking Spider; centipedes; millipedes; Green Tree Ant; Looper Moth; mosquitoes; longicorn beetles; stag beetles; lacewings; assassin bugs; mantids; cockroaches; peripatus; leeches.

Above: The Maiala section in Brisbane Forest Park (Queensland) is one of the best, most accessible areas for nature-lovers and offers numerous self-guided nature walks.

their drier locations with plenty of accessible nutrients and water-holding clays that reduce the need for high rainfall. Water supply essentially makes nutrients accessible to plant root cells. There is little more of this forest beyond the enriched soils of the Illawarra and Kiama area, and the Kangaroo Valley — originally an area of significant subtropical luxuriance due to high rainfall on the surrounding 750 metre escarpment and the area's extensive exposure to good soils. The most southerly and coolest pocket is probably a hectare or so on the north-easterly face of Mount Dromedary, New South Wales, which once grew Red Cedar.

SUBSISTENCE AND SURVIVAL IN SUBTROPICAL ENVIRONMENTS

In Australia's subtropical ecosystems the life-sustaining environment is not a level playing field. As with any habitat, environmental factors, temperature, soil nutrients, sunlight and atmosphere are provided in unique measure. Millions of

Above: The view from Point Lookout, on the New England scarp east of Armidale, New South Wales, gives a panorama of rainforest wilderness par excellence to the headwaters of the Bellinger River and far-off Dorrigo.

years of geological, faunal and floral evolution has fitted particular organisms to a certain mix of environmental resources. Each organism that colonises a new environment modifies the habitat for others — some of which may have been there for many generations and others that may themselves be recent colonisers. Many colonial species may be considered weeds or pests until they are either eradicated by the living ecosystem or become successfully incorporated within it. However, even successful colonisation does not eliminate hardship. In fitting as much life into these prime conditions as possible, most rainforest space is used. There is brutal competition for sunlight.

While some species of figs, Red Cedars, Black Booyong, Blue Gums, Hoop Pines and Brush Box may actually break right through the canopy and become emergents, others, such as vines and Strangler Figs, must hitch a ride on host plants to get into the upper canopy and to the source of light. Many epiphytes, ferns and orchids, for example, use the trees as hanging garden space, inching themselves nearer to the light. The more unfortunate seedlings — and some may have been seedlings for 50 years! — must wait until a storm knocks a hole in the "roof" or until an elderly giant dies, crashing to the ground and tearing down its vine-linked neighbours.

Despite the apparent inhospitality of the subtropical rainforest floor, what is going on there is almost as important as any event in the light-gathering canopy. Where there is so much life, there is subsequently much death and decay — and that is the primary function of the ground layer. This damp, rotting, fungi-strewn, wormy, beetle-filled, invertebrate-riddled layer is a living recycling unit. Here, the wastes of the forest are miraculously turned back into living forest food. This explains why rainforest trees are so shallow-rooted that many require buttressed-root supports. Plants, animals and the recycling decomposers all combine to create one system.

Above: Looking down onto the Illawarra rainforest below Sublime Point, Bulli, New South Wales. This is Red Cedar and Cabbage Tree Palm country, stretching along the Illawarra escarpment below the infertile Hawkesbury sandstones. Note the huge figs emerging above the canopy.

Above: Noisy Pittas forage in the leaf litter for invertebrates.

Birds of the Subtropical Rainforests

Figs and palms of the rainforest are prolific fruit producers, attracting great flocks of pigeons and numerous Regent and Satin Bowerbirds, as well as parrots and cockatoos. The latter move from rainforest to rainforest, following the flowering and fruiting sequence as it varies with the climatic pattern. The other great food producer is the litter of the forest floor; this is where the insectivores and invertebrate-feeders gather. Fallen fruit also brings some pigeons, such as the Emerald Dove and others, to the floor.

Classic Birds: Lyrebird; Pacific Baza; Collared Sparrowhawk; Grey Goshawk; Buff-banded Rail; White-headed Pigeon; Wompoo Fruit-Dove; Rose-crowned Fruit-Dove; Emerald Dove; Brown Cuckoo-Dove; Wonga Pigeon; Sulphur-crested Cockatoo; Rainbow Lorikeet; Scaly-breasted Lorikeet; Australian King-Parrot; Crimson Rosella; Oriental Cuckoo; Brush Cuckoo; Fan-tailed Cuckoo; Shining Bronze-Cuckoo; Koel; Channel-billed Cuckoo; Australian Owlet-nightjar; Striated Pardalote; Brown Gerygone; Lewin's Honeyeater; Rose Robin; Eastern Yellow Robin; Logrunner; Olive Whistler; Golden Whistler; Black-faced Monarch; Rufous Fantail; Grey Fantail; Spangled Drongo; Varied Triller; Black-faced Cuckoo-shrike; Noisy Pitta; Paradise Riflebird; Green Catbird; Regent Bowerbird; Satin Bowerbird.

Above, left to right: Emerald Dove; female Satin Bowerbird

Above: Ferns, fruits and mosses all flourish in the moist, humid rainforest environment. Australia has around 900 species of moss. These bryophytes represent the first land plants, evolutionarily a step ahead of algae, and require much moisture.

Flora of the Subtropical Rainforests

These communities are home to the massive Blush Tulip Oak, Yellow Carabeen, Brown Pine, and once-giant Red Cedar, Flooded Gum, Brush Box, Strangler Figs, Giant Stinging Trees (with their dinner-plate-sized, deceptively soft green leaves that have severe stinging hairs) and Bangalow Palms. Native Peppers, cunjevoi, climbing and epiphytic ferns and tree ferns are common ground plants. Strangler Figs and other figs, as well as great Blue Gums and Blackbutt Eucalypts, are the pillars of the forests and many forest trees lean on them for support. This ecosystem absorbs the majority of soil nutrients, so dead trees must be quickly recycled, allowing nutrients to again go into circulation. The main recyclers are invertebrates, fungi and bacteria. Without fungi, the forest would not be sustainable. Myriad fungi colours (particularly brilliant oranges, reds, blues and yellows) and forms create massive brackets of white, spongy, "blackfellow's bread", or the exquisite "lanterns".

Classic Plants: Hoop Pine; Red Cedar; Booyongs; Yellow Carabeen; Rosewood; figs; lilly pillies; Leopard Ash; Tuckeroo; Cedar Wattle; Native Elderberry; Native Tamarind; Black Bean; Durobby; Brush Cherry; Sour Cherry; Firewheel Tree; Stinging Tree; Coachwood; Crab Apple; Blue Quandong; Fraser Island Turpentine; Kauri Pine; Bangalow Palm; Cabbage Tree Palm; Walking-stick Palm; Rattan Palms; large epiphytes such as ferns, orchids and aroids; lianes; fungi.

Above: The subtropical rainforest environment depends upon efficient recycling of matter. On the forest floor, in the leaf litter and on tree trunks, a variety of decomposers, in the form of lichens, algae and fungi, are at work. Fungi are especially crucial as they can decompose the woody tree component lignin to break down even hard tree trunks.

Above, clockwise from top left: Short-beaked Echidna; Red-legged Pademelon; Long-nosed Bandicoot; Spotted-tailed Quoll.

Above, clockwise from top left: Ringed Thin-tailed Gecko; Eastern Tiger Snake; Green Tree-frog.

Mammals of the Subtropical Rainforests

There is little food for inhabitants of the subtropical rainforest ground floor; most ground-dwelling creatures are predators that are able to live off others, or animals that can sustain themselves, either in the litter or on fallen fruit or grasses in open patches or adjacent areas. High in the canopy, the sustenance situation is very different. Climbing reptiles, possums, small mammals and bats raid a rich pantry of foods, leaves, flowers, fruits and seeds. Herbivores include possums, very small wallabies, pademelons and bandicoots, which mix invertebrates with smatterings of plant roots and fallen fruit. Insectivores are those such as the Short-beaked Echidna, the many tree-frogs and some skinks, while the carnivores include monitors, geckoes, tiger snakes, pythons and others.

Classic Mammals: Dingo; Bush Rat; Water-rat; Lesser Long-eared Bat; Little Brown Bat; Large-footed Mouse-eared Bat; Eastern Horseshoe Bat; Queensland Blossom Bat; Black Flying-fox; Little Red Flying-fox; Grey-headed Flying-fox; Short-beaked Echidna; Spotted-tailed Quoll; Brown Antechinus; Common Planigale; Long-nosed Bandicoot; brushtail possums; Red-legged and Red-necked Pademelons.

Frogs and Reptiles of the Subtropical Rainforests

Amphibians and reptiles, being "cold-blooded" animals, require sunlight in the subtropical environment in order to be active. Hence, they find typical vantage points on sunlit boulders by river verges or where storms have broken the canopy. Much of the larger vertebrate fauna, as well as invertebrates, is arboreal — a definite advantage for pythons, tree snakes and geckoes. The damp, dense litter of the forest floor favours invertebrates, along with numerous amphibians, skinks and small mammals. A number of ground-feeding birds find paradise in rainforest leaf litter. Birds, skinks, amphibians and rodents are a rich food resource for death adders and tiger snakes.

Classic Frogs and Reptiles: Common Eastern Froglet; Fletcher's Frog; Ornate Burrowing-frog; Great and Giant Barred Frogs; Mount Glorious Torrent Frog; Green Tree-frog; Orange-eyed Tree-frog; Lesueur's Frog; Northern Leaf-tailed Gecko; Southern Angle-headed Dragon; Eastern Water Dragon; Lace Monitor; Copper-tailed Skink; Major Skink; Land Mullet; Challenger's Skink; Pink-tongued Lizard; Eastern Blue-tongue; Diamond Python; Brown and Common Tree Snakes; death adders; Eastern Small-eyed Snake; Mainland Tiger Snake; Rough-scaled Snake.

Where Are They? These rainforests exist at higher altitudes (450–1200 metres) from west of Gladstone (Kroombit Tops National Park) south to Batemans Bay (Budawang–Morton National Park) on poorer soils in the north and richer soils in the south.

What Do They Look Like? A closed, even-height canopy with two strata of trees. A low diversity of tree species (3–15 species), most commonly with simple leaves with toothed margins. Palms are rarely present. There are few buttressed trees or large vines. A few species of large epiphytes. Ground ferns are common.

Critical Conditions: Moderately high rainfall (over 1000 millimetres); higher rainfall required on soils high in silica (sandstone, rhyolite, trachyte, metamorphics) and less rain on basalts, silts and shales.

Above: Warm-temperate rainforest in Murramarang National Park, NSW, shows ferny floor, heavy litter and few tree species.

Warm-temperate Rainforests

The first impression of a warm-temperate rainforest is one of comparative tidiness and uniformity compared with the baroque of tropical and subtropical associations. The festooned, buttressed giants of those forests are replaced with comparatively unbuttressed trees of a more uniform height. The even canopy usually reaches 25–30 metres and the number of tree species forming the canopy is small, often being only between three and fifteen. The most common floristic ingredient … is the Coachwood — a beautiful straight tree whose smooth grey bark is decoratively encrusted with pink, orange, grey and white lichens.

Alex Floyd (whose work led to many national park dedications in NSW) in *Rainforests of Australia*, 1985.

Water supply and drainage, temperature, and especially soil nutrient supply (stemming from the dissolution of rock) largely determine the distribution of temperate rainforest communities. The decomposing rock upon which the community has grown becomes a determining factor for which species will live in the warm-temperate plant community. Warm-temperate rainforests push the boundaries of rainforest structure because lower temperatures reduce the chemical reactivity of nutrients in the soil, making nutrients less readily available. This problem is obviously lessened if soils are rich in nutrients and if there is ample water supply to aid the slow erosion of rock, because mineral content that leaches from the bedrock is the primary source of nutrients. These nutrients are supplemented, of course, by cyclic elements of the weather and seasonal animal movements.

Temperate rainforests are split into two distinct groups: warm-temperate rainforest and the southern cool-temperate rainforest, which requires higher, cooler altitudes in its northern reaches. In Lamington National Park, these two temperate rainforest types exist at relatively low altitudes due to the nutrient-poor soils that are derived from silica-rich rhyolite lavas. These soils are not productive enough to carry the more luxuriant subtropical rainforest that grows at lower, warmer levels. Dominant species of the temperate rainforests differ. In high, cold and very wet

Above: Aerial shot of a warm-temperate rainforest near Belmore Falls in Morton National Park, New South Wales. Turpentine trees are breaking up the uniform canopy, while the pale-coloured tree heads are Coachwoods in flower.
Right: Verdant foliage in warm-temperate rainforest within Dorrigo National Park, northern New South Wales.

Above, top to bottom: Upper levels of Dorrigo National Park are cool enough for warm-temperate rainforest to grow; typical forest floor at Platypus Creek, Dorrigo National Park, NSW.

Classic Conditions for Warm-temperate Rainforests

The warm-temperate rainforest zone occurs where subtropical rainforest conditions ascend above sea-level warmth or where soil fertility is low and winter months are cool and damp. In these environments, Coachwoods become dominant while lilly pillies and many year-long warmth-lovers drop out. Red Cedars, however, are sustained; other species, such as Sassafras, become more dominant in cooler climes — a good example of this cool edge is the Robertson Brush east of Moss Vale, New South Wales.

Best Examples: *Qld* — Lamington National Park; *NSW* — Mount Warning and Washpool National Parks; Dorrigo and New England National Parks; Werrikimbe National Park; Blue Mountains National Park; Mount Wilson; Morton, Budderoo, Macquarie Pass and Budawang National Parks.

Sounds: Lyrebirds; Wonga Pigeons.

Smells: Spicy crushed Sassafras leaves.

Sensation: The texture of Coachwood bark.

conditions (1750–3500 millimetres per year), at high altitudes (900–1500 metres) and in Australia's far south, instead of Coachwood or Crab Apple dominating, beeches, such as Antarctic Beech and Southern Beech, play a dominant role. In the very far north (as at Mount Bartle Frere in Queensland), Northern Sassafras and a particular species of Crab Apple become more frequent.

WANDERING THE WARM-TEMPERATE ZONES

One of my favourite places to familiarise myself with this kind of rainforest is on the edge of the largest remaining Coachwood forest in the world — Washpool National Park, just across the Gwydir Highway from Gibraltar Range National Park in New South Wales. This area, along the edge of the New England escarpment, experiences high rainfall (approximately 1000 millimetres per year), primarily in summer squalls but also in some surges of cool, wet winter weather. The self-guided walk, with its fourteen information posts linked to excellent guide notes, is just over a kilometre long and commences at the Coachwood Picnic Area.

At a starting height of 800 metres, the track continues down a sloping spur to Coombadjha Creek, where the current has forged an open valley through granite and masses of rhyodacite (a rock with crystals of calcium feldspar, which weathers to a nutrient-rich clay — an improvement on nearby grey granite soils). This edge of the forest was logged in 1966 and the track clearly shows the regrowth of the forest, with pioneering species such as *Callicoma* (the Black Wattle, which despite its cream, fluffy, wattle-like flower heads isn't a wattle at all!), Blackwood (which is a wattle) and bushy lilly pillies around the edge to seal essential humidity inside the forest. Native Raspberry also binds the edge, as do the leftover effects of a bushfire that burned the forest when it dried out due to logging activity.

Above: In the mid-storey level of warm-temperate rainforests, Coachwoods, Rough Tree Ferns and Crow's Nest Ferns grow, but few other epiphytes are found.

The walk meanders 300 metres through the forest to the creek, then another 400 metres along a delightful stream that cascades among boulders and slips through quiet "Platypus pools" on its way through the Gibraltar Range and down to the Nymboida Range. It then returns to the Coachwood Picnic Area via a 400 metre Blue Gum Walk through a community that resembles both wet sclerophyll forest and rainforest country.

The walk evokes many impressions and sensations. First, one is struck by the nobility of the smooth, slender, cloud-grey trunks, mottled with clinging lichens, that lunge upwards into the dappled-green Coachwood canopies. Guessing at their age is made difficult by their habit of producing an ever-widening cluster of trunks that embrace several generations of suckers, which themselves have become trees. In the centre of the cluster is the "grandfather" of them all, now merely a low hump or perhaps even totally rotted away. These Coachwoods set the canopy height, but are aided by similarly skyward-seeking Jackwood (Silver Sycamore to Illawarra locals), Sassafras (with its wonderful spicy smell of crushed leaves) and the Scrub Beefwood (named for its raw, meat-red timber, which never seems to quite make the height).

The surrounding rainforest floor is quite open. Here, slender vines shoot upwards past scattered Walking-stick Palms, Native Pepper and Prickly Tree Ferns. By the creek are "gardens" of King, Fishbone and Umbrella Ferns, flourishing in emerald splendour as they relish the brighter light. The creek itself makes its flow among the towering walls of a living green canyon, the trees that line the waterway having arched out to capture light over the water.

In the deep, damp leaf litter on the floor, competition for life remains equally intense. In these lower echelons of the rainforest, the Possumwood, which never really succeeds on the rainforest floor, does a very possum-like thing. Its tiny seeds — almost all of which hit the litter and are consumed by ants, beetles or rot — take to the trees, sometimes lodging on the scaly trunk of one of three species of tree fern or becoming trapped in rough Corkwood bark where they germinate, and, for a while, become epiphytic until their roots reach the ground. They have most success by the creek, where they may develop into small bushy trees that grow up to 8 metres tall. Other epiphytic species of these forests are limited to ferns and a few orchids. Bird's Nest Ferns, Elkhorns and Strap Ferns, with bundles of compost collected in their funnel-shaped forms, are the most common, along with numerous delicate mosses.

In the half-light of early morning, late afternoon or by the bright glow of a spotlight, walkers here are likely to see Common Ringtail and Brushtail Possums high in the tall gums, as well as Greater Gliders — their eyes beaming in the spotlight like twin silvery stars. On the ground, particularly near the edge of the eucalypt forest, reside the very rare Parma Wallaby and, on or near the ground, the uncommon Rufous Scrub-bird. Sacred and Azure Kingfishers dart, in a sudden, gleaming flash of colour, to hunt in the creeks.

While wandering in this rainforest cathedral or contemplating its wonders from a warm, sunny perch on a midstream boulder, the extreme importance of the few high-altitude remnants of rainforest habitat in eastern Australia become apparent. Over the past million years this continent passed through many long, dry and droughty cycles, during which vegetation was forced to retreat from

Right: Coachwoods in warm-temperate rainforest in Morton National Park, NSW, find perfect habitat around the vapour-misted depths of Fitzroy Falls, which are also bordered by Blackbutt and Sydney Blue Gum.

Flora of the Warm-temperate Rainforests

Probably the most unpleasant plant in the warm-temperate rainforest is the Lawyer Vine, a climber with a tough, thin stem and severe tearing spines. Except for a few heavy lianes and a number of smaller vines, most vines have been left behind in the tropical forests. The wonderful smooth grey trunks of the Coachwood, lichen-blotched and with serrated leaves, contrast with the smooth, shiny deep-green leaves of lilly pillies, which bear masses of creamy to pink succulent berries, and the gleaming green canopy of the Silver Sycamore. In spring, the cedar's new red pinnate leaves, which once gave the trees' locations away to the "red gold"-seeking timber-getters, light up the canopy, while the white flowers of the Coachwood revert to the red bracts of the old flower.

Classic Plants: Coachwood; Sassafras; Antarctic Beech; Red Ash; Native Clerodendrum; Brown Kurrajong; Native Laurel; Red-fruited Olive Plum; figs; Cheese Tree; Native Hibiscus; Native Olive; Brown Beech; Blueberry Ash; Sweet Pittosporum; Possumwood; Bastard Rosewood; lilly pillies; Red Cedar; Water Gum; Cabbage Tree Palm; Crow's Nest Fern; fewer epiphytes; many ground ferns; Soft, Slender and Rough Tree Ferns; fungi; lichens.

Above: Fungi festoons a buttress root in Lamington NP, Qld.

environments that could no longer sustain life. Today, for example, trees that have their main populations on the coast are also growing on the southern side of the Warrumbungle mountains of central New South Wales. These protected, cooler and wetter aspects are now refuges, but in wetter times they were once continuous forests that swept down to the coast. Similarly, the mountainous areas of Mount Bartle Frere, Mount Warning, Point Lookout and Barrington Tops provide cooler, wetter high-country aspects that are havens for innumerable species that retreated before the many arid periods this land has endured. Later, when the dry periods began to wane, wind, water, gravity, birds and other animals moved fruits and seeds back into territory that was becoming hospitable once again. These taller, sheltering mountains were rainforest "arks", keeping threatened species alive. Many incredibly ancient rainforest plants and their dependent animals — including communities of the Daintree as well as of the Coachwood and Beech forests — owe their longevity to the geography of mountainous eastern Australia.

Above: A bushwalker admires the luxuriant rainforest in Blue Mountains National Park, New South Wales.

Above, clockwise from top left: Yellow-tailed Black-Cockatoo; Crimson Rosella; Pied Currawong; Wonga Pigeon.

Birds of the Warm-temperate Rainforests

Not only does the over-arching canopy of this rainforest produce typical "soft" fruits, such as that of the lilly pilly, but the numerous emergent Blue Gum, Brown Barrel, Blackbutt and Forest Oaks grow hard fruit and seeds as well as succulent flower buds that attract flocks of lorikeets, parrots and the large Yellow-tailed Black-Cockatoo, which is particularly enticed by the Casuarina. On the ground, the Wonga Pigeon finds its prime habitat, along with the Superb Lyrebird, which is common in the Illawarra forests. In the more open forests, once the lilly pilly fruits are finished, Currawongs chip away at bark, searching for invertebrates. Smaller birds, such as fairy-wrens and the Eastern Whipbird, delight in the shelter of dense thickets that are scattered through the forest.

Classic Birds: Superb Lyrebird; Albert's Lyrebird; Pacific Baza; Brown Goshawk; Brown Cuckoo-Dove; Wonga Pigeon; Red-tailed Black-Cockatoo; Yellow-tailed Black-Cockatoo; Sulphur-crested Cockatoo; Rainbow Lorikeet; Australian King-Parrot; Crimson Rosella; Blue-winged Parrot; Brush Cuckoo; Fan-tailed Cuckoo; Shining Bronze-Cuckoo; Koel; Sooty Owl; Marbled Frogmouth; Australian Owlet-nightjar; Noisy Pitta; Rufous Scrub-bird; White-throated Treecreeper; Striated Pardalote; Large-billed Scrubwren; Yellow-throated Scrubwren; Brown Thornbill; Lewin's Honeyeater; Rose Robin; Pink Robin; Scarlet Robin; Eastern Yellow Robin; Pale-yellow Robin; Logrunner; Eastern Whipbird; Golden Whistler; Rufous Fantail; Grey Fantail; Black-faced Cuckoo-shrike; Pied Currawong; Regent Bowerbird; Satin Bowerbird; Bassian Thrush.

Invertebrates of the Warm-temperate Rainforests

Moths and butterflies are the egg producers and disseminators of their Lepidopterous world. The abundance of rainforest plants provides a wealth of food resources for the longer-lived larval phases of this group's life cycle. From egg to adult, some species rely totally on a single plant species. Should any plant species disappear, we rarely know which invertebrate species might consequently also vanish. This is the holistic concept of ecosystem — the bigger picture that looks beyond individual animals to the populations and the principles that govern their survival.

Classic Invertebrates: Forest snails; amphipods; crayfish; Golden Orb-weavers; funnel-webs; huntsmans; Leaf-curling Spider; centipedes; millipedes; longicorn beetles; lacewings; assassin bugs; King Cricket; mantids, cockroaches; leeches.

Above: The Sydney Funnel-web Spider is a robust predator, if (fortunately for its prey) a lazy one. It is highly venomous and builds its sock-like web in a damp litter burrow, either trapping careless wanderers in its sock or hunting at night. Direct sunlight rapidly kills this funnel-web, as does dry litter because the spider imbibes water through its food and skin.

Above: The life cycle of the Four O'clock Moth (*Dysphania fenestrata*), like that of most moth and butterfly species, relies on one or a number of particular food plants. These moths pupate on the Corky Bark tree (*Carallia brachiata*), providing a source of food for pupae as they undergo their transformation from larva to moth.

Above, top to bottom: Carpet Python; Orange-eyed Tree-frog; Southern Forest Dragon.

Frogs and Reptiles of the Warm-temperate Rainforests

Many warm-temperate rainforests are situated high on mountainsides with many rocky exposures, as around the cliffs of the Blue Mountains and the Illawarra escarpment. Such climes are perfect habitat for multifarious reptile species, especially tiger snakes and whipsnakes. Being on craggy escarpments, these forests usually have permanent creeks running through them, which encourage dragon, gecko and skink species. The wonderful clinging toes of Green Tree-frogs allow them to spend nearly all of their lives high in leaves of the canopy, coming down only to breed in water pooled in nearby gullies and creeks.

Classic Frogs and Reptiles: Common Eastern Froglet; Fletcher's Frog; Ornate Burrowing-frog; Great and Giant Barred Frogs; Sphagnum Frog; Green Tree-frog; Lesueur's Frog; Northern Leaf-tailed Gecko; Common Scaly-foot; Southern Angle-headed Dragon; Eastern Water Dragon; Lace Monitor; Copper-tailed Skink; Land Mullet; Murray's Skink; Pink-tongued Lizard; Eastern Blue-tongue; Diamond Python; Brown and Common Tree Snakes; death adders; Eastern Small-eyed Snake; Broad-headed Snake; Mainland Tiger Snake; Rough-scaled Snake.

Above, clockwise from top left: Swamp Rat; Eastern Pygmy-possum; Mountain Brushtail Possum; Grey-headed Flying-fox.

Mammals of the Warm-temperate Rainforests

Warm-temperate rainforest habitat frequently merges into wet sclerophyll forest with grassy floors; consequently, the Parma Wallaby and bandicoots often tend to shelter in the rainforest before moving into the adjacent forest to feed among grasses and ferns. Fruiting trees, such as the lilly pilly, attract bats and possums, while the fallen fruit is excellent food for rodents and also supplements the omnivorous diet of antechinuses. Mammals that are attracted to the fruits are themselves an attractant for predatory reptiles, such as the Diamond Python, and quolls.

Classic Mammals: Dingo; Bush Rat; Smoky Mouse; Parma Wallaby; Swamp Wallaby; Water-rat; Lesser Long-eared Bat; Little Brown Bat; Large-footed Mouse-eared Bat; Common Bent-wing Bat; Eastern Horseshoe Bat; Little Red Flying-fox; Grey-headed Flying-fox; Platypus; Short-beaked Echidna; Spotted-tailed Quoll; Brown Antechinus; Common Planigale; Long-nosed Bandicoot; Common Ringtail and Brushtail Possums; Mountain Brushtail Possum; Eastern Pygmy-possum; Red-necked Pademelon.

The Platypus — a Curious, Highly Successful Beast

Most people see their first Platypus in the wild at early morning or at dusk, as this bizarre-looking creature surfaces to make ripples of bright water across some serene pool of a cool mountain stream. In springtime Platypuses will be active, for this is mating time. In the shortening days of autumn, they reach their maximum weight, with plenty of fat stored for the stressful days of winter ahead. A prodigious number of crustaceans, worms and the like, secured from the river bed, have gone into building this stored energy — a Platypus can consume half its body weight in an evening's feed! — all hunted with eyes and ears closed, using only electrolocation. During life-sustaining activity, all animal life produces weak electrical fields. For the shrimp, a major component of the Platypus's diet, a tail flip produces a detectable electrical field 10 centimetres away. The Platypus's leathery bill has an intricate network of receptor pores in flaps where the bill connects with the head, giving a three-dimensional electrical view of potential prey, even beneath the creek bed. This type of direct electrical imaging is so unique in the animal world that it is now accepted that such evolution occurred over a very long time — time enough to develop a completely new animal sensory system! Fossil evidence now shows that the development of this species has been active for over 100 million years and that it split from its egg-laying monotreme cousin, the echidna, some 60 million years ago. Life for the Platypus has obviously been highly successful: it remains quite common in its natural habitat and has outlived thousands of other species thanks to its unique in-built imaging system.

Above: The Platypus delights in cold, clear streams that transect many warm-temperate rainforests, such as Platypus Creek in Dorrigo National Park, New South Wales. These waters provide abundant food, shelter and soft banks where Platypuses dig nesting burrows.

Where Are They? From Mongarlowe (southern NSW) to south-west Tasmania. In high areas in the north to sea level in Tasmania, and including Gippsland to the Otways in Victoria.

What Do They Look Like? Closed forest with few flowering species. They have large numbers of mosses, lichen and fern species in the understorey and growing as epiphytes. There are few heavy epiphytes and few, if any, buttresses; vines are also sparse.

Critical Conditions: High rainfall and mist interception at cool temperatures. They grow on all rock types.

Above: Cool temperate rainforest surrounds Liffey Falls on the slopes of the Great Western Tiers, Tasmania.

Cool-temperate Rainforests

*The Tasmanian temperate rainforest is richer in moss and lichen species than in higher plants. These lower plants cover rock, soil and trunk of myrtle [*Nothofagus cunninghamii*], sassafras [*Atherosperma moschatum*], leatherwood [*Eucryphia lucida*], horizontal [scrub] [*Anadopetalum biglandulosum*], celery-top pine [*Phyllocladus aspleniifolius*], Huon pine and other smaller tree and shrub species. The bizarre palm-like pandani [*Richea pandanifolia*] is a heath which can gain the canopy of the elfin, tangled rainforest. Elsewhere, the floor of the rainforest can be a shaded park with straight-boled trees and long green views, occasionally interrupted by the umbrella of a man fern [*Dicksonia antarctica*].*

The interdependence of different species is seldom more evident than in rainforest, where the closed canopy of trees creates the constantly humid, cool and shaded environment necessary for the delicate filmy ferns and other hygrophytes. Here, the root systems of trees often fuse and the very soil that supports the forest can consist of the accumulation of red, fibrous peat from the litter of hundreds of generations of trees. If fires gain access to this organic soil on the few days each year that it is dry, the consequences are disastrous, unburned trees collapsing with the loss of their supporting soil.

Part of Dr Bob Brown's wonderful writings in one of the most beautiful books ever published, *Wild Rivers* (1983), illustrated with the equally brilliant photographs of Peter Dombrovskis.

A mysterious quality pervades Tasmania's cool-temperate rainforests and this sense of mystery has remained with me, in sharp clarity, fifty years after my first walk to Frenchmans Cap. It was about 7.00 p.m. and we had just cleared the knee-deep mud across the Button Grass/Tea-tree swamp of Philps Lead (it had been a fairly dry season), when the track rose up through a few eucalypts, their leaves rattling in a fresh, cool westerly. Then the track transported us into a "tunnel" of green gloom. The air was still and silent, the utter silence broken only by the distant but piercing "chi-chi-chiewit" of a Scrubtit. Here, in place of mud, ankle-deep yellow-green mosses, like a living shag-pile carpet, blanketed the floor. They rose in curious bumps and hummocks and crept up the lower twisted trunks of the myrtles, making the trunks seem like a company of black, gyrating dancers clad in orange-green and scaly blue-green lichen socks. As we neared the ridge-top, a patch of light illuminated a clump of ferns nestled in place where a very old tree had been thrown by a gale. Over the ridge, the myrtles shrank in size to become dense bushes in harmony with their small, exquisitely detailed leaves. We were back in gum country, and then all too soon through this back to the quaking bog and sedges at the northern end of Lake Vera, our campsite for the night.

The few tree species in these rainforests are compensated by many mosses, lichens and ferns, usually with a uniform canopy, particularly in the smaller stands by the creek and lakesides, in the gullies or on high, protected aspects where they break into several layers with the pines, *Richea* and horizontal scrub. The latter is an awful community to walk through: its tall, slender trunks bend and become horizontal and over time weave a platform that is raised a metre (or many metres) above the ground. It is a truly closed community that develops in places of very high rainfall (1750–3500 millimetres) on cool-temperature lands.

Right: Ancient Antarctic Beech forest along the Border Track in Lamington National Park, Qld. Everything is muffled by a blanket of mosses and lichens. Note the old soil level shown by the original roots on the tree to the right.

Best Examples: *Qld* — Lamington National Park. *NSW* — Mount Warning, Washpool, Dorrigo and New England National Parks; Werrikimbe National Park; Barrington Tops and Blue Mountains National Parks; cascades around Jamberoo; Macquarie Pass National Park. *Vic* — Errinundra, Great Otway, Lind and Alfred National Parks. *Tas* — Mount Field National Park; roadside en route to Lake Pedder; Cradle Mountain–Lake St Clair National Park; Franklin–Gordon Wild Rivers tour; Southwest National Park.

Sounds: Cooing pigeons; dripping rain; cascades.

Smells: Wet; earthy; fungi-smelling.

Sensations: Feel enclosed in this silent world.

Above, top and bottom: Cool-temperate rainforest flourishes around Marysville, near the Yarra Ranges, Victoria.

Across Bass Strait, the myrtle forests of the Otways, the Strzeleckis and Central Highlands have close affinities with Tasmanian cool-temperate rainforest, being, as they were, once connected to Tasmania at a time of lower sea levels. However, these forests, unlike Tasmania's pristine wilderness, have been significantly damaged by fire and human intervention. The pockets that survive are small, and due to fire are being invaded by eucalypts. The Gippsland to south-eastern New South Wales area fluctuates between being cool, warm-temperate or subtropical rainforest habitat. Several very interesting cool-temperate areas, which have different cool-temperate affinities than those further south, exist in the high country. Errinundra Plateau, Nadgee's Coast and Howe Ranges, South Coast Range (Tantawanglo) and the Mongarlowe areas have mixes of the Mountain Tea-tree, Mountain Plum Pine, Sassafras, Blackwood, Gippsland and Monga Waratahs, Black Oliveberry, Tree Lomatia, Silver Wattle, Mountain Ash, Shining Gum, Brown Barrel and numerous mosses, lichens and ferns, including Shield Ferns and the Soft Tree Fern. Along the coast in the Cann River area, from Howe Range to Mount Dromedary, the warm-temperate forests begin to tail off. Here lilly pillies exist in a location far from the next stand north; Cabbage Tree Palms grow, and around the foot of the Howe Range in Nadgee is the southern limit of the King Lily (*Thelychiton speciosus*), known in these parts as the Rock Lily.

Wildlife mostly stays clear of cool-temperate rainforest, but makes extensive use of its edges as shelter. Only the Tasmanian Long-tailed Mouse occurs primarily in the rainforest, with the Tasmanian Pademelon and the Masked Owl being the largest animals regularly encountered. There is insufficient sunlight to maintain thermo-regulation for reptiles, apart from the arboreal skinks that climb into sunlight.

Flora of the Cool-temperate Rainforests

The simplest cool-temperate rainforest lies in the coolest, wettest environments, such as the highest areas of Lamington National Park, or in areas furthest south, as in southern Tasmania. Further north, as the temperature rises, fern cover increases on the floor, providing that the canopy lets enough light through. The "carpet" of mosses and lichens can often be 15 centimetres thick, or more. In Tasmania, trees include the rich honey-producer, Leatherwood, the spicy-smelling Sassafras, the Giant Grass-tree (or Pandani), the notorious horizontal scrub and, occasionally, Huon and Celery-top Pines.

Classic Plants: Deciduous Beech; Myrtle; Antarctic Beech; Dogwood; Smooth-barked Sassafras; Coachwood; Leatherwood; Swamp Gums; Shining Gum; Cedar Wattle; Celery Wood; Wild Quince; Southern Marara; King's Lomatia; Celery-top Pine; Huon Pine; King Billy Pine; Mountain Pepperbush; Broad-leafed Pepperbush; Forest Nightshade; Prickly Coprosma; Black Oliveberry; Silky Lomatia; Mountain Walnut; Mountain Laurel; Rough Possumwood; Mountain Plum Pine; Victorian Christmas Bush; tree ferns; Maiden Hair Fern; Mother Spleenwort; Rainbow Fern; Soft Water Fern; Coral Ferns; Shield Ferns; King Fern; numerous fungi.

Above: Richea pandanifolia grows in thickets bordering rainforest on the Tasmanian Highlands and the south-west. *Right, top to bottom:* The Styx Valley, Tasmania, clothed in cool-temperate rainforest; richer forest in warmer conditions in Yarra Ranges National Park, Victoria; rainforest beneath the scarp of St Columba Falls, Tasmania.

Frogs and Reptiles of the Cool-temperate Rainforests

There are frequently ponds and tarns located near rainforest pockets, particularly in Tasmania, and many frogs favour these still waters and boggy areas over fast-running streams. One such frog, the Eastern Banjo Frog, is often heard in the vicinity of these wet areas where it hunts small insects by night. Brown Toadlets inhabit forest close to creeks and breed in the cool weather. Another rare frog that may be seen is the Green and Golden Bell Frog. The cool environment of this rainforest is not very conducive to cold-blooded animals, so reptile life is quite limited and most species are darker coloured, helping them to absorb heat. The best example is the black Chappell Island Tiger Snake.

Classic Frogs and Reptiles: Common Eastern Froglet; Tasmanian Froglet; Loveridge's Frog; Eastern Blue-tongue; Diamond Python; tiger snakes.

Invertebrates of the Cool-temperate Rainforests

With such a depth of moss blanket covering deep, wet litter, including large lumps of wood, it is not surprising there is a myriad of micro-organisms living in cool-temperate forests. These include many bacteria and small insects such as springtails, bristletails and silverfish that consume and turn over cellulose in the rotting wood, which is shot through by mycelium of fungi. Larger tunnellers, such as beetle larvae, beetles and mole crickets, continue turning over the litter. Lying in wait for wandering beasts are leeches, which, in between feeding on the blood of hapless passers-by, maintain themselves on vegetable sap. As for all sustainable living systems, there are the primary consumers of plants, predatory secondary consumers and the recyclers.

Classic Invertebrates: Amphipods; crayfish; huntsman spiders; funnel-webs; centipedes; millipedes; Alderfly; mantids; cockroaches; leeches.

Above: Eastern Blue-tongues inhabit cool-temperate rainforest on the continent's mainland, but are not found in Tasmania, where the Blotched Blue-tongue is resident.

Above, top to bottom: A female Scarlet Robin diligently prepares her nest; male Gang-gang Cockatoo.

Birds of the Cool-temperate Rainforests

Many cool-temperate rainforest birds sustain themselves by scratching about in the thick moss mats and decaying timber for beetle larvae, other invertebrates and worms. The birds found here are many of those that also inhabit wet sclerophyll forest, along with a few notable additions. The Bassian Thrush is a classic example of beautifully camouflaged brown patterning, and scrubwrens and the mouselike Scrubtit also blend perfectly into this environment. Adding contrast to the gradients of shaded green are the Pink, Flame and Scarlet Robins in Tasmania, along with the Rose Robin on the mainland. Golden Whistlers, Shining Bronze-Cuckoos and the high-pitched Grey Fantail add their songs to this otherwise ghostly quiet habitat. Above the tree tops, Swift Parrots and Crimson Rosellas flash in the sunlight, while Wedge-tailed Eagles soar watchfully far above. Beneath the canopy, in the dim, green twilight, silent operators such as the Masked Owl and Australian Owlet-nightjar watch closely for telltale movements from their small mammal or insect prey.

Classic Birds: Bassian Thrush; Green Rosella; Tasmanian Scrubwren; Scrubtit; Strong-billed Honeyeater; Yellow-throated Honeyeater; Lyrebird; Wedge-tailed Eagle; Grey Goshawk; Wonga Pigeon; Yellow-tailed Black-Cockatoo; Gang-gang Cockatoo; Sulphur-crested Cockatoo; Fan-tailed Cuckoo; Shining Bronze-Cuckoo; Sooty Owl; Dusky Robin; Rose Robin; Pink Robin; Scarlet Robin; Grey Fantail; Pied Currawong; Black Currawong.

Above, top to bottom: Spotted-tailed Quoll; Dingo; Tasmanian Pademelon.

Above: The Swamp Wallaby is the only living member of the genus *Wallabia*. It prefers habitats with a dense understorey.

Mammals of the Cool-temperate Rainforests

Flora is the foundation of any living system, and with such limited floral diversity, the cool-temperate rainforests of Tasmania have a similarly low number of permanent mammal species. On the mainland, where these forest types are scattered among other plant communities and also provide a refuge in time of drought, there are many temporary occupants. However, at least in Tasmania, where the introduced fox has not yet secured a foothold, some species such as the Eastern Quoll still survive in these forests. This little predator/scavenger feeds on ground birds, bandicoots and rats, with some offal thrown in. The fierce, tiny Brown Antechinus thrives by rifling among piles of rotting logs and the thick moss cover to feed on beetles, spiders, crustaceans, amphipods and cockroaches at night. The Short-beaked Echidna scratches away here, too. Ringtailed possums make their nests in the lower canopy. Wombats, Tasmanian Devils and Spotted-tailed Quolls wander in from surrounding habitat. At night, Lesser Long-Eared Bats sweep the canopy, both above and below.

Classic Mammals: Dingo; Bush Rat; Water-rat; Tasmanian Long-eared Bat; Eastern Horseshoe Bat; Little Red Flying-fox; Short-beaked Echidna; Spotted-tailed Quoll; Eastern Quoll; Brown Antechinus; Dusky Antechinus; wombats; Common Ringtail Possum; brushtail possums; Eastern Pygmy-possum; Tasmanian Pademelon; Swamp Wallaby.

Where Are They? In the highest mountainous eastern aspects of the Wet Tropics World Heritage Area and the top of Mount Gower, Lord Howe Island.

What Do They Look Like? Wind pruned and streamlined, low-profile closed canopies with 1–2 layers. They have a small number of species and no buttresses but many species of moss, lichen and fern, along with many epiphytes.

Critical Conditions: Very wet conditions; cloud prevalent; cool temperatures; few soil limitations.

Best Examples: *NSW* — Mount Gower. *Qld* — Areas accessible only to experienced bushwalkers.

Sounds: Howling wind.

Smells: Wetness; damp litter and vegetation.

Sensations: Cool; clammy.

Above: The scarlet flowers of the Australian Rhododendron bloom in winter in the mountains of Queensland's Wet Tropics.

Flora of the Cloud Forests

If one climbs far enough up a mountain to enter the mist-shrouded land of near perpetual cloud, then one finds oneself in the temperate world of a forest similar to the cool-temperate rainforest. In this environment, mosses, ferns and specialised trees, such as *Pittosporum* spp., Antarctic Beech and Big Mountain Palms, thrive. Shrubs, too, such as the Australian Rhododendron and the Mountain Rose, are well represented and, being lower, are favoured by the lack of exposure to high winds. Most of the trees and shrubs in this habitat have tough, small leaves.

Classic Plants: Tea-tree; *Planchonella* spp.; Pepperwood; Tree Heath; Malletwood; Native Holly; Rex Satinash; Pimply Ash; Lignum; Basswood; Mountain Silkwood; *Orites fragrans*; Walking-stick Palm; *Cyathea rebeccae*; Bristly Tree Fern; *Dianella* spp.; *Gahnia* spp.; Coral Fern; Iron Grass; Lawyer Vine; Sarsaparilla; *Pandorea nervosa*; Twining Guinea Flower; Misty Bells; numerous orchids and ferny epiphytes.

Cloud Forests

They have a Tolkien-like atmosphere ... with mosses, filmy ferns and other ferns, lichen and fascinating fungi ...

Descriptions of cloud forest from Jean Edgecombe's *Lord Howe Island, World Heritage Area* (1987).

Perched high on mountain tops and exposed to wind and other severe weather conditions, this is a rainforest type able to survive extremes of nature. Wind aside, its lofty location assures cloud forest high moisture, thanks to the many hours each day when this forest is submerged in cloud. While suited to high altitudes, cloud forests cannot withstand freezing temperatures, forcing these communities well into the tropics or, as in the cloud forests of Lord Howe Island, to be surrounded by the temperature-ameliorating ocean. Thus, while Point Lookout in New England National Park fits the cloudy altitudinal conditions, it does not quite qualify as cloud forest because it experiences sub-zero winter temperatures that support only a few rainforest species covered by a protective blanket of low Antarctic Beech canopy. Snow grass, snow gums and hardy leguminous shrubs fit the conditions much better.

Northern cloud forests are found beyond Cairns on the peaks of Mounts Bellenden Ker, Bartle Frere, Broken Nose and Finlayson, as well as Thornton Peak. Granitic Thornton Peak is perilous, with sharp rock exposures and massive boulder fields. The wind-whipped canopy of cloud forest thickets fits in among the boulders, and dense sedge and fern mats cover the floor. Punctuating the canopy are eucalypt and acacia emergents. Worth special mention in this habitat is the continent's only native rhododendron, the Australian Rhododendron, with its beautiful crimson, bell-shaped flowers. The communities, however, tend to be parts of a mosaic of other mixes of rainforest species. In some ways, these cloud forests have similarities with the Errinundra area of Gippsland and it is interesting that numerous plant and invertebrate species have their nearest relatives down south.

Many cloud forests are notoriously difficult to access. More scientific investigation is needed, but it seems that few wildlife species count cloud forest as core habitat, preferring to treat them as places to wander and forage for food. Two animal species are known to depend entirely upon northern cloud forests: the Thornton Peak Melomys, a small native rat, and a tree-frog species, the Armoured Mistfrog. The Bartle Frere Skink (*Leiolopisma jigurru*) is one of the restricted species, with its nearest relatives 1500 kilometres to the south, while a stag beetle on Mount Lewis has its nearest relatives in the Andes. These, and other species, pose questions that relate to the ancient patterns of vegetation and climates over Australia.

To the south is a pocket of cloud forest on Mount Gower, Lord Howe Island. The 875 metre climb to Mount Gower's small sloping plateau is quite difficult, but with a guide it is probably more accessible than the cloud forests of the tropics. On the plateau is a low (8 metre), somewhat tangled two-tiered rainforest made up of Hotbark, *Dracophylum* spp., Island Apple, Big Mountain Palm, Pumpkin Tree and *Pittosporum* species. The wind-pruned canopy is streamlined without emergents, but there are many small epiphytes, twining herbs, Mountain Rose shrubs, stiff sedges and five fern species, including a *Cyathea* tree fern, all rising from a dense moss- and lichen-covered floor — that is, where the floor has not been disturbed by nesting Providence Petrels or by the endangered Lord Howe Woodhen.

Above: Cloud-capped mountains Gower and Lidgbird on Lord Howe Island. *Right:* Misty forest on the heights in Eungella National Park.

Fauna of the Cloud Forests

These forests are widely distributed, from Cooktown to New England and out to Lord Howe Island, so regional climate largely determines the animals that inhabitat cloud forests. Being on high mountain tops, these forests, with their damp, cool conditions, are not only habitat for permanent species but, when drought arrives, also act as vital refuges for beasts from lower altitudes. Among the residents are a number of skinks, most of which are dark toned, such as the Bartle Frere Skink and Thornton Peak Skink. The most spectacular bird is the Golden Bowerbird, which builds an astonishing metre-high bower. Macleay's Fig-Parrots feast on figs, as do Wompoo Fruit-Doves. Busily checking the litter and epiphytes are the Mountain Thornbill, the Atherton Scrubwren and the Grey-headed Robin. On the ground, Musky Rat-kangaroos and Northern Bettongs forage. In the evening, Mountain Brushtail and Common Ringtail Possums clamber through the dense low canopy.

Many animals of the lower wet tropical rainforest also use cloud forests as part of their habitat, with some exceptions such as the Thornton Peak Melomys, the Armoured Mistfrog and the Bartle Frere Skink; however, much more investigation is required to be certain that all of the animals endemic to this habitat have been uncovered. In the case of Mount Gower, it is unlikely that any vertebrates are endemic to the mountain top, but this may not be so for invertebrates. At any rate, this cloud forest has not been affected by feral pig and goat populations, whereas the rest of the island habitats below Mount Gower's cliifftops have.

Monsoon and Dry Rainforests

Monsoon is said to have been derived from the Arabic mausim *meaning season, and if one were looking for a land of distinct seasons it would be difficult to find a better example than the Top End of Australia, from Port Hedland to Princess Charlotte Bay, Cape York. This is the land of the 'Wet' and the 'Dry'. The monsoon climate determines the nature of the monsoon forest, or, to be technically correct, of the monsoon vine forest.*

Rainforests of Australia, ed. Penny Figgis, Weldon, 1985.

The common factor for this group of forests is a regular severe drought season, consistent with the arrival of the South-East Trade Winds that follow the decline of the north-west monsoon. Seasonal drought is accentuated by the composition of the underlying soils: some, such as those on granitic parent material, are considered "droughty soils" and are largely composed of silica grains, particularly where clays have washed out during earlier climatic cycles. Over the past million years, plant species were (and still are) continually tested by climate change. Species not fit to survive prolonged drought either died out or remained hidden in refuges, such as the sheltered gullies and spring-fed gorges on the edge of the Kakadu sandstone escarpment. When long-term climatic change brought more humid conditions, the "refugees" became free to range once again. On their migrations chasing Carpentaria Palm fruit, pigeons from the Torres Strait (as well as the Rose-crowned Fruit-Dove and the Banded Fruit-Dove), couriered in the seeds of other rainforest species, enriching the populations of "refugees".

This process of retreating and regenerating species is still continuing. Humid conditions last only for a short, intense wet season (greater than 500 millimetres) each year, leaving May to November almost rainless. Later, the intensely hot dry season swelters at more than 35°C. Yet even these conditions are inconsistent — this climate experiences irregular, severe cyclonic disturbance, which may bring the annual average rainfall in a single day! Few plants can handle this severe environmental pressure. Those tough few that can, "bounce back" as evidenced at Port Essington's historic settlement, Victoria — an area that was cleared to bare earth in 1845 is once again a monsoon vine forest. Similarly, Channel Island, cleared in 1940 and once Darwin's leprosarium, is now, once again, vine forest.

Above: Abundant ferns and epiphytes during the wet season's flourish of growth typify monsoon and dry rainforest.

Above, top to bottom: Hoop Pine shows the location of dry rainforest and monsoon forest on Hook Island, Queensland; Bunya Pine forests in the Bunya Mountains, Queensland, are unique dry rainforest.

Right: Monsoon forest seen through a cave mouth, Kakadu National Park, Northern Territory. *Far right:* Deep green monsoon forest blankets the tributary gorges of the East Alligator River, Kakadu National Park, Northern Territory.

Where Are They? From Cape York (Qld) to the Kimberley (WA). Trees form a canopy in isolated wetter areas with rainfall over 400 millimetres in the monsoon rainfall belt that experiences the Wet (December–April/May) and Dry (May–November).

What Do They Look Like? Green pockets and patches amid dry open forests, woodlands and scrubland. They are frequently seen in gorges and gullies and fringing river estuaries.

Critical Conditions: Adequate soil moisture throughout the year with annual rainfall of at least 400 millimetres in a four-month wet season; prefer hot to very hot (more than 30°C) day temperatures from August to March.

Above, top to bottom: The mound nests of the Orange-footed Scrubfowl can be seen in dry-season monsoon forest on Channel Island off Darwin, Northern Territory. These particular incubator nests were so large that they appeared on the contour map; monsoon forests are usually two-storeyed with an upper canopy of Carpentaria Palms (within their range, or other palms elsewhere), and the giant An-binik trees (*Allosyncarpia ternata*), below which the mid and ground storeys are a tangle of fine vines, shrubs and young palms.

NATURE OF MONSOON AND DRY RAINFORESTS

Monsoon forest is a kind of "cover-all" name that actually comprises a variety of structures and plant and animal species. As could be expected, with these forests ranging from Cape York (which is closest to the richest rainforests on the continent at Daintree–Bartle Frere), to the Kimberley and 2400 kilometres to the west, there is much variation in the species that populate such forests. The richest and most diverse are at the east edge of the continent; the most depauperate are in the west.

Climate and season also dramatically affect the nature of the monsoon forest. "White feller" immigrants may only perceive two seasons in Australia's north, the Wet and the Dry, but Aboriginal people, whose lineage stretches back some 50,000 or more years through a number of climatic changes and major sea level changes, recognise some six different and dynamic seasons — far too many to describe in detail here, but each splendidly described in Ian Morris's 1996 natural history guide, *Kakadu National Park, Australia*. For the purposes of this book, my recollections of part of this awe-inspiring World-Heritage-listed area must suffice.

Off the South Alligator River estuary lies the elliptical-shaped Field Island, almost surrounded by zoned bands of nineteen mangrove species that provide prime habitat for Estuarine Crocodiles, Black Flying-fox colonies and nesting Intermediate Egrets. Behind the small beach, and beyond an ancient Macassan trepang (sea cucumber) fishing camp, run the parallel lines of old shorelines. On the damp hollows, where a veneer of sand overrides laterite and clay, are long, deep-green 10-metre high "mounds" of vine forest. These vine forest mounds, with the mangrove incursion, tall paperbarks, more vine forest, eucalyptus forest of Darwin Stringybark, sandy patch, shrubland, vine forest again, and so on, through to the far side mangrove belt, lend the island a striated appearance.

The edge of vine forest is protected by masses of slender vines, some bearing yams, others the poisonous crimson- and black-seeded Abrus. Adding pastel to Nature's palette are the pale-pink Hibiscus flowers, growing alongside acacias as well as Screw Palms. Beyond the humidity enclosing barrier of vines, the forest becomes cooler and more open, with a shading canopy of evergreens, such as Terminalia species, and emergent Leichhardt Trees. Here, too, are dry season deciduous plants, such as the Kapok Bush and Gyrocarpus with its "helicopter-like" flying winged seeds. Sometimes these areas are graced by a Banyan Fig, its widespread, embracing limbs making up the very heart of these stands. Denser parts of the canopy of Tuckeroo (Cupaniopsis spp.) are broken only by the feathery heads of Carpentaria Palms, while the spreading canopy of the Maranthes tree, resplendent with succulent, pink and ivory fruit, draws a crowd of pigeons and Flying-foxes. The fallen fruit garnishes the dry litter surface on the ground level, catering for the Brush-tailed Tree-rat, Chestnut Rails, Orange-footed Scrubfowl and numerous invertebrates attracted by the fruit's pungent aroma. In the highest stringybark lurks the White-bellied Sea-Eagle, patiently scanning the surroundings and waiting for a careless animal to stray beyond the cover of the vine forest and onto the unprotected beach.

The hot 5-kilometre walk along the sandy track to Boroalba Spring monsoon forest winds through a cool, humid oasis beneath the green canopy at the entrance to the sandstone gorge of Baroalba Creek. As the valley walls draw closer, deep sandy soils cover the floor. Paperbarks, Pandanus Palms, grevilleas, Ghost Gums and An-binik (Kakadu's most memorable tree) close in. In this more protected site, the monsoon forest is less like a thicket; instead, a 20–35 metre canopy,

Above: The Northern Quoll is the most diminutive of the quoll species; it is also the most aggressive. It is endangered, due in part to the devastating affect of the introduced and poisonous Cane Toad.

Mammals of the Monsoon and Dry Rainforests

Small pockets of rainforest that experience seasonal inundation by monsoonal rains and seasonal dry weather are scattered about tropical Australia. Mammals in particular use these habitats as refuges and these sanctuaries also provide a variety of soft foods, such as berries. A diversity of rich invertebrate life provides prey for the small mammal insectivores, while the abundance of small mammals and reptiles lures larger mammal, reptile and bird predators, such as Northern Quolls, Northern Brown Bandicoots and the smaller, yet equally rapacious, Common Planigale.

Classic Mammals: The list of mammals is much the same as for those of the dry rainforest. Spectacled Flying-fox; Little Red Flying-fox; Black Flying-fox; Rock Ringtail Possum; Large Rock-Rat; White-tailed Rat; Cape York Melomys; Prehensile-tailed Rat; Arnhem Land Rock-Rat; Cinnamon Antechinus; Feathertail Glider; Red-legged Pademelon; Black Wallaroo; Monjon Wallaby; Striped Possum.

Above: Delicately patterned Marbled Velvet Geckoes hide under bark or in crevices by day, emerging at night to forage for insects.

Frogs and Reptiles of the Monsoon and Dry Rainforests

Monsoon forests are rich habitats that serve as refuge for woodland beasts during the dry season. As a bonus, these habitats are usually situated near water: a spring, stream or wetland. The heaviest reptile is the Yellow-spotted Monitor, although some of the pythons (such as Oenpelli, Water, Olive, Diamond and Scrub Pythons) would clearly top the list if they occupied these territories. Of the venomous "Elapid" snakes, the Northern Death Adder is common, as are whipsnakes, Slaty Greys, King Browns and taipans — by far the deadliest. Numerous skinks and geckoes feed in the litter, on tree trunks and on exposed rock.

Classic Frogs and Reptiles: Northern Territory Frog; Robust Whistlefrog; *Carlia* spp. skinks; Common Tree Snake; Marbled Velvet Gecko; monitors; 10,000 species of invertebrates were collected in Kakadu monsoon vine forests in 1980.

Above: Curcuma Lilies grow on damp sandy soils in sheltered gullies and caverns in Kakadu National Park, Northern Territory.

Flora of the Monsoon and Dry Rainforests

Because the plants of this system are tropical, they must survive a parched dry season of at least five months — in short, they must adapt well to the serious stress created by a severe water shortage. Consequently, most species are deciduous, dropping almost all of their leaves in the dry season or, in the case of the Kapok Bush, becoming completely leafless during drought.

Most species grow individually rather than in stands, notably the Kapok, the monumental Leichhardt Tree, Giant and Weeping Paperbarks, and Ghost Gums, as well as the perpetually green broad-crowned An-binik. Over (and under) the floor twine yam vines; the beautiful huge, pink-flowered Curcuma Lily; Native Ginger; Freshwater Mangroves and, of course, Pandanus, Cluster and Rock Figs — sustenance for pigeons and fruit bats.

Classic Plants: An-binik; various *Terminalia* spp.; *Lophopetalum arnhemicum*; Blue Quandong; Emu Apple; Red Ash; Milkwood; Yellow Tulipwood (*Drypetes lasiogyna*); Pink Mahogany (*Dysoxylum oppositifolium*); Horsfieldia; *Xanthostemon* spp.; native plums; *Calophyllum* spp.; Carpentaria Palm; *Pandanus* spp.; paperbarks; Round Yams; Kentia Palms; Northern Grevillea; Rock Fig; Banyan Fig; Cluster Fig; Leichhardt Tree; Tuckeroo; *Maranthes* tree; *Polyalthia* spp.; Hyacinth and Nervillea Orchids; cunjevoi; *Curcuma* Lily; Basket and numerous other ferns; mosses; Supplejack; Lawyer Vine; *Flagellaria* spp.

Above: Monsoon forest surrounds the deep plunging cascades of Twin Falls in Litchfield National Park, Northern Territory.

Best Examples: *NT* — Kakadu National Park; Litchfield National Park; Howard Springs; Berry Springs Nature Park; Channel Island; Gurig Gunak Barlu National Park. *WA* — Mitchell Plateau; Bell Gorge. *Qld* — parts of Iron Range National Park and upper Cape York.

Sounds: Honeyeaters in grevilleas; the screech of flying-foxes.

Smells: Spicy, damp vegetation.

Sensations: Moist relief from the sweltering heat.

mainly of An-binik, strives upward above cool, crystal-clear waters teeming with Sacred Saratoga, Eel-tailed Catfish and Primitive Archerfish. Deeper into the forest, a number of plant species (some buttressed) vie for dominance: the Little Gooseberry (Buchanania arborescens); a native plum; the beautiful, shiny-leaved and threatened Blush Touriga (Calophyllum sil); Carpentaria Palms and White Apples. A number of long, slender lianes loop around and link the trees. On the drier slopes of the forest edge, the Lawyer Vine and Abrus add variety to the densely tangled mats of Supplejack (Flagellaria indica).

Masses of tangled roots in the valley bed spread the water into numerous pools and runnels, all with pure-white sandy beds. Nestled in the damp, spring-fed seepage areas of the sandstone walls are numerous mosses and some of the 26 species of fern that grow in this marvellous example of monsoon forest.

These pockets of refuge from the inclement weather, particularly during the dry season, are safe havens for a multitude of animal life, from the rock-loving Black Wallaroos to the Nabarlek, Rock Ringtail Possum, Chestnut-quilled Rock-Pigeon and gorgeous Rainbow Pitta.

Birds of the Monsoon and Dry Rainforests

Mobile animals seek to escape the devastating dry season drought by sheltering in the mosaic of monsoon forest refuges across the continent's Top End. Traditional Indigenous owners, understanding the crucial importance of this guaranteed food source in times of scarcity, rigorously protected these areas from fire. For birds, these safe havens played a huge role in their evolutionary histories. The animal residents of monsoon forests fluctuate from season to season, with the greatest variety being around August to October. As the wet season begins in late October, the animals start dispersing to their primary habitat areas. Of all of the animals, the birds disperse furthest.

Classic Birds: Torresian Imperial-Pigeon; Banded Fruit-Dove; Emerald Dove; Rose-crowned Fruit-Dove; Yellow Oriole; Figbird; Spangled Drongo; Rainbow Pitta; Orange-footed Scrubfowl; Great Bowerbird; White-lined Honeyeater; Red-winged Parrot; Varied Lorikeet; Oriental Cuckoo; Common Koel; Rufous Owl; Striated Pardalote; Helmeted Friarbird; Rufous-banded Honeyeater; Lemon-bellied Flycatcher; Grey Whistler; Little Shrike-thrush; Shining Flycatcher; Leaden Flycatcher; Rufous Fantail; Northern Fantail; Varied Triller; Black Butcherbird.

Below, left to right: Flocks of Red-winged Parrots provide wonderful flashes of colour in an otherwise neutral green environment; a Rufous Fantail checks in on its small chick; Figbirds are common visitors to monsoon forests. They arrive in small noisy groups to harvest figs and other fruits.

Where Are They? *NT* — Darwin lagoons and East Point. *Qld* — Bunya Mountains National Park; Whitsunday Islands; Mount Barney National Park; Carnarvon National Park and north of Injune along Carnarvon Development Road; Taroom area; Springsure; Blackdown Tableland and Expedition National Parks; Normanby River; Lakefield National Park; Great Sandy National Park. *NSW* — Warrumbungles (head of Wombelong Creek); Sawn Rocks; Castletop and Mount Waa–Mount Kaputar National Parks; Mount Lindsay; Royal National Park at Curracorang. *WA* — Tunnel Creek and Windjana Gorge; Bell Gorge.

What Do They Look Like? From very dense but low (15 metre) scrub to dense thickets with thorny vines. They often form on more eastern coastal sites, usually with tall Araucarian pine emergents. Old Scrubfowl nests mark past "forest" locations.

Critical Conditions: More than 750 millimetres of effective rain; few if any frosts; hot summers (more than 28°C) with some fire protection.

Best Examples: *Qld* — Carnarvon Development Road (Injune–Rolleston); Bunya Mountains and Expedition National Parks; Stradbroke Island; Great Sandy National Park (Cooloola). *NT* — Darwin lagoons; East Point Reserve, Darwin. *WA* — Tunnel Creek; Windjana Gorge. *NSW* — Mount Kaputar National Park; Cape Byron; North Entrance Dunes.

Sounds: Australian King-Parrots at Bunya Mountains; silence at Kaputar.

Smells: Dry and spicy.

Sensations: Variable — cool to hot and prickly.

Dry Rainforests

In the flats, over which we travelled following Zamia Creek, I was surprised to find Erythrina, *which I had been accustomed to meet with only on the creeks, and at the outskirts of mountain brushes, near the sea-coast. The White Cedar [*Melia azedarach*] grows also along Zamia Creek, with casuarina, and a species of* Leptospermum. *On my return I found that the party had been out wallabi [sic] shooting, and had brought in three; they were about two feet long [61 cm]; body reddish grey, neck mouse grey, a white stripe on each shoulder, black muzzle, and black at the back of the ear; the tail with rather long hair [apparently Bridled Nailtail Wallaby]. The flying squirrel [*Petaurus sciureus*] which was not different from that of the Hunter; and a* Centropus phasianellus [*the swamp pheasant of Moreton Bay*] *was also shot … on the west side of the hill, a noble fig-tree spread its rich dark-green shady foliage; on the steep slopes* Erythrina *was frequent. I could not help contrasting the character of this place with the moist creeks and mountain brushes of the Bunya Bunya country.*

Dr Ludwig Leichhardt, traversing Queensland's central tablelands, November 1845.

Leichhardt describes one of the dry rainforest communities he saw south-east of Carnarvon Gorge in pre-settlement conditions. He had just struggled through numerous scrubs of what he called "Bricklow" (Brigalow), along with Bottle Trees, Cypress Pine and vines, which are typical specimens of these communities. In wonderful detail, Leichhardt describes the great faunal abundance of the places he visited, probably because his whole expedition to Port Essington depended heavily upon living off the land. While travelling these regions prior to the onset of the wet season, the most common repetitive reference is to fire, and the evidence of a considerable Aboriginal population. Fire is one of the major limiting factors for the extension of dry rainforest scrubs and vine thickets.

Climatically, as one moves across the eastern escarpment down the length of the Great Dividing Range to progressively drier, rain shadow western areas (and in areas where some country rock provides droughty and/or infertile soils), fewer and fewer rainforest species are able to survive. Those species that do survive, do so due to the efficient adaptations of moisture conservation and nutrient use. These adaptations include the production of smaller leaves, waxy leaf surfaces, a reduced number of leaf stomates (breathing pores), deciduousness, smaller plant structure, increased active root systems and development of associations with other species. They form communities that comprise both dry rainforests and others, which probably should not be claimed to be rainforest but certainly contain both plant and animal species that also occur in rainforests. Dry rainforests lie somewhere between rainforest and scrublands or thickets of dense scrub. The one thing they have in common is their structure — sometime in their life they will potentially have a closed canopy, although most of the time much light will still penetrate through the canopy of vines and small leaves.

Left: Livistona palms grow on spring and seepage areas in the otherwise-dry Echidna Chasm of Purnululu National Park, Western Australia. A few other species, more typical of rainforests, have slowly colonised these places, forming the nucleus of a dry rainforest.

Right: Damp gullies that cut through the giant sandstone-pillar forest on impermeable stone at the Lost City, Northern Territory, have been colonised by seeds carried by Torres Strait Pigeons and other birds from monsoon forests further east, forming dry rainforest in these locations.

Frogs and Reptiles of the Dry Rainforests

Because this habitat is relatively open, it provides a warm habitat for reptiles, but remains too dry for most amphibians. Pythons and geckoes are well suited to this environment, while skinks find cooler shelter and invertebrate food among the eroding rock slabs and concentrated leaf litter on the gully floors. Dragons, too, find reasonable conditions in dry rainforests.

Classic Frogs and Reptiles: Northern Velvet Gecko; Rusty-topped Delma; Burton's Snake-lizard; Chameleon Dragon; Frilled Lizard; Two-lined Dragon; Gould's Monitor; Spotted Tree Monitor; *Carlia* spp.; Major Skink; Eastern Blue-tongue; Black-headed Python; Children's Python; Diamond Python; Common Tree Snake; Common Death Adder; taipan; King Brown Snake; Western Brown Snake.

Above: Prickly Knob-tailed Gecko (*Nephrurus asper*).

Flora of the Dry Rainforests

In many locations where these forests exist, arid conditions during the dry season are exacerbated by surrounding rock; for example, in the Limmen region of the Northern Territory, Palm Valley, the Bungle Bungles in Purnululu NP, Jasper Gorge and some escarpment areas of Kakadu. Rock Figs and Cluster Figs, both of which produce excellent pigeon and Great Bowerbird food, can survive both the rocky geology and the heat. Sandstone Pandanus helps shade and cool the dry rainforest while several species of *Livistona* palms are scattered throughout the community.

Clasic Plants: Bunya and Hoop Pines; Brigalow; Northern Cypress Pine; Bottle Tree; Green Plum; Native Gardenia; Rock Fig; Cluster Fig; Sandpaper Fig; Banyan; Kapok; Hoya; Australian Ebony (*Diospyros compacta*); Native Cherry; Silkwood; Helicopter Tree; White Cedar; Quinine Tree; Bakupar (*Pouteria sericea*); *Terminalia* spp.; Crinum Lily; Beach Arrowroot; Burdekin Plum; Galip Nut Tree; Broad-leafed Paperbark; Ironwood; Arnhem Land Quandong; *Bauhinia binatum*; Fan-leafed Cabbage Palm; Cooktown Orchid; Deciduous Kurrajong; Crow's Ash; Carpentaria Palm; Currant Bush; Yellow Tulip Oak; Mock Olive; Staghorns.

It is very significant that Leichhardt compares the area he describes with the Bunya Mountains and their elevated "island" of magnificent Bunya Pine dry rainforest, with its floor of ferns and gullies of cunjevoi and Lawyer Vine. Again, this area is incredibly rich in fauna, which uses the dry rainforest (surrounded as it is by very much drier lowland) as shelter and food supply. The edge of the forest is protected by barriers of dense thorny thickets. Each year, the giant 50 metre Bunya Pines produce huge, pineapple-sized cones with large "nuts". This food source annually attracted Aboriginal peoples for sumptuous feasts and elaborate ceremonies. Providing spectacular skylines for numerous dry rainforests on the wetter edge of the rain shadow, as well as in drier parts of heavier rainforests, is the Hoop Pine (*Araucaria cunninghamii*), another very large conifer with Gondwanan ancestry. It is a tall, emergent co-dominant pine whose dark green, wedge-shaped silhouette rises above the canopy, as on the granite offshore islands of the Whitsundays.

Many mixes of species in marginal areas might classify as one of these rainforests — the dense, thorny thickets on limestone knolls near Katherine (NT); lagoon-edge forest around Top End lagoons; riverside forest at Mataranka (NT); gulllies in the Warrumbungle and Nandewar Mountains (NSW); headland thickets, such as Seal Rocks, Cape Byron, Yacaaba Head (NSW), and East Point near Darwin; dune swale thickets behind many beaches with banksia, Tuckeroo, lilly pillies, Boobialla, Tylophora, and Duboisia; boab scrubs around Victoria River (NT) and the King Leopold, Oscar and Napier Ranges (WA); and coastal gully scrubs in the Kimberley.

Above: Male bowerbirds construct elaborate bowers to impress females. These architectural masterpieces are not nests, rather they are dance venues where the male and female conduct their courtship.

Birds of the Dry Rainforests

Dry rainforest communities have a wide variety of plant types, even if they are stunted by the arid conditions. These plants create bird food, such as nectar-rich flower, seeds, soft fruits or berries, and attract flying and ground insects and invertebrates. This is usually one of the "fringe" communities bordering other habitats, so there are usually plenty of birds.

Classic Birds: Wonga Pigeon; Common Bronzewing Pigeon; Partridge Pigeon; White-quilled Rock-Pigeon; Rose-crowned Fruit-Dove; Brown Cuckoo-Dove; Bar-shouldered Dove; Brush Cuckoo; Fan-tailed Cuckoo; Little Bronze-Cuckoo; Channel-billed Cuckoo; Pheasant Coucal; Tawny Frogmouth; Sacred Kingfisher; Blue-winged Kookaburra; Noisy Pitta; Purple-crowned Fairy-wren; Lovely Fairy-wren; Red-backed Fairy-wren; Large-billed Gerygone; Green-backed Gerygone; Blue-faced Honeyeater; Yellow-tinted Honeyeater; Brown-backed Honeyeater; Bar-breasted Honeyeater; Rufous-banded Honeyeater; White-throated Honeyeater; Red-headed Honeyeater; Dusky Honeyeater; White-browed Robin; Golden Whistler; Grey Shrike-thrush; Leaden Flycatcher; Northern Fantail; Willie Wagtail; White-bellied Cuckoo-shrike; White-breasted Woodswallow; Grey Butcherbird; Fawn-breasted Bowerbird; Star Finch; Australian King-Parrot; Wedge-tailed Eagle (inland); Pacific Baza; Grey Goshawk.

Above, clockwise from top left: Dry rainforest of the Arnhem Land escarpment and plateau is the only haunt of the endemic Black Wallaroo; the timid Nabarlek is a small rock-wallaby; Rock Ringtail Possums live in small family groups.

Mammals of the Dry Rainforests

Mammals of the dry rainforests are the same as those that inhabit the monsoon and dry rainforest. While there are a few large areas of dry rainforest, such as Forty Mile Scrub National Park near Mount Garnet, small pockets throughout tropical Australia prove the most crucial for wildlife, acting as bases of shelter, from which mammals can access wide areas of open habitat. In rocky escarpment habitat, these safe havens supplement the dry food diet of many animals with soft foods, such as berries, and are also rich in invertebrates, catering for the small mammal insectivores. The populations of small mammals and reptiles draw larger mammal, reptile and bird predators, such as Northern Quolls, Northern Brown Bandicoots and ferocious smaller species, such as the Common Planigale.

Classic Mammals: Spectacled Flying-fox; Little Red Flying-fox; Black Flying-fox; Rock Ringtail Possum; Large Rock-Rat; White-tailed Rat; Cape York Melomys; Prehensile-tailed Rat; Arnhem Land Rock-Rat; Cinnamon Antechinus; Feathertail Glider; Red-legged Pademelon; Black Wallaroo; Monjon Rock-wallaby; Striped Possum; Red-necked Wallaby; Eastern Wallaroo; Antilopine Wallaroo.

Signs of Past Times

There are many places in dry rainforest where the vegetation hints at vastly dissimilar climates during earlier times. Perhaps the best known survivors are the Cabbage Palms (*Livistona mariae*) of Palm Valley in the West MacDonnell Ranges in Central Australia. These palms, relics of previous times, have survived in this isolated "desert" valley only because of an underlying impervious sandstone that is tilted towards the valley. This sandstone carries springwater and releases it into the valley, which is aligned to provide some shelter from the harsh sun. In a similar way, springwater keeps the soils of deeply entrenched Carnarvon Gorge damp — this dampness is a refuge for the more common Cabbage Palm in the dry sandstone country. Figs are another tough genus of the wet forest. Figs can withstand arid temperatures when sufficient moisture is available; thus, we find figs around Uluru and many other Red Centre locations, as well as at Hurleys Spring in the Warrumbungle Range.

Above, top to bottom: Palm Valley's Cabbage Palms are relics of a past climate. They survive along Palm Creek because the thick, absorbent, soft red sandstone, from which the surrounding country formed, lies over a harder, impervious rock. This caused stored water to be released slowly, and kept the palms irrigated while the surrounding country baked and all other ancestors of the ancient rainforest died out; the colourful fruit of a Rock Fig.

Woodlands

LEGEND
- Monsoon & tropical woodlands
- Temperate woodlands
- Riverine woodlands
- Semi-arid shrub with savanna
- Arid & semi-arid low woodlands

Previous pages: Eucalypt and bluebush woodland east of Norseman, Western Australia. *Right:* A ground storey of diverse flowering shrubs in Sydney woodlands, including the Pink Wax Flower (*Eriostemon australasius*), is typical of that found in sandstone-based national parks, which shelter more than 2000 flowering species.

Above: The Waratah is the State emblem of New South Wales. Its genus name *Telopea* means "seen from afar", while its species moniker *speciosissima* honours it as "most beautiful".

Woodlands

… the timber around is thinly scattered, I do not suppose there are more than ten Gum Trees on an Acre, their bark is amazingly thick at least 2 inches [5 centimetres]; the soil is exceedingly rich and produces the finest grass intermixed with variety of herbs; the hills have the look of a park and Grounds laid out …

Asstistant Surveyor G.W. Evans, first to see Bathurst Plains, south-east of Bathurst, NSW, 6 December 1813.

… made the Bogan at spot, where its banks were beautiful, and the grass of better quality than any we had seen for some time. The Acacia pendula [Myall] grew there in company with the pine (or callitris), the casuarina and eucalyptus, besides many smaller trees, in graceful groups, the surface being very smooth and park-like.

Major Thomas Mitchell, near Peak Hill, 7 September 1835.

Journals kept by explorers provide the first written observations of the continent's woodlands from a European perspective. Major Mitchell and many others — including John Oxley (NSW), Hume and Hovell (Vic), Leichhardt (Qld and NT), Sturt (SA and south-west Qld), Giles (Central Australia and WA), the Gregory brothers and Roe (WA) — were pioneers who traversed Australia's rugged interior. While some of them loosely called woodlands "forests", they all agree that woodlands are places of well-spaced trees (often beautifully and uniquely shaped, as were English broadleaf trees) with a floor covering of abundant grasses, many herbs and, in places, a shrubby cover. Early explorers frequently described woodlands as park-like. Kangaroos and Emus — not by chance the animals of the coat of arms — were commonly described fauna, as were parrots, cockatoos and bronzewing pigeons. The effects of fire in these places were also often recorded.

Of the European settlers who followed in the explorers' footsteps, pastoralists were the first to recognise the potential of woodlands, quickly populating tracts of land with sheep and cattle — both great consumers of grass and palatable young trees. Over the next 150 years, these prime grass-producing lands also attracted the attention of agriculturists. Commercial grass, wheat, rice and crops of cotton,

Above: A woodland profile — temperate woodland, left, is dominated by eucalyptus; tropical woodland, right, is much more diverse, with larger leafed trees that are significantly deciduous in the dry season.

Above, top to bottom: Tall eucalypt woodland in Stirling Range National Park, Western Australia; this alpine woodland of snow gums defines woodlands' sparse distribution of trees.

Right: Temperate woodland in Sydney's surrounding sandstone country is dominated by Scribbly Gums and grass-trees.

grain sorghum and canola all benefited from the excellent environmental conditions. Temperate woodlands' versatility and popularity render it a very threatened community. Tree cover is cleared and vanishes altogether or is converted into scrubland that is covered with unpalatable tall shrubs and trees.

CLIMATE, ENVIRONMENT AND TREE SHAPE

The climatic zone that produces woodland is a kind of "average" Australian community condition, lying between the wet country of the rainforests/forests and the arid central lands of the Outback. It should be no surprise that the "old Australians", the Gondwanans, which have had the longest period to adapt to the changing Australian conditions, are the dominant trees of the temperate woodlands and make up a significant number of dominants in tropical woodlands. These are trees belonging to the family Myrtaceae (such as eucalypts, tea-trees and paperbarks), casuarinas, acacias and members of the Proteaceae family (for example banksias, dryandras, hakeas and grevilleas). Accentuating the dry climatic effect is the sheer antiquity of Australia's land surfaces. So much leaching of soluble minerals from the soil has occurred that dominant plants have had to develop special characteristics to survive on nutrient-deficient soils, particularly those lacking in phosphates. These adaptations have taken a significant amount of time, and in some cases have demanded close symbiotic relationships with other organisms. There are, then, a number of kinds of woodland with different mixes of dominant trees that relate to differences in the environmental conditions.

Despite differing environmental "ingredients", many of the woodland trees remain eucalypts, and many of the flourishing species are of box. Yellow Box, Red Box, Grey Box and Bimble (or Poplar Box) are just some of these. Box trees were named not for a particular shape, but because the first species to receive this moniker produced a pale timber similar to boxwood and happened to have what we now think of as the typical "box" form. Box tree trunks are routinely less than half the height of the tree, with a fork low to the ground. Like other eucalypts, all of which are evergreen, boxes use chlorophyll to trap the sun's heat and convert it to energy year-round. Their leaves hang vertically, usually with one edge facing upwards to the sun. Leaf cells that receive the most sunlight consequently grow larger, causing the leaf to grow sickle-shaped.

Above, top to bottom: Snow gum woodland blankets the Australian Alps, NSW, during winter; subtropical eucalypt woodland grows on a sandstone foundation at Mount Moffat, Carnarvon Gorge, Qld. Like all plants, trees depend upon chlorophyll to harness the sun's energy. Aside from the power of sunlight, they must be nourished by dissolved nutrients which they absorb from the soil via their root system. These roots sometimes also have fungal helpers: mycorrhiza. If soil moisture or nutrients are deficient, trees must be well separated in order to remain healthy. Sparse covering allows for the availability of sunlight all around the tree. Hence, woodland trees are relatively low, with a short main trunk, spherical canopies and leaves that start to grow low to the ground. In contrast, forest trees, which must battle close neighbours for sunlight, are very tall and wedge-shaped with flattish canopies.

Above, top to bottom: Classic woodland of White Gums, Grey Ironbarks and grass-trees, Warrumbungle National Park, NSW; Cypress Pine woodlands, Yathong Nature Reserve, NSW; coastal sandstone woodland (with waratahs, Scribbly Gums and Red Bloodwoods) in Brisbane Water National Park, NSW, covers soils of iron enriched with laterite. The scattered, shorter trees of these communities allow light through to the ground, encouraging a layer of grass and shrubs rooted in the topsoil.

Where Are They? *NSW* — New England National Park; Barrington Tops National Park. *ACT* — Namadgi National Park; Kosciuszko National Park. *Vic* — Alpine National Park; Mount Buffalo National Park; Baw Baw National Park; Monaro Gap. *Tas* — Ben Lomond National Park; Mount Field National Park; Cradle Mountain–Lake St Clair National Park; Walls of Jerusalem National Park; Southwest National Park.

What Do They Look Like? Low eucalypt trees are fairly dense when young but become scattered in old-growth woodland; grassy and shrubby floor.

Critical Conditions: They require space immediately below the tree line on subalpine plains and ridges, but above the frost hollows.

Above: High alpine areas show the limit of tree life at the tree line. Above that, the climate is too cold for successful germination and the trees cannot compete with better-adapted smaller vegetation, such as alpine herbs and grasses. *Below:* Although at high altitude, warmer conditions in New England National Park at this latitude have produced conditions where snow gums can grow larger than those down south. Here, by Point Lookout, snow gums are surrounded by subtropical vegetation with a dense carpet of snow grass as a ground storey, through which other plants have difficulty growing.

Cool and High Country Eucalypt Woodlands

Although other regions of Australia may contain more eucalypt species than the Kosciuszko-to-coast corridor, it is ecologically richest, with eucalypts able to exploit every habitat available to trees from the climatic tree line to the ocean's edge. No other genus of trees [anywhere on Earth] has been shown to do this. The wide [genetic] adaptive capacity of Eucalyptus … provides suitable genetic combinations able to take advantage of almost any ecological challenge that might arise.

Alec Costin, Dane Wimbush and Jamie Kirkpatrick, *An Assessment of the Values of Kosciuszko National Park*, 2002, p. 411.

Two hundred years ago, eucalypts were restricted to the Australian continent and New Guinea. Today, the genus *Eucalyptus* is the most widespread on Earth! On Australia's steepest climes, subalpine woodland grows on heights of up to 1860 metres on Kosciuszko's Main Range. In Tasmania, the Tasmanian Snow Gum (*Eucalyptus coccifera*) grows at slightly lower altitudes, along with Yellow Gum.

The Kosciuszko tree line is populated by a lone subspecies of snow gum (*Eucalyptus niphophila* — from the Greek *niphos* meaning snow, and *philos*, loving). About 100 metres lower down, the Common Snow Gum (*Eucalyptus pauciflora*), also known as White Sallee or Cabbage Gum, takes over, along with the beautiful, bronze-barked Black Sallee in damper areas. In forests below about 1450 metres, these species begin to merge with other gums, such as Mountain Gum and Candle Bark. Below that level, snow gum woodlands mixed with White Gums occur on areas of the Monaro and mingle with Mountain Gums on Barrington Tops and the heights of New England National Park in New South Wales. On the Victorian High Plains, on Mount Baw Baw and skirting the top of Mount Bogong, are pure stands of snow gum woodland. When wet, snow laden or covered with an icy glaze, these graceful gums are some of the most exquisite examples of Nature's artistry.

Above, top to bottom: The view of Mount Feathertop from Mount Hotham in the Victorian Alps shows heavy Alpine Ash forests in the deep valleys. As the slopes climb ever higher into zones of cold and violent weather, these thick stands thin into more sparsely populated woodlands; in places where these trees attempt to grow too closely together, they struggle for light and become malnourished, developing into spindly trees that are easily damaged by the inclement weather.

Flora of the Cool and High Country Eucalypt Woodlands

A lack of moisture and/or fertilisation requires that trees spread apart, providing light all around and allowing the leaves on side branches to be useful energy collectors. Because of this, the general shape of woodland trees is hemispherical, with a short main trunk dividing low to the ground. Sunlight on the floor beneath allows a thick understorey to form, usually of sclerophyllous shrubs, many with a high oil content. This density of vegetation with its flammable oil-producing trees creates potentially explosive environments, especially in hot, dry times, so bushfires are common in woodland communities. But these areas are also wonderfully diverse and the understorey can be vividly colourful in spring. Many understorey plants are "borrowed" from heathland habitats.

Classic Plants: Snow gums, including White and Black Sallee; Spinning Gum; *Eucalyptus niphophila*; Tasmanian Snow Gum and Yellow Gum; snow grass (*Poa caespitosa* var.); shrubs, including *Kunzea* spp., *Oxylobium* spp., *Epacris* spp., Mint Bush, *Hovea* spp.

Above, top to bottom: This *Hovea*-covered slope in alpine woodland is a fire scar caused by sheep graziers, who burned the country to encourage grass cover. The shrubs are now self-perpetuating because they withstand fire better than young gum trees; a typical winter scene in the Australian Alps shows the wide-stretched limbs of a snow gum as it shivers in the winter air.

Above, top: A snowscape of Mount Wellington, which rises above Hobart, Tasmania, shows a stand of gums huddled together and surrounded by the inhospitable, boulder- and snow-strewn winter habitat. *Centre, left to right:* The skeletal branches of a long-dead snow gum that perished in an earlier fire in Mount Field National Park, Tasmania, are dressed in Old Mans' Whiskers lichen and become a support for *Banksia marginata*; Red Cheeseberry (*Cyathodes petiolaris*); Crimson Mountain Rocket (*Bellendena montana*) lights up the spring highlands in Tasmania. *Bottom:* The stressed, bent limbs of an ancient snow gum near the tree line are twisted and gnarled into abstract from seasonal loads of heavy snow and powerful, bitingly cold winds.

The Victorian High Plains (excluding Bogong, Pretty Valley and Mounts Howitt and Baw Baw, which are granitic) are predominately volcanic in origin, giving them a more subdued landscape with "stickier", richer black soils. Here the snow gums are larger and the woodland floor has a higher percentage of soft, herbaceous plants. Tasmanian highlands tend towards a mix of larger plants, such as myrtle and tea-tree in the subalpine woodland, as well as pines and a dense understorey of shrubs and Button Grass in wet places.

Most of the very old, gnarled trees that can live longer than 200 years have not survived the frenzy of deliberate burning that took place when cattle and sheep grazed the High Country from the 1840s to 1960s. Cattle still roam much of the High Plains of Victoria. Even if fire destroys the snow gums' trunks and branches, these stately trees survive by initiating a vigorous growth of shoots from the basal lignotubers. From these shoots grow a tangled mass of thin stems, known as the mallee form. If these stems survive 50 or more years without succumbing to a major fire, many of them then die, leaving a few to expand into a main trunk again. Recent studies of old-tree annual growth rings, in order to check for fire scarring, have indicated that major fires occurred at 50–70 year intervals, with rare stands experiencing fire-free periods of up to 150 years. Old-growth snow gum woodland is a community of scattered trees with a lumpy or rough canopy that causes wind turbulence and subsequently traps more snow.

Increased burning by summer graziers was not meant to be wanton environmental vandalism, it was to replace the shrub understorey with abundant snow grass (*Poa* spp.). Those of us who bushwalked the High Country before the 1960s may look back fondly on days when the small, knotted snow grass tussocks seemed endless and designed for wonderful walking and camping, but the environmental cost was far too great and could not be borne forever. In the south-eastern High Country, from New England through to Mounts Bogong and Buffalo, the dominant High Country rock is granite, which produces sandy, easily eroded and droughty soils. When burning became a near-annual event, the covering grasses were burned off in autumn, resulting in a nutritious green pick during the thaw.

However, these burnt areas left wet soil unprotected, to be easily loosened by the penetration of ice needles. Once the ice melted, the soils loosened and the surface was carried away with the draining waters. This not only affected the woodlands, but carried on down-slope to the valley bogs and streams, which, under the more rapid run-off, further incised their channels. With the lowering of the water tables in late summer, the deep channels dried out — widespread environmental change was the result.

LIFE IN NATURE'S WINTER BOARDING HOUSES

The winter extremities of alpine woodland deem it a lean habitat for small mammals in the cooler months. At best, it is an ephemeral habitat for large macropods in summer, although they move away down the mountain in winter. Woodlands at lower altitudes, and thus with taller trees, do retain Swamp Wallabies and some Eastern Grey Kangaroos. When the country is under a blanket of snow, the largest mammal game enough to endure the winters is the Common Wombat, which can retreat to the shelter of its burrows.

For other animals, such as bats, dead tree hollows become very uncomfortable when icy. Ringtail possums make their leafy nests in the denser woodland in sheltered aspects, while Dusky and Brown Antechinuses inhabit the lower, warmer

Above, top to bottom: Crimson Rosellas inhabit eucalypt forests in the continent's south-east; Green Rosellas are found only in Tasmania and are commonly seen in dense forest.

Birds of the Cool and High Country Eucalypt Woodlands

Bird communities develop and are sustained according to the way in which habitats provide basic needs, including nectar, fruit, seeds and prey animals. Shelter is vital, particularly if the climate experiences rapid weather changes, such as severe winds and cold spells. High Country woodlands are the most secure habitat for many birds, as this habitat has a rich litter layer, loose bark, foliage, masses of seasonal flowers, holes and hollows. Compared with other parts of the high, cold country (such as grassland and shrubland) the woodlands are the greatest attractant for birds. Even so, during very severe winter periods birds' mobility allows them to escape to warmer places. Almost all birds flee when snow settles during winter.

Classic Birds: Australian Pipit; Little Raven; Australian Kestrel; Crimson Rosella; Flame Robin; Grey Shrike-thrush; Grey Fantail; Brown and Striated Thornbills; White-eared, Brown-headed, White-naped and Crescent Honeyeaters; Yellow-tailed Black-Cockatoo; Gang-gang Cockatoo; Forest Raven (Tas); Green Rosella (Tas); Pied Currawong.

Above: Weather-beaten and scorched snow gums on Mount Buller. *Below:* A boulder stream edged with snow gums in Mount Field National Park, Tasmania. Such streams act as massive fire breaks that compartmentalise large alpine area wildfires. Note that the age-weathered dead timber is rarely burned and becomes special shelter for small reptiles.

Best Examples: *NSW* — Kosciuszko National Park at Deadhorse Gap; Charlottes Pass; Guthega; Smiggins Holes; Blue Cow; Currango and about Jagungal; Mount Ginini; Barrington Tops National Park. *ACT* — Mount Franklin and Mount Kelly in the Brindabellas. *Vic* — Mount Selwyn; Round Mountain area; Victorian High Plains; near Cleve Cole Hut; Mount Bogong; walk to Mount Feathertop from Hotham; Mount Arbuckle and Mount Howitt. *Tas* — Mount Field National Park and Lake Windermere.

Sounds: Wind whispering through the gums.

Smells: In summer, eucalyptus; in winter, sterile cold.

Sensations: Chill wind; burning sun; crunch of ice underfoot.

woodlands. The rare Mountain Pygmy-possum lives among some boulder streams that have a woodland cover, and Broad-toothed Rats sometimes live near creeks.

Cold-country reptiles find it somewhat easier, hibernating in a retreat deep under rotting logs, beneath boulders or among exfoliated slabs of granite, usually where there is a cover of leguminous shrubs such as mint bushes. Also sheltering under bark and in crevices are a variety of invertebrates, including flies (28%), bugs (18%), springtails (14%), beetles (10%), wasps (9%), invertebrate larvae (8%), mites (3%), amphipods (3%), spiders (3%), moths (1%), as well as centipedes, millipedes, cockroaches, thrips, grasshoppers, worms and isopods. Some of these animals undergo massive population surges seasonally or when environmental conditions are favourable, such as with the Bogong Moth and grasshoppers.

Invertebrates of the Cool and High Country Eucalypt Woodlands

In the freezing, sub-zero temperatures of the highlands, invertebrates must conserve energy and heat. For this reason, many invertebrates that contribute to this ecosystem are slow moving and dark-hued, if not entirely black, so as to rapidly absorb heat when the sun shines. The speckled Alpine Grasshopper and fat katydids with brilliant red mid-parts, along with the Metallic Cockroach, are the more striking examples. Among the spiders, the wolf spider and the Alpine Grass Funnel-web are notorious. In the streams, crayfish and aquatic larval insects are extremely active.

Classic Invertebrates: Southern Eucalyptus Leaf Beetle; a psyllid (*Ctenarytaina* sp.); Tasmanian Gelonus Bug; Paropsis Leaf Beetle (*Trachymela fumata*); weevils; numerous sap-sucking bugs; Shield Bug; native bees (*Lasioglossum, Leioproctus, Exoneura, Hylaeus* spp.); numerous flies; Metallic Cockroach; Alpine Hairy Cicada; Bogong Moth; Helena Moth; Jack Jumper Ant; wolf spiders; funnel-web spiders.

Above, left to right: Bogong Moth; wolf spider.

Above, clockwise from top left: Common Ringtail Possums flee the colder country during the winter but are seasonal summer visitors; hardy Tasmanian Devils are at home in all habitats throughout Tasmania, with individuals protecting a home territory of approximately 10–20 hectares; a winter resident of these High Country parts, the Common Wombat opens many burrows in the woodlands, frequently undermining trees but also providing shelter for other animals.

Mammals of the Cool and High Country Eucalypt Woodlands

Australia's highest woodlands are not a prolific habitat for mammalian life. Perhaps the most obvious mammal of the High Country woodlands is the Common Wombat. The presence of this tenacious excavator is evidenced by the many burrows, which leave raw, visible earthworks across the landscape. Even in winter, when the ground is frequently snow-covered, muddy wombat tracks are seen radiating from burrows, as at the Eucumbene River crossing. Eastern Grey Kangaroos rarely ascend into the mountains, but are very common in the high woodlands during summer, attracted by the fresh ground-cover grasses. Dingoes, too, hunt high in the mountains, sometimes travelling long distances in a day if food is scarce. The war between dingoes and pastoralists on the Monaro is a classic mammal conflict: humans versus wildlife. Feral horses (or brumbies) are another highly controversial animal on High Country plains, such as in the woodlands at Currango.

Classic Mammals: Eastern Grey Kangaroo; Swamp Wallaby; Common Wombat; Mountain Pygmy-possum; ringtail possums; Eastern Pygmy-possum (Tas); Bennett's Wallaby (Tas); brushtail possums (Tas); Dusky and Brown Antechinuses; Short-beaked Echidna; Bush Rat; Broad-toothed Rat; at least five bat species; Long-tailed Mouse (Tas); Spotted–tailed Quoll (Tas); Dingo; Tasmanian Devil (Tas).

Above, top to bottom: The endangered Northern Corroboree Frog, from Kosciuszko National Park's highest country, uses both high sphagnum wetlands in summer and adjacent woodlands in winter; inoffensive yet venomous Highland Copperheads inhabit wet depressions within the subalpine woodland, where their primary food source is small amphibians.

Frogs and Reptiles of the Cool and High Country Eucalypt Woodlands

Cool streams and wet depressions running through the High Country woodlands are conducive environments for invertebrate larvae. In turn, these young invertebrates act as a food resource for larger beasts, including frogs, crayfish and cold-water fishes, such as Brook Trout. Some seven or so skink species, hiding under rock and bark in the cold country, hunt insects in a habitat where only two snakes are present: the White-lipped Snake and the Highland Copperhead. Further north, and at lower altitudes, a range of other snakes become common. The Black Island Tiger Snake is common in Tasmania and Eastern Tiger Snakes are locally very common around New England and the Barrington Tops, while Eastern Brown Snakes venture in from lower altitudes, as do Yellow-faced Whipsnakes and Red-bellied Black Snakes near the water. A critical feature is the prevalence of loose bush, rock and logs — the essential reptilian furniture.

Classic Frogs and Reptiles: Highland Copperhead Snake; White-lipped Snake; Mountain Heath Dragon; Southern Water Skink; Snowy Mountains Rock Skink; Tan-backed Rock Skink; Mountain Log Skink; High Plains Skink; Metallic Skink; Northern Corroboree Frog (near breeding pools).

FIRE IN THE AUSTRALIAN BUSH

The impact of wildfires on the Australian bush is far-reaching and has roughly six phases. First, fire "fuel" builds up (usually light fuel of leaf matter and grass) as successive plants flourish after the previous fire. As years go by, heavier material from trees is accumulated into the available kindling. Seasonally, the litter begins to decay at its damp base. The early regrowth is keenly sought out by macropods moving in on fresh regrowth. The damp base of the litter continues to decay because fungi, bacteria and invertebrates are at work. After about five years, the annual addition to the litter will begin to equal the decay and the invertebrate-rich litter will be as stable as it will ever be.

The second phase is weather-dominated. After hot dry and windy weather, the fuel load dries and awaits ignition, which may be lightning or a natural cause but is more usually careless human error. At this point, larger, more mobile herbivores have moved to greener pastures. In the third phase, the fire spreads, modified by the quality of the fuel load, wind intensity and direction, and the slope of the land. A hot fire scorches the canopy, usually causing serious injury or death to both plants and animals. In fire-prone habitats, life forms may have evolved survival strategies, like the hard, fire-resistant seeds of acacias and banksias, and the tunnelling habits of wombats.

During the fourth phase, survivors begin a fruitless search for food. In their hunt they are totally exposed to the light, heat and predators. Famine rules the land for the less mobile. Changing weather initiates the fifth stage: the rains come. Underground seeds germinate, living root stocks and tubers begin to shoot. Life returns in a glut of fresh, nutrient-rich green food and quickly seeding grasses. Insect life explodes with a plague of invertebrate herbivores and the House Mouse dominates until antechinuses and avian predators re-colonise.

Finally, after about five years and numerous plant and animal surges, the impact of the fire on the ecosystem begins to lessen and the web of life is largely rebuilt. Prescribed-burning programs, at irregular intervals, upset this delicate equilibrium.

Above: Looking north from Siding Spring Mountain in Warrumbungle National Park, NSW. This fire was the product of aerial incendiary bombing under a fuel-reduction program.

No. 1 This dry sclerophyll forest in Nadgee Nature Reserve (NSW) has reached the stable phase, some nine years after the previous fire. At this point, it is still producing considerable quantities of fresh, young leaf material and flowering, and is sustaining a peak population of grey kangaroos, brushtail and ringtail possums and Sugar Gliders. Lace Monitors and a variety of skinks are common, along with Red-bellied Blacks and Eastern Tiger Snakes and a diverse bird population.

No. 2 Successive extremely dry years were followed by a week of 38°C daytime temperatures and a 60 kilometre per hour north-westerly wind. Smouldering piles of heavy eucalyptus bark re-ignited into flame and quickly spread to the reserve. Overall, this fire burned for ten days, consumed 18,000 hectares of the reserve and left a number of intensively burned firestorm areas.

No. 3 Fire has just passed this grass-tree. The "grassy leaved" top has not burned, thus protecting the growing buds and the shoot at the core of the crown. The grass-tree usually develops a highly flammable collar of dead leaves below the green crown; this produces a rapid flash of heat when burning, which, combined with the green crown above, causes a teardrop-shaped convection system that protects the heart of the canopy — an effective adaptation against fire.

No. 4 Immediate deaths in the holocaust — a Common Ringtail Possum, all but burned to the bone, dangles suspended in *Melaleuca* scrub. We found, to our astonishment, eleven such skeletons over about half a hectare, caught up by chance or by the remains of their prehensile tails. Before the fire, we were unaware that such a high possum population was present. It took a number of years before a ringtail population rediscovered this stand of *Melaleucas* and re-colonised it.

No. 5 The speed of this fire was so great that even grey kangaroos were trapped and incinerated. Despite the extreme, widespread burn, there were some unburned pockets of refuge, usually on small patches that had been burned shortly before, or in areas of dramatically different habitat or among beach dunes. Most survivors suffered scorched feet, making locomotion difficult for weeks. The first wave of regrowth was grass, which dominated for several years, giving these animals a rapid start.

No. 6 Primary habitat in Nadgee for this Eastern Pygmy-possum is tall coastal heath and sclerophyll woodland with numerous large banksias. How this one survived is difficult to imagine, unless it was secreted in a protected tree hollow. It has climbed the burned banksia, probably to search for seed in the fire-opened capsule. As a nocturnal wanderer, this possum is highly vulnerable to attack by Brown Falcons, Sea-Eagles or Diamond Pythons in this exposed habitat.

No. 11 The Rough Barked Apple tree, an *Angophora* species closely related to eucalypts, is an even better producer of epicormic shoots. *Angophora* bark is a superior insulator, meaning that very thin limbs actually remain alive. However, this entire forest crop of new leaves is a problem due to its sheer volume. Any animals that can subsist on epicormic leaves are now on "easy street". To counter this, the plant protects itself by producing leaves that are toxic to many.

No. 7 How this large Diamond Python survived the fire is anybody's guess! Its next challenge is to find living prey when only famine abounds. The python has wandered out of the woodland onto the heath in its search. With luck it may locate a foraging pygmy-possum, like the one shown above. In the first few days there was a glut of hungry skinks — most died of starvation due to the near-total absence of insects. But with death and decay came flies, and so the residual skinks now have flies on the menu.

No. 12 This beetle, along with a caterpillar species, became a major plague animal for flora after the Nadgee fire. Literally countless numbers of these beetles gorged on new shoots and, after some days of heavy winds, blew into the sea. One could lift a shovelful of them from along the tideline. The infesting caterpillars spun cocoon-like webs across clumps of shoots and rapidly devoured all enclosed leaves. Many trees that survived the fire were killed by insects.

No. 8 *Banksia serrata* cone. Fire, heat, exposure and wind all dry out woody structures. Plants in the Proteaceae family, the banksias, hakeas and woody pears, for example, require strong drying processes for their woody fruits to shrink and release winged seeds. After the fire, the ash, dust and loose-sand-covered ground is full of nutrients. What better place to shed seed a few days after the fire? Seeds will flourish in this rich, fertile seed bed following the next shower — an excellent adaptation to bushfire.

No. 13 Germinating acacias, probably the tenacious Sydney Golden Wattle, spring up in the ash bed. So successful was such germination that we recorded upwards of 2000 eucalypts per square metre of the study plot! Yet, within six months, we established a survival rate of less than 5%. No doubt, in the race for survival, the victors had some attributes that were superior to their siblings — natural selection at its finest.

No. 9 The thick, corky bark of banksia plants insulates and protects critical buds embedded in layers of growth cells in the plant's woody trunk. When living leaves are scorched or burnt off, plant hormones — signalling a crisis because the energy supply has been shut down — trigger these embedded buds to commence growth. The shoots in this image have broken through the bark and already entice Yellow-tailed Black-Cockatoos, which harvest the released banksia seed.

No. 14 One might walk a piece of bushland for many years without seeing a grass-tree flower, but if the country is swept by fire (or, for that matter, if a nearby fire fills the air with smoke) then the grass-tree miraculously rapidly grows its great flowering spike. This "kangaroo tail" is a wonderful nectar-full insect attractant. Recently, smoke has been found to contain a number of trace nutrients that promote germination. Also, over two years following fire, four times as many ground orchids were recorded.

No. 10 Similarly, stringybark and bloodwood trees are covered by a layer of porous, insulating bark that protects shoots embedded in the sheets of sap-carrying cells. These epicormic shoots, so typical of eucalypts, burst prolifically into life, covering the blackened trees with pinkish-hued new leaves. This huge stock of fresh leaves is purely an emergency stock that supplies the immediate requirements after the fire. Only some of the new branches will survive; when no longer required, the majority die.

No. 15 This photo is of a similar location as picture No. 1 but taken three years after the fire. Note the heavy growth of grass on the floor. Grass was then overtopping young shrubs and trees and for a time was a real fire risk for those smaller plants. A fire at this stage would threaten many of the shrub species locally as the previous seed store in the soil had been almost totally used and no new seeding was imminent. It was five years later still before a fair degree of safety had returned.

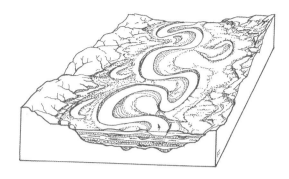

Where Are They? Ribbons of woodland situated along watercourses, especially in inland Australia and where water overflows inland.

What Do They Look Like? Green columns and winding ribbons of trees meandering across dusty plains, frequently with "untidy" hummocks of Lignum beneath trees or, in the continent's east, plump green tree masses that squat by the watercourses and cover a grassy understorey.

Critical Conditions: Warm to hot summers and alluvial soils with natural, seasonal flooding. The Murray–Murrumbidgee receives two floods, an early winter flood and a late-spring–early-summer flood. Trees need deep roots that immerse in groundwater.

Best Examples: *NSW* — Carrathool Bridge; Euabalong; Murray River; Kinchega National Park; Mutawintji National Park; Nocoleche Nature Reserve; Culgoa National Park; Lachlan River, accessed by Lachlan Valley Way; Darling River; Murray River valley. *SA* — Flinders Ranges; Murrumbidgee River.

Sounds: Chortling kookaburras; screeching parrots.

Smells: Swampy sweetness.

Sensations: Cool, serene shade.

Riverine Woodlands

The river [Darling] preserved a breadth of one hundred yards [90 metres], and a depth of rather more than twelve feet [4 metres]. Its banks were sloping and grassy, and were overhung by trees of magnificent size. Indeed, its appearance was so different from the water-worn banks of the sister stream [Murray], that the men exclaimed, on entering it, that we had got into an English river ... for the greenness of its banks was as new to us as the size of its timber. Its waters though sweet, were turbid, and had a taste of vegetable decay, as well as a slight tinge of green ... We noticed that the country had, at some time, been subject to extensive inundation, and was, beyond doubt, of alluvial formation.

Charles Sturt, at the junction of the Murray and Darling Rivers, January 1830.

Riverine habitats produce a distinct ribbon of life, along which plants and animals exist in zoned communities. They are essentially one long "edge" habitat — an interface between water, wetland and land. A healthy river carries on its banks and in its waters, a rich faunal habitat that passes through farmlands and even through cities. However, this aquatic system of life has its limitations, which are set by the water surface. The "dry" land riverine systems of the plains are defined by a belt of forest and woodland that is dominated almost entirely by two eucalypts, the River Red Gum (the "Blue Gum" of the explorers) and the Coolibah. Animal life is not so prescribed. Many species use the woodland as shelter and nesting habitat, but may also spend much of their time in or on the water or out on the semi-arid and arid plains.

EVOLUTION OF A RIPARIAN ECOSYSTEM

Apart from Antarctica, all of the Earth's surfaces are covered by a network of drainage channels comprising gullies, creeks and rivers. Even beneath the sands of the Great Sandy Desert there remain the channels of old palaeo-river systems. Water always seeks the lowest levels, and as it moves it carries sediment loosened

Above: A fringing riverine woodland of paperbarks lines the Fitzroy River in Western Australia.

Above: A floodplain of the Endeavour River, inland from Cooktown, Queensland, is covered by strips of riverine forest and woodland with a smattering of mangrove closed forest, habitats determined by drainage, soils and ancient river courses. *Right:* Tropical riverine woodlands of paperbarks and eucalypts surround the upper Drysdale River, WA.

Above, top to bottom: Flora must be sturdy enough to endure seasonal flooding, such as here along the Murrumbidgee River, NSW; waterweeds flourish, but can clog these systems.

Flora of the Riverine Woodlands

Only sturdy or very supple trees survive the surging floodwaters. The rough-barked bottoms of River Red Gums and paperbarks buffer much of the damage, the latter are also very flexible and bend. Associates of the River Red Gum are the Coolibah, from the warmer north, and the Yapunyah, a beautiful pink-trunked honey producer from the Paroo River system. Speaking of honey, one must not forget the glorious Yellow Box, which has its range in the hills as well as the floodplain. Another typical riverine woodland tree is the River Oak, a casuarina that whistles in the wind and grows hard, cone-covered seeds that attract Yellow-tailed Black-Cockatoos. In the arid areas, Lignum, a hummocky tangle of wiry stems makes excellent shelter (unfortunately mainly for feral pigs) and great nest pedestals for Ibises and other wetland birds.

Classic Plants: River Red Gum; Coolibah; Yapunyah; Black Box; Poplar Box; Carbeen; River Oak; Yellow Box; Lignum; *Acacia victoriae.*

by weathering and erosion. Abrasive sand and gravel, empowered by the rushing water, become the cutting tools that deepen and widen the river channels. Doubling the speed of a river increases the sediment load it can carry up to 64 times! Young, fast streams run off the mountain sides and create faster rivers that are more quickly incised by waterfalls, rapids and riffles. As their pace slows on the flatter country, rivers cut and swing sideways to avoid obstacles. In doing so, their lacerating power is transferred to the sides of the channel, somewhat like the weight of a sled rider on a curving luge course. The river then begins to score out its meandering course.

Older streams run more slowly and drop their load of scouring sediment and wind across lands that have been levelled by the eroding and depositing processes of earlier times. Flowing rivers in Australia's east are short and fast for most of their length, influenced by the run-off of the Great Dividing Range, which runs close to the eastern coast. These rivers meander only after reaching the narrow coastal plain. Over the Dividing Range, the heads of the western rivers rise in the mountains, which, geologically speaking, were uplifted not long ago. These rivers have young courses lined by River Oaks, until they reach the ancient plains out west. The Murray–Darling system's journey across these vast, near-level plains leads the rivers into straying senility. They twist and turn, taking much longer to reach the sea than is necessary. On their journey, they drop countless tonnes of silt, which build up the river bed and cover the plains during flood times.

A RIVERSIDE REGULAR — THE RIVER RED GUM

The River Red Gum (*Eucalyptus Camaldulensis*) is the epitome of woodland flora. It is found along almost all seasonal watercourses across arid and semi-arid Australia (except the south-west), and along tributaries in the south-east. This magnificent tree, the most widely distributed of all eucalypts, possesses a thick, short trunk branching out to heavy boughs that support a wide-spreading hemispherical canopy. In some areas (such as near Barmah, where the Murray's course was partially blocked by a local geological uplift that forced its waters to spill out across the wide floodplain) River Red Gums have developed a forest form, with longer trunks in stands where the trees grow close together. The deep-red timber is dense and heavy, one of the best woods to use for a hot, "smokeless" campfire. These stalwarts of the river system fired most of the Murray–Darling paddle-steamers and riverfront sheep-station steam engines. Few of the stately 400-year-old veterans have survived close to settlement, except where they happen to remain in reserves along the rivers, such as at Euabalong, Carrathool, the lower Darling, Mutawintji, Kinchega, the Flinders Ranges, Wilcannia and Dubbo–Narromine along the Macquarie River. Along Stephens Creek, north-east of Broken Hill, are very beautiful, pendulous types of the River Red Gum, the seeds of which were grown in India and now grace many wet areas there.

The heavy branches of River Red Gums, like those of the "widow-maker" Ghost Gums, have a habit of falling suddenly and leaving a dry stub that rots to form large, round hollows — "Nature's boarding houses", where bats, possums, parrots and cockatoos shelter. River Red Gums require a natural regime of flooding in order to reproduce successfully. They share this dependency on floodwaters with many species of inland fish, such as the Murray Cod and Macquarie Perch. For these species, the damming of rivers over the past 75 years to control flow has made reproduction a matter of chance. Water temperature, flow patterns and flood timing have changed at the hands of humans.

Above, top to bottom: River Red Gums, veterans of the Murrumbidgee floodplain, soak up water through deep underground root systems; larger trees line the dry beds of watercourses and short river systems in the Flinders Ranges, South Australia.

Above: A young Red Kangaroo stands stock still in Kangaroo Grass at Uluṟu, Northern Territory.

Mammals of the Riverine Woodlands

Situated as it is on excellent water supplies and fertile soils, this habitat has the capacity to nourish large, mature trees as well as a ground storey of dense grasses or sedge, so one can expect a healthy population of arboreal and ground-dwelling animals. Veteran trees of the riverine woodlands justifiably earn the title of Nature's boarding houses, with hollows, broken limbs, accommodating forks and abundant fallen logs creating plenty of furniture for mammal species. Just as important are piles of driftwood and other ground-storey debris washed up by floodwaters. Depending on the location (tropical or temperate) one could expect to see Koalas (in the River Red Gum food trees), possums (although brushtails are mysteriously vanishing from the interior) and the arboreal Yellow-footed Antechinus, along with the Brush-tailed Phascogale. Floodplain soils are frequently self-mulching or cracking soils that provide ample shelter for both Common and Fat-tailed Dunnarts. Echidnas are never far away, nor are the Red and Eastern Grey Kangaroos. Pockets of scrubby understorey are often home to Western Greys, or "Scrubbers" as they are sometimes called. Bats, too, are well represented.

Classic Mammals: Eastern and Western Grey Kangaroos; Red Kangaroo; Common Wallaroo; Common Brushtail Possum; Koala; Feathertail Glider; Sugar Glider; Squirrel Glider; Brush-tailed Phascogale; Yellow-footed Antechinus; Short-beaked Echidna; Common Dunnart; Fat-tailed Dunnart; Little Red Flying-fox; Yellow-bellied Sheathtail Bat; White-striped Mastiff-bat; Little Mastiff-bat; Greater Long-eared Bat; Lesser Long-eared Bat; Gould's Wattled Bat; Chocolate Wattled Bat; Little Broad-nosed Bat; Western Broad-nosed Bat; Little Forest Bat; Mitchell's Hopping-mouse.

North of Wilcannia and into the arid and semi-arid tropics, the Coolibah becomes a dominant watercourse tree. Two of the most famous trees are the DIG tree of Burke and Wills on Cooper Creek (vandalised in 2002) and the "Jolly Swagman's" campsite under the Coolibah on a creek north of Winton. The Coolibah that forms large woodland areas on outwash country in the MacDonnell Ranges' valleys is smaller than the River Red Gum, and much shorter and lighter in the trunk. Its straggly, bluish crown casts only light shade and is supported by silvery white branches that rise from a dark-grey, rough-barked skirt. Coolibah wood makes even better campfires than that of River Red Gums. Some of the finest Coolibah woodlands almost reach forest proportions in Culgoa National Park. On the Paroo River, near Wanaaring, another eucalypt dominates the flood areas — the handsome, honey-producing Yapunyah. Along with River Red Gums, Coolibah, Flooded Box (Black Box) and a dense understorey of Lignum, Yapunyah make up extensive woodlands about the Paroo River system and its tributaries and swamps.

Frogs and Reptiles of the Riverine Woodlands

This is prime habitat for freshwater amphibians and, because frogs constitute so much of the diet of reptiles (particularly snakes), most herpetologists know the riverine woodlands intimately. Shelter is plentiful here, with soft cracking earth, piles of drift debris, high and dense grass tussocks, river banks tunnelled by other animals, warm sandbanks for egg incubation, logs and trees — all near readily available freshwater. Such semi-wetlands are rich in invertebrate foods too. In the rivers, snags, algal and aquatic plant beds, mudbanks, sandbanks and reed/sedge beds attract turtles and frogs. During the parched months of the tropical dry season, much of the water-covered mud dries out and cracks deeply. Beneath the dry crust lies the perfect wet "cool-room" for freshwater turtles, who rest almost in a torpor for the duration of the Dry.

Classic Frogs and Reptiles: Eastern Water Dragon; Broad-shelled Turtle; Eastern Snake-necked Turtle; Krefft's Turtle; Murray River Turtle; Tessellated and Wood Geckoes; Northern Dtella; Marbled Velvet and Robust Velvet Geckoes; Hooded Scaly-foot; Bearded Dragon; Lace Monitor; Gould's Monitor; numerous skinks, including *Cryptoblepharus boutonii*; Short-legged Ctenotus (*Ctenotus strauchii*); Tree Skink; White's Skink; Grey's Skink; South-eastern Morethia Skink; Shrubland Morethia Skink; Red-tailed Soil-crevice Skink; Western and Eastern Blue-tongue Lizards; Shingleback; Children's Python; Carpet Python; Common Death Adder; copperheads; Yellow-faced Whipsnake; De Vis' Banded Snake; Red-naped Snake; Grey Snake; Eastern Tiger Snake; King Brown Snake; Spotted Black Snake; Red-bellied Black Snake; Western and Eastern Brown Snakes; Black-headed Snake; Bandy Bandy; Eastern and Sloane's Froglets; Water-holding Frog; Eastern and Giant Banjo Frogs; Long-footed Frog; Ornate Burrowing-frog; Spotted Grass-frog; Crucifix Toad; Red-groined Toadlet; Green and Golden Bell Frog; Green Tree-frog; Peron's Tree-frog; Desert Tree-frog.

Above, left to right: Mertens' Water Monitor uses its laterally compressed tail to herd aquatic animals, such as small fishes and tadpoles, into the corner of waterholes, enclosing the prey in a rapidly shrinking space until the lizard can bend its neck back to reach around and snap it up; the Eastern Snake-necked Turtle spends much of its life in the water, but will journey over land if its environment dries up.

Above, top to bottom: A typical Inland river scene of the lower Murray River shows floodplain forest or woodland fringing the river bank, along with introduced willows; an aerial view of a reach in the Murray River near Mildura, Victoria, shows the traces of past watercourses and billabongs. The history of the river's flow clearly determines where the forests and woodlands thrive. Chocolate-coloured soil on the right is floodplain soil, while the paler, orange soils on the left are wind-drift sand that has blown from the north-west and is now a veneer over the heavy soils. These sandy soils have better drainage and are therefore more suited to irrigation.

Birds of the Riverine Woodlands

Permanent watercourses lined with mature trees that contain plenty of shelter, situated near plenty of seeding grasses, describes the perfect parrot and cockatoo habitat. Little Corellas and Galahs gather in great flocks, sometimes of thousands of birds, and noisily roost in River Red Gums.

At Depot Glen, where Charles Sturt was "holed-up" for six months in 1845, the birds demonstrated their preferred times for drinking and roosting. Galahs arrived first, followed by Little Corellas then green clouds of Budgerigars screamed in to the water's edge, rapidly filled their "tanks" and went to perch. Smaller parties of "Pink Cockatoos" (Major Mitchell's Cockatoo) pushed their way in anytime. Clouds of midges and other insects formed over the water, and Willie Wagtails, Grey Fantails and other small insectivores skimmed over the water, wet mud and trees. The Magpie-lark delights in these habitats and, like swallows and martins, makes its nest from mud. Swarms of grass-eating finches move to the river frequently during the day, after filling on dry grass-seed from nearby plains. Quarrelling Apostlebirds spend much time foraging through the understorey shrub and scrub.

Classic Birds: Emu; Major Mitchell's Cockatoo; Red-tailed Black-Cockatoo; Galah; Little Corella; Cockatiel; Eastern Rosella; Yellow Rosella; Blue Bonnet; Regent Parrot; Red-rumped Parrot; Ring-necked Parrot; Budgerigar; Mulga Parrot; Tree Martin; Black-capped Sittella; Yellow-tailed and Little Thornbills; White-winged Triller; White-browed, Black-faced and Dusky Woodswallows; Black-faced Cuckoo-shrike; Pallid Cuckoo; Horsfield's Bronze-Cuckoo; Black-winged Currawong; Australian Magpie; Magpie-lark; Grey and Pied Butcherbirds; Barn Owl; Barking Owl; Boobook; Wedge-tailed Eagle; White-bellied Sea-Eagle; Little Eagle; Black-breasted Buzzard; Black-shouldered and Letter-winged Kites; Collared Sparrowhawk; Brown and Black Falcons; Whistling Kite; Australian Wood Duck; Black Duck.

Above, top to bottom: The rare Hooded Parrot occupies a small range in the far Northern Territory; Bourke's Parrot is frequently seen in the mid-Darling River woodlands. Its dusky plumage camouflages well with the red earth, while the shimmering blue of its wings and underside reflect off the water when it comes to drink. *Left, top to bottom:* Post-wet-season flooding down the Channel Country of south-west Queensland reinvigorates the surrounding plains; River Red Gums along the Lyons River, north of Gascoyne Junction, Western Australia.

Above, top to bottom: A Major Mitchell's Cockatoo takes up residence in a large hollow in a hardy eucalypt; another uncommon parrot is the very beautiful, fast-flying and long-winged Princess Parrot, which nests in tree hollows. *Right:* A rabble of bickering Little Corellas. Flocks this size can easily defoliate River Red Gums.

Where Are They? *NSW* — Western Slopes and near Western Plains; Hawkesbury sandstone country. *Vic* — eastern Riverina. *WA* — Wheatbelt; Norseman–Kalgoorlie is a more arid form of woodland.

What Do They Look Like? Spaced trees allowing hemispherical canopy development with grassy and/or shrubby floors.

Critical Conditions: Temperate winters and hot summers; winter rains; only moderate available soil moisture; drought-prone country.

Above: Mixed woodland in Warrumbungle National Park is dominated by Cypress Pine, White Gum and acacias, such as the Western Golden Wattle shown here. The floor cover is grassy with a smattering of small shrubs, mainly legumes.

Below: Coolibah woodland with a Curly Mitchell Grass, Neverfail Grass and copperburr ground coverage, near Culgoa National Park, New South Wales.

Other Woodlands

We passed through many miles of beautiful granite ranges, very thinly timbered indeed … we reached an elevated part of the country … and as far as the eye could reach the country appeared good undulating forest, very open, with here and there, spaces devoid of trees altogether; a very fine pasture country … beyond that, it looked beautiful, and we all exclaimed – "There is Australia Felix!"… I have no doubt that it will soon be occupied by sheep.

A Month in the Bush of Australia by "A Gentleman" travelling from Sydney to Port Phillip, part following Major Mitchell's blazed track in the Campaspe River country of Victoria, 1838.

The above account of a temperate woodland dominated by eucalypts describes just a sample of a huge area of woodland habitat. Woodland stretches north from the edge of Victoria's mallee to meet an east–west-running belt of the same country inland from Kingaroy in Queensland, covering the western slopes and edging out onto the western plains. True to the "Gentleman's" prediction, it became the major sheep and wheat country of eastern Australia.

This large tract of woodland is broken only by the rivers of the Murray–Darling, some natural grasslands of Mitchell Grass, outlying pockets of tropical brigalow woodland, forests about the volcanic Nandewar and Warrumbungle Mountains and the Macquarie Marshes. Today it is a vastly changed area. Dense acacia woodlands of Myall with an Old Man Saltbush understorey once covered much of the Riverina and the central area east of Cobar, but there has since been a radical change in woodland species. The more palatable shrubs and trees, such as Wilga, Kurrajong, Myall and Mulga, have been eaten away. In their place, trees such as the eucalypt, Poplar Box and the aggressive Budda (*Eremophila mitchelli*), along with White Cypress Pine (since the myxomatosis virus reduced the rabbit population) now form extensive, dense woodland and scrubland communities that drive out even the sheep. However, the most significant change has been the conversion of most of these woodlands to grassland in the form of wheat, oats and barley crops.

Apart from changes to the vegetation of the woodland habitat, another great change was in the placement of tens of thousands of ground tanks, dams and water-bore drains, which provided open water across the pastoral landscape. Reading the early explorers' journals, one is struck by the scarcity of water in pre-European settlement times. Many expeditions would have failed were it not for the accompanying resourceful Aboriginal guides, who knew where to look for water. During prolonged dry periods, broken only by random occurrences of rain, this lack of water was the major limiting factor in the ecology of large herbivores.

With the conversion of woodlands to watered grasslands, populations of large macropods dramatically increased, both in size and in distribution. Red Kangaroos broadened their range. Eastern and Western Grey Kangaroos, which had a merging habitat in the natural woodlands, inland scrublands and tall shrublands, were pushed further inland as woodlands were cleared and readily available water inland allowed massive population increases. Smaller kangaroos and wallabies, and other small mammals, did not benefit as much because they were less mobile and more dependent on ground cover, such as dense shrubs and heavy tussocks to protect them from dingoes, dogs, foxes and feral cats. The tussocks were eaten by stock and the shrubs burned or cut away to allow short grasses to grow.

Above, top: Red and orange grevilleas and acacias flower in the dry tropical woodland/scrub of White Mountains National Park, west of Charters Towers, Queensland. *Centre:* Bimble Box woodland on Yanda Creek, Gunderbooka National Park, New South Wales. *Bottom, left to right:* Cypress Pine woodland; Sydney Red Gum (*Angophora costata*) and Red Bloodwood coastal dune woodland in Myall Lakes National Park, New South Wales, is a community very similar to the Hawkesbury sandstone flora.

Above: Banksia species are classic "habitat hoppers", ranging from the south-west to the far south and east, from the tropics to Tasmania. Many birds and animals rely on them for food.

Blending Boundaries

"Other woodlands" may seem a rather general category, but a word of warning is that habitats are often indistinct. The concept of habitat is defined by the requirements of animal occupants, not necessarily those of plants. Boundaries mix and merge, particularly where a species occupies adjoining habitats. Many plant genera, such as *Banksia*, are widespread and may have representatives across many habitats. When one thinks about plant needs and distribution one finds that banksias are basically a heathland species, although the Coast Banksia can also grow successfully on Point Lookout in New England National Park, in winter snow country! The message is not to think of boundaries drawn on maps as being sharp delineations of habitat — sometimes they may be, but mostly there is a "grey area". "Other woodlands" is an attempt to sort out some of those areas that don't clearly fit into any other chapter.

Classic Plants: Yellow Box; Black Box; Inland Grey Box; White Box; Red Box; Bimble Box; Yellow Gum; Scribbly Gum; White Gum; Red Bloodwood; Yellow Bloodwood; Sydney Red Gum; Black Oak; Belah; Rosewood; River Red Gum; Dwyer's Red Gum; Grey Gum; Coastal Ash; Myall; Kurrajong; White Cypress Pine; Wilga; Budda; Brown Mallet; Wandoo; Gimlet; York Gum; Salmon Gum; Flooded Gum; Redwood; Kangaroo Grass; Wallaby Grass; speargrass; wire grasses; snow grasses; Waratah; boronias; Heath-leafed and Old Man Banksias; *Hakea* spp.; Wellington, Cootamundra and numerous other wattles; Showy and Golden Dryandras; Pingle; Painted Featherflower; Native Cauliflower; Flat-stemmed Wattle; Firewood Banksia; Bull Banksia; Acorn Banksia; various grevilleas; *Hovea stricta*; Starflower; various *Diplolaena* spp.; various *Isopogon* coneflowers; cat's paws; numerous *Daviesia*; *Gastrolobium*; *Templetonia*; *Gompholobium* and *Urodon* peas; Gungurru.

Above: Another small but incredibly significant patch of woodland is the Desert Bloodwood dominated woodland on the south side of Uluru and in Kantju Gorge, Uluru–Kata Tjuta National Park. This provides shelter and nesting sites near waterholes for Major Mitchell's Cockatoo and the Little Corella along with Little Woodswallows and Australian Magpies.

Best Examples: *NSW* — Royal and Hawkesbury River National Parks; Blue Mountains National Park, Barren Grounds Nature Reserve; Yathong Nature Reserve; Pilliga Nature Reserve; Warrumbungle National Park; Cocoparra National Park; The Rock Nature Reserve; Flagstaff Nature Reserve. *WA* — Bold Park; Wongamine Nature Reserve; Wandoo Conservation Park; Dryandra Nature Reserve, Boyagin Rock; Paynes Find–Wubin, Mount Lesueur area reserves; Stirling Range National Park; Salmon Gums and Norseman areas. *Vic* — Pyramid Hill; Glenrowan area.

Sounds: Squawking parrots; the buzz of flies.

Smells: Warm eucalyptus; scorched gum leaves.

Sensations: Dry heat.

Similar temperate eucalypt woodland also covered parts of south-western Australia, from Geraldton to Albany (WA) with eucalypt species such as Brown Mallet, Wandoo, Powderbark Wandoo, Gimlet, York Gum, Salmon Gum, Flooded Gum and Redwood. Much of this country has a rich, natural understorey of flowering shrubs but, again, much of it was converted into wheat farms and experienced a similar wildlife problem as in the east. Those woodlands that retain the heavy, shrubby understorey with its considerable litter are the remaining core habitat of the exquisite Numbat. During severe drought, endemic wildlife of the more northern woodlands also faces invasion by hordes of Emus moving south-westerly out of the arid country in search of food and water.

THE GEOLOGICAL FOUNDATION OF WOODLANDS

Where there is a shortage of soil moisture for significant periods, temperate woodlands usually occur instead of forest. The woodland described by the "Gentleman" at the beginning of this section was on granitic soils, which are notoriously droughty and contain a very high level of silica — the most resistant crystal in the granite mix. The other two components, feldspar and mica, break down to form clay, which is washed through the soil. Wide areas of temperate eucalypt woodland form on these soil types, with the exception of shale soils,

places capped by basalt (such as Mounts Banks and Hay), on the richer Narrabeen and Coal Measure rocks of the Jamison Valley or on floodplains (as at Blue Gum Forest). Some more exposed sites with very shallow deposits of these soils encourage heathlands. On a basalt-derived soil that is rich in minerals, the Campaspe River country would produce forest.

On the tracts of infertile soils derived from sandstones (principally silica) that cover the Sydney Basin, one would expect a woodland cover. The immense crescent of sandstone national parks that grace Sydney are topped largely by woodlands, most composed on Hawkesbury sandstone and featuring exquisite Scribbly Gums, Red Bloodwoods, the closely related pink- and purple-barked Sydney Red Gum (*Angophora costata*) and *Casuarina* species. Few grasses adorn the understorey (except Kangaroo Grass, *Themeda* sp.) but a profuse shrub and herb layer boasts some 700 flowering species, including *Boronia*, Waratah, *Eriostemon*, *Epacris*, *Acacia*, *Dampiera* and *Patersonia* species, particularly where the woodland adjoins heathland. Some of this Scribbly Gum woodland almost appears to be heath, overtopped by scattered gums. Woodlands of the higher, wetter sandstone areas, such as the Barren Grounds and Blue Mountains National Parks, add to their list of floral species the Coastal Ash, Yellow Bloodwood, Dwyer's Red Gum, White Gum and Grey Gums. As for all woodland communities, fire plays a significant role in species selection and survival.

Above: High, sandstone-based woodland of Kings Tableland, Blue Mountains National Park, New South Wales.

Frogs and Reptiles of the Woodlands

An unusual species that inhabits these usually very dry environments is the Turtle Frog. Resembling a flabby little turtle, this amphibian occupies an arc of habitat north of the great south-western forests. It is a termite-eating frog that requires little or no water to breed.

Classic Frogs and Reptiles: Turtle Frog; Red-crowned Toadlet; Brown Toadlet; Red-groined Toadlet; Green Tree-frog; Broad-palmed Rocketfrog; Peron's Tree-frog; Desert Tree-frog; Western Spiny-tailed Gecko; Wood Gecko; Ocellated Velvet Gecko; Reticulated Velvet Gecko; Marbled Gecko; Thick-tailed Gecko; Marble-faced Delma; Common Delma; Burton's Snake-lizard; Hooded Scaly-foot; Bearded Dragon; Spotted Dragon; Western Bearded Dragon; Nobbi; Western Netted Dragon; Gould's Monitor; Black-tailed Monitor; Lace Monitor; Striped Skink; Tree Skink; White's Skink; Red-throated Skink; *Lerista* sp.; *Morethia* sp.; Broad-banded Sand-swimmer; Western Blue-tongue; Eastern Blue-tongue; Shingleback; *Typhlina* sp.; Children's Python; Diamond Python; Common Death Adder; Copperhead; Yellow-faced Whipsnake; Rosen's Snake; Bardick; Red-naped Snake; Broad-headed Snake; Western Black-naped Snake; Eastern Tiger Snake; Mulga Snake; Spotted Black Snake; Red-bellied Black Snake; Dugite; Western Brown Snake; Eastern Brown Snake; Myall or Curl Snake; Black-headed Snake; Bandy Bandy.

Mammals of the Woodlands

The most impressive is undoubtedly the Numbat. Human occupation and modification of much of its extensive former range means that it now exists only in remnant Wandoo woodland/forests and Jarrah areas of South-West WA. It survives entirely on a diet of termites and its protection critically depends upon the "furniture" of the habitat. Burning programs are inimical to this animal. Other vulnerable species are the Western Brush Wallaby (although common in certain areas) and the Woylie, which is being reintroduced to protected woodland areas in the Stirling Ranges.

Classic Mammals: Short-beaked Echidna; Eastern and Western Grey Kangaroos; Common Wallaroo; Swamp and Red-necked Wallabies; Common Wombat; Numbat; Western Quoll; Brush-tailed Phascogale; Red-tailed Phascogale; Yellow-footed Antechinus; Common Dunnart; Fat-tailed Dunnart; White-tailed Dunnart; Southern Brown Bandicoot; Northern Brown Bandicoot; Koala; Common Ringtail Possum; Greater Glider; Sugar Glider; Squirrel Glider; Common Brushtail Possum; Eastern Pygmy-possum; Western Pygmy-possum; Feathertail Glider; Honey Possum; Woylie; Rufous Bettong; Tammar Wallaby; Western Brush Wallaby; Quokka; White-striped and Little Mastiff-bats; Greater, Lesser and Gould's Long-eared Bats; Gould's and Chocolate Wattled Bats; Large Pied Bat; Little Broad-nosed Bat; Great Pipistrelle; Southern Forest and Little Forest Bats; Ash-grey Mouse; Western Mouse.

Above, clockwise from top: Black-headed Python; Western Blue-tongue; Short-beaked Echidna; Numbat; Northern Brown Bandicoot; Bearded Dragon.

Birds of the Woodlands

As well as being readily accessible to grasses and grasslands, woodlands are rich in nectar-bearing plants that attract copious numbers of insects. For this reason, bird populations are quite diverse and some species maintain high populations when food is plentiful, particularly honey-eating birds (such as lorikeets), which follow the seasonal honey flow.

Mobile, seed-eating birds, such as parrots, inland pigeons and finches, are common visitors that are easily able to fly to find liquid sustenance. Galahs and Crested Pigeons, which John Oxley first noted out near present-day Condobolin in 1817, are common even along the coasts, where forests have been replaced by farmland. Treecreepers and bark chippers, which prey on invertebrates, are also common and include Pied and Grey Currawongs. Thornbills and Rufous Whistlers inspect the foliage for insects — the former in the lower canopy and the latter, the higher.

Classic Birds: The species list is similar to that for riverine woodlands with the addition of the Red-backed Kingfisher; Rufous Treecreeper; Splendid Fairy-wren; Blue-breasted Fairy-wren; Striated Pardalote; Speckled Warbler; Western Gerygone; White-throated Gerygone; Weebill; Western Thornbill; Yellow Thornbill; Chestnut-rumped Thornbill; Inland Thornbill; Red Wattlebird (race: *woodwardi*); Little Wattlebird (race: *lunulata*); Regent Honeyeater; Singing Honeyeater; White-eared Honeyeater (race: *novaenorciae*); Brown Honeyeater; New Holland Honeyeater (race: *longirostris*); White-fronted Honeyeater; White-cheeked Honeyeater (race: *gouldi*); Brown-headed Honeyeater (race: *leucogenys*); Western Spinebill; Hooded Robin; Flame Robin; Red-capped Robin; Western Yellow Robin; Jacky Winter (race: *assimilis*); White-browed Babbler; Grey-crowned Babbler; Crested Bellbird; Golden Whistler (race: *fuliginosa*); Grey Shrike-thrush (race: *rufiventris*); Pied Butcherbird; Grey Currawong; Double-barred Finch; Zebra Finch; Diamond Firetail; Welcome Swallow; White-backed Swallow; songlarks; Silvereye.

Above, clockwise from top left: Diamond Firetail; Red-capped Robin; Black-shouldered Kite; White-cheeked Honeyeater; Red-backed Kingfisher.

Above: The Yellow-faced Honeyeater, seen here feeding its chicks, occupies woodland on high ranges and coastal plains.

Above: Boabs dominate the open savanna woodland along with *Acacia* spp., a number of bloodwoods, *Eucalyptus* spp. and speargrass by the Oscar Range, near Fitzroy Crossing in the Kimberley, Western Australia.

Where Are They? Stretching in a great northern arc inside the forest belt from Roma (Qld) to Broome (WA); although, as one travels west, these communities become less easy to distinguish from the open forests. Much of Western Australia's Kimberley is more akin to woodland and savanna than to the forest end of the treed spectrum.

What Do They Look Like? Open and park-like; most with grassy and shrubby floors. The trees tend to have wide canopies that graduate into forest on the wetter side and into grassland on the drier side.

Critical Conditions: A tropical wet and dry climatic system with only moderately available soil moisture, sometimes geologically controlled.

Above: Spread the trees of tropical woodland a little further apart and add grass, frequently a native sorghum, and the habitat becomes savanna, shown here in the Pilbara, WA.

Tropical and Savanna Woodlands

The natives seemed to have burned the grass systematically along every watercourse, and around every water-hole, in order to have them surrounded with young grass as soon as the rains set in. These burnings are not connected with camping places ... Long strips of lately burnt grass were frequently observed extending for many miles along the creek. The banks of small isolated water-holes in the forest, were equally attended to, although water had not been in either for a considerable time. It is no doubt connected with a systematic management of their runs, to attract game to particular spots ... The natives, however, frequently burn the high stiff grass, particularly along shady creeks, with the intention of driving the concealed game out of it.

Ludwig Leichhardt, near the Albert River in the Gulf of Carpentaria, making probably the first comment by Europeans on the habitat management of Aboriginal burning practices in the tropical savanna woodlands, 2 August 1845.

Perhaps the best understanding of Australia's tropical and savanna woodlands can be gleaned by studying Leichhardt's Journal. For all but a few months of his eighteen-month journey, Leichhardt travelled through extensive ecosystems of tropical eucalypt woodlands and savanna, Brigalow and Bottle Tree woodlands and the mixed woodlands about the Roper River and southern Kakadu. His approach to travelling through totally foreign country is impressively scientific and his journal clearly describes not only his observations, but also his reflections on them. The greatest testament to his logic was that he wandered from Brisbane to Port Essington in just over a year and a half, all the while living principally off the land. Not only was finding water always a challenge, but many of the untried native fruits, seeds and other plants were toxic. Yet he and his party arrived (except for Gilbert, who was speared) in good health. He routinely noted remnants of Aboriginal foods about their camps, as well as documenting what Emus and other birds had been eating. The help and advice of his two Aboriginal assistants was also crucial. Compare Leichhardt's result with the ultimately fatal Burke and Wills expedition and the Stuart expeditions fifteen years later and it is easy to see that Leichhardt's comprehensive, level-headed approach was critical to his success.

Above: Savanna makes perfect cattle country right around the world. *Right:* Lennard River Gorge cuts through the King Leopold Ranges in Western Australia. The ground cover is a typical mix of tropical woodland and savanna, with the trees thinning out on drier slopes or tops.

Above: A Leichhardt's Grasshopper alights on its favoured *Pityrodia* plant, on which its life cycle is based. Its vivid colours warn would-be predators that it contains toxic materials in its body.

Flora of Tropical and Savanna Woodland

Each year, plants in the monsoon tropics must survive a humid wet season followed by a severe five-month drought. Many are part deciduous to reduce water loss by transpiration. Common eucalypts are bloodwoods, stringybarks and the Darwin Woollybutt with its wonderful orange blooms. Particularly beautiful is the Swamp Bloodwood with its mop of rose-pink blossoms and large gumnuts that attract Red-tailed Black-Cockatoos. The understorey includes many wet-season flowering plants and others such as Bush Apples, Billygoat Plums and soft-fruiting species that entice both mammals and birds.

Classic Plants: Brigalow; Bottle Tree; Bimble Box; Carbeen; Long-fruited Bloodwood; Ghost Gum; Northern Salmon Gum; Woollybutt; Rusty Jacket; Silver Box; Darwin Box; River Red Gum; ironbark; Scarlet Gum; *Eucalyptus setosa*; Elephant Ear Wattle; Hickory Wattle; Ghost Wattle; Lancewood; Elegant Wattle (*Acacia umbellata*); Native Cherry; Quinine Tree; Fern-leafed Grevillea; Christmas Holly Grevillea; Beefwood; Bloodroot; Woody Hakea; *Hibiscus* spp.; Sand Palm; *Kimberley Bauhinia*; Woodland Paperbark; Emu Apple; Long-leafed Geebung; *Pityrodia* spp.; Cocky Apple; *Sesbania benthamiana*; *Syzygium eucalyptoides*; Bush Apple; Nutwood; Billygoat Plum; *Terminalia pterocarya*; Fringed Lily; *Verticordia* spp.; Vigna; Bridal Tree; grasses such as *Heteropogon* spp.; *Bothriochloa* spp; *Dichanthium* spp.; speargrass and native sorghums.

Anyone who travels the Australian tropics from the end of June to the start of November will notice that bushfire is a common environmental factor. From the observations of Leichhardt, Stuart and the Gregory brothers, intentional burning seems to have been an Aboriginal practice but, as Leichhardt implies, it was not deemed appropriate for all of the landscape. Wildfires devastated the landscape long before Aboriginal occupation, which began approximately 60,000 years ago. By the mid-Tertiary Period, some 20 million years ago, the Australian continent had drifted far enough north to come under the influence of (and the increasing power of) the monsoon. Large, lightning-lit infernos have raged ever since the monsoon originated. The monsoon-driven climate created two seasons in the Australian tropics: the Wet and the Dry (although Aboriginal and Torres Strait Islander people recognise more). Fire is a regular threat at the end of the dry season, in the pre-monsoon season of *Gunumeleng* of the Gagudju people (one of the six seasons that they perceive). Vast storm cells form on the rising, heated air and amass incredibly powerful cumulus clouds that climb into the stratosphere. These may move and build extremely rapidly, travelling westwards from Arnhem Land at 100 kilometres an hour. Sometimes cumulus clouds drop great quantities of rain; at other times none, but always the country is lashed by wind and lightning. Wherever there is dry, unburned country, fire follows.

Even before the rain arrives, and probably due to the rising humidity, many of the plants sense the coming weather shift and begin their annual rejuvenation. Deciduous and partially deciduous trees, such as the Kapok and a number of eucalypts, throw new shoots. After a period of quiescence, the Northern Hyacinth and Nervillea shoot, along with other ground orchids and the huge, stinking Elephant Yam (*Amorphophallus paeoniifolius*), pink-flowered *Curcuma* lilies and cycads. At this time, too, Carpentaria Palms, White Apples and Green Plums begin to drop ripe fruit. The heralds of the wet season, nymphs of the brilliantly coloured, vermilion and electric-blue, Leichhardt's Grasshopper become obvious on scattered stands of aromatic *Pityrodia* bushes of the sandstone woodlands. It is remarkable that through 20 million years of rigorous change, such a diversity of life flourishes, particularly after the almost-annual trial-by-fire.

Trial-by-fire, as well as trial-by-season and its associated environmental factors, happened perhaps a million or more times! In drifting close enough to Asia to be affected by the monsoon, Australia also drifted close enough for some Asian plants and animals (especially birds, bats and rats) to migrate. So easy was this journey that 43% of north Australian plants also occur in Asia. Birds disperse 63% of all vine forest (Top End tropical rainforest) species, while 20% are dispersed by wind. Those Asian species that remain had, or developed, adaptations to their makeup that allowed them successful passage through Australia's environmental trials.

So what were these strategies that enabled introduced species to flourish? Some — the true perennials, such as palms, large eucalypts (Darwin Stringybark and Woollybutt) and kurrajongs — have the advantage of deep roots. Others — annuals and ephemeral plants — have shallow roots to soak up brief rainfalls whenever they occur. Some plants, such as Vigna, Fringed Lily, many ground orchids and the Quinine Tree, have tubers to store both food and water. Deciduous plants, like the Billygoat Plum, Croton and *Ipomoea* vines, protect themselves from dehydration by dropping their leaves, which also prevents the canopy from burning. Native Cherry (*Exocarpus* spp.), the herb Striga and mistletoes are parasites whose food source is other well-fed plants and, while mistletoe plants are susceptible to fire, they survive in woodlands and savanna because the main fire stays in the understorey while they are usually well above, near the end of

Above, clockwise from top left: Sand Palm/cycad/eucalypt woodland on the Kakadu lowlands, Northern Territory; native sorghum goes up in flame in the mid dry season; plants must endure humidity, fire and raging wet season floods; such extremes of habitat make these woodlands seasonally very dry, but post-fire they grow very lush in the early wet season; post-fire growth shoots from underground stems; fire devastates the landscape, clearing woodland and leaving little but blackened trunks and termite mounds until the rains bring renewed growth.

Above, top to bottom: The Boab is an indicative plant of tropical savanna in the Kimberley, Western Australia; savanna woodlands in Keep River National Park, on the border of Western Australia and the Northern Territory; Desert Bloodwood savanna in the south-west Northern Territory.

Best Examples: *Qld* — Expedition National Park; Carnarvon National Park; Hughenden area; Undara Volcanic National Park; Camooweal to Lawn Hill National Park and area. *NT* — Hells Gate area and Wollogorang; Cape Crawford area; Daly Waters area; Mataranka area; Katherine area and southern Kakadu; Gregory National Park; Keep River National Park. *WA* — Gibb River Road (Kimberley); Mitchell Plateau area; Windjana Gorge–Tunnel Creek area; Fitzroy Crossing area; Duncan Road–Buntine Highway country.

Sounds: The crunch of dry grass underfoot.

Smells: Smoke; spicy dry air.

Sensations: Sticky wet-season humidity; dry heat.

tree branches. Other plants have perennial underground root stocks with buds that survive when all of their upper parts are burned. Grasses, such as the many species of native sorghums, have sharply pointed, hard-coated seeds with large tightly wound spiral awns. When these get wet in the first rains they expand and unravel. The seed stands on its point on the softened soil surface and rotates like a drill, burying and self-sowing itself ready for germination. The vine *Vigna lanceolata* has two options: it produces two pods, the main one above the ground with a number of seeds and the other below the ground surface with a backup seed protected from fire. Plants that evolved these adaptations survived to later pass on the genes within which such useful survival strategies were encoded.

Such are the processes in the trials of life that produce the wonderful diversity of plant and animal life within the living systems of all communities, including those of the tropical woodlands and savannas. These include the dense Brigalow and Bottle Tree woodlands of central south-eastern Queensland and the mixed eucalyptus woodlands and savannas with their bluish *Heteropogon*, *Bothriochloa* and *Dichanthium* grass understoreys, which sweep in a great arc across northern Australia from Roma to Broome. There are also the areas of greatest mix, the woodlands of *Eucalyptus* such as Ghost Gum, the very beautiful large-leafed, rust-coloured gum, which sheds a pale purplish bark to reveal almost "human" limbs, *Eucalyptus bigalerita* (my favourite), and others mixed with many of the tropical trees of the vine and monsoon forests. Always, however, the woodlands let great amounts of sunlight penetrate their rounded and scattered trees, which encourages a vigorous growth of grass and shrubs, perfect habitat for the largest of the wallaroos, the fawn-like Antilopine Wallaroo and a magnificent seed eater, the Red-tailed Black-Cockatoo.

Above, left to right: Although flamboyant looking, the Frilled Lizard camouflages well among the fallen twigs and leaves of woodland; Water Python.

Frogs and Reptiles of the Tropical and Savanna Woodlands

Tropical woodlands and savannas near wetlands are rich in amphibious life. Early wet-season storms fill billabongs and lagoons and inspire a cacophony of frog calls. Reptile populations boom and roads become killing fields as Water Pythons, Olive Pythons, Carpet Pythons, Slaty Grey Snakes, whipsnakes, tree snakes, King Brown Snakes and even taipans bask on the warm, wet bitumen. Even Freshwater Crocodiles become roadkill in the wet, as they move overland to swap billabongs.

Classic Frogs and Reptiles: Water-holding Frog; Spencer's Burrowing-frog; Spotted Grass-frog; Trilling Frog; Orange-crowned Toadlet; Desert Tree-frog; Spiny-tailed Gecko; Fat-tailed Diplodactylus; Jewelled Gecko; Tessellated Gecko; Wood Gecko; Tree Dtella; Bynoe's Gecko; Beaded Gecko; Marbled Velvet Gecko; Beaked Gecko; Thick-tailed Gecko; *Delma tincta*; Hooded Scaly-foot; Ring-tailed Dragon; Mallee Dragon; Military Dragon; Dwarf Bearded Dragon; Central Netted Dragon; Western Netted Dragon; Painted Dragon; *Lophognathus gilberti*; *L. longirostris*; Thorny Devil; Perentie; Pygmy Mulga Monitor; Gould's Monitor; *Varanis tristis*; Pygmy Spiny-tailed Skink; Desert Skink; Tree Skink; Fire-tailed Skink; Centralian Blue-tongue; Western Blue-tongue; Eastern Blue-tongue; Shingleback; Woma; Children's Python; Carpet Python; Desert Death Adder; Yellow-faced Whipsnake; Red-naped Snake; Small-scaled Snake; King Brown Snake; Ringed Brown Snake; Western Brown Snake; Eastern Brown Snake; Myall Snake; Black-headed Snake; Bandy Bandy.

Above, clockwise from top left: Rainbow Bee-eaters, dry season immigrants from the south; the Blue-winged Kookaburra occupies a smaller range than its Laughing cousin; Sulphur-crested Cockatoos are common and full of character; White-bellied Cuckoo-shrikes forage in foliage for insects and fruit.

Birds of the Tropical and Savanna Woodlands

Numerous parrots are at home in this woodland of abundant grasses and suitable nesting trees. Flashy Red-winged Parrots, yellow and blue Northern Rosellas and screeching Rainbow Lorikeets exceed expectations of vibrancy. Grass seeds attract the spectacular Gouldian Finch, populations of which are recovering from too much habitat burning. Squatter and Partridge Pigeons strut about in pairs and small groups, and proud, graceful Brolgas "dance" in the swampy hollows.

Classic Birds: Emu; Stubble Quail; Brown Quail; Cattle Egret; Great Egret; White-faced Heron; White-necked Heron; Brolga; Black Kite; Square-tailed Kite; Whistling Kite; Black-breasted Buzzard; Wedge-tailed Eagle; Spotted Harrier; Black-shouldered Kite; Collared Sparrowhawk; Brown Goshawk (race: *didimus*); Grey Goshawk; Red Goshawk; Nankeen Kestrel; Australian Hobby (race: *murchisonianus*); Brown Falcon; Australian Bustard; Red-backed, Little and Red-chested Button-quails; Bush Stone-curlew; Australian and Oriental Pratincoles; Oriental Plover; Masked Lapwing (race: *miles*); Banded Lapwing; Crested Pigeon; Common Bronzewing; Squatter Pigeon; Peaceful Dove; Diamond Dove; Red-tailed Black-Cockatoo; Little Corella; Cockatiel; Sulphur-crested Cockatoo; Galah; Rainbow Lorikeet; Varied Lorikeet; Red-winged Parrot (race: *coccineopterus*); Pale-headed and Northern Rosellas; Budgerigar; Pallid Cuckoo; Black-eared Cuckoo; Horsfield's Bronze-Cuckoo; Channel-billed Cuckoo; Pheasant Coucal; Barking Owl; Southern Boobook; Barn Owl; Masked Owl; Grass Owl; Tawny Frogmouth (race: *phalaenoides*); Spotted Nightjar; Australian Owlet-nightjar; Red-backed Kingfisher; Sacred Kingfisher; Blue-winged Kookaburra; Laughing Kookaburra; Rainbow Bee-eater; Dollarbird; Brown Treecreeper; Black-tailed Treecreeper; Purple-backed Fairy-wren (race: *assimilis*); Red-backed Fairy-wren; Red-browed Pardalote; Striated Pardalote (race: *uropygialis*); Western Gerygone; White-throated Gerygone; Weebill (race: *flavescens*); Yellow-rumped Thornbill; Silver-crowned Friarbird; Little Friarbird; Blue-faced Honeyeater; Yellow-throated Miner; Noisy Miner; Singing Honeyeater; White-lined Honeyeater; Grey-fronted Honeyeater; Yellow-tinted Honeyeater; Brown Honeyeater; Bar-breasted Honeyeater; Rufous-throated Honeyeater; Painted Honeyeater; Black-chinned Honeyeater; White-throated Honeyeater; Banded Honeyeater; Mistletoebird; Yellow Chat; Hooded Robin; Lemon-bellied Flycatcher; Jacky Winter (race: *pallida*); Grey-crowned Babbler; Black-capped Sittella; Crested Bellbird; Rufous Whistler; Grey Shrike-thrush; Restless Flycatcher; Leaden Flycatcher; Grey Fantail (race: *albicauda*); Northern Fantail; Magpie-lark; Willie Wagtail; White-winged Triller; Black-faced, White-bellied and Ground Cuckoo-shrikes; Olive-backed Oriole (race: *affinis*); Figbird; woodswallows; Grey and Pied Butcherbirds; Australian Magpie; Pied Currawong; Australian Raven; Torresian Crow; White-winged Chough; Apostlebird; Spotted and Great Bowerbirds; Singing Bushlark; Australian Pipit; Pictorella Mannikin, Zebra, Double-barred, Long-tailed, Black-throated, Masked, Painted and Gouldian Finches; Welcome Swallow; Tree Martin; Fairy Martin; Rufous Songlark; Brown Songlark.

Mammals of the Tropical and Savanna Woodlands

Aside from introduced horses, donkeys, buffaloes, cattle and pigs, the largest mammal here is the superbly camouflaged Antilopine Wallaroo. The Agile Wallaby develops large populations close to damp areas that have a green grassy pick. Long-haired Rat populations boom in some seasons and when they do, owls move in to feed. Pale Field Rats are another common native rodent. Bats find superb habitat in these northern areas, where they hunt insects and other food, and trees and caves provide ample shelter. Great camps of Black and Little Red Flying-foxes rest in riverbank scrub and forest and range far and wide in the evening. Blossom Bats are particularly active in flowering eucalypts. A delightful resident is the endangered Northern Quoll, which has suffered a population decline since invasion by Cane Toads.

Classic Mammals: Bridled Nailtail Wallaby; Common Wallaroo; Eastern Grey Kangaroo; Red Kangaroo; Antilopine Wallaroo; Rufous Bettong; Spectacled Hare-wallaby; Agile Wallaby; Northern Nailtail Wallaby; Whiptail, Red-necked and Swamp Wallabies; Short-beaked Echidna; Northern Quoll; Brush-tailed Phascogale; Red-cheeked Dunnart; Long-tailed Planigale; Koala (residual populations); Northern Brown Bandicoot; Greater, Sugar and Feathertail Gliders; Squirrel Glider (south); Common Brushtail and Northern Brushtail Possums; Little Red Flying-fox; Black Flying-fox; Ghost Bat; Dusky Horseshoe Bat; Orange Horseshoe Bat; Common Sheathtail Bat; Hoary Bat; Northern Mastiff-bat; Lesser Long-eared Bat; North Queensland Long-eared Bat; Gould's Wattled Bat; Little Broad-nosed and Western Broad-nosed Bats; Little Cave Bat; Brush-tailed Tree-rat; Black-footed Tree-rat; Western Chestnut Mouse; Delicate Mouse; Long-haired Rat; Dingo.

Above, top to bottom: Antilopine Wallaroos are the largest native herbivores of the grassy savanna; Agile Wallabies are also very common in this habitat.

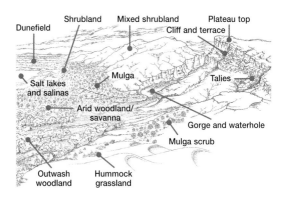

Above: The variety of habitats in arid Australia. The rich outwash area is central to life here. This diagram depicts the MacDonnell Ranges, Northern Territory.

Where Are They? Outwash woodlands form where rivers and streams run out onto plains situated against mountain ranges in the arid zone; for example, Big John Creek (SA); Gammon Ranges (SA); Olga Gorge (NT); Hugh River (NT); Finke River (NT); Simpsons Gap (NT); Preservation Creek (NSW).

What Do They Look Like? Heavily wooded areas with diverse trees situated at the foot of ranges and watered by flooding. River Red Gums are frequently a dominant species.

Critical Conditions: Arid zone; short, intense storms with severe and/or flash flooding off mountains.

Above: Outwash channels carrying run-off from the Hamersley Range, Western Australia. Trees and tall shrubs mark the places where extra moisture has remained in sandy channels.

Outwash Woodlands

I suddenly found myself under the shadow of a huge rock … On ascending it, I was much gratified to discover, not more than a mile and a-half from me, the eucalypts of a creek, which meandered through this dense wilderness. I soon gained its banks, but was disappointed to find that its channel was very flat and but poorly defined, though the timber upon it was splendid — elegant upright stems, supporting umbrageous tops — whose roots at least must surely extend downwards to a moistened soil. On each side of the creek was a strip of open ground, so richly grassed and so beautifully decked with flowers … Upon the side opposite, stood an extraordinary ridge or hill, consisting of a huge red turtle-back [with] enormous egg-shaped [granite] tors.

Ernest Giles, in the Musgrave Ranges of northern South Australia, 27 August 1873.

As with Stuart's journals, the pioneering Giles devotes much space in his Journal to the challenge of finding water in Central Australia. In his search for the life-giving fluid, he discovered that outwash woodland areas, such as the one described above, were vital animal habitats in arid Australia — a conclusion confirmed by current scientific research. Plant communities, which form the basis of all habitat, are composed of intermingling plant species with common environmental needs. We think of these communities as broad "habitats" but, from the point of view of the animals that populate that environment, some parts of a habitat's composition are more desirable than others, especially those that provide specific shelter, food and space needs for breeding and important behavioral activities.

Outwash woodlands near ranges (especially the Barrier, Grey, Flinders, Musgrave, Everard, Mann, East and West Macdonnell, Petermann, Kata Tjuta, James, Davenport, Hamersley, Kennedy, Augusta and Chichester Ranges) are some of the most crucial habitats for many aridland species. To discover them, let us wander for a moment in one of the classic examples of outwash woodlands, and a place where famous "bush outfitter" R.M. Williams began his entrepreneurial leather-working career — Italowie Gorge in the Gammon Ranges of South Australia.

Above: An outwash stream in Karijini National Park, Western Australia, has carved out deep waterholes in places, providing permanent water for wildlife. Outwash woodlands create real refuges in times of drought, particularly for seed-eating birds such as finches, parrots and cockatoos. *Right:* While the Murchison River is not an outwash area, this pool in Kalbarri National Park, Western Australia, is typical of outwash waterholes and the woodland covering the broad, river-cut plain between the rugged sandstone walls is very similar.

Best Examples: *NSW* — Barrier–Grey Range; Stephens Creek; Mutawintji National Park; Koonawarra; Bunker Creek; Evelyn Creek. *SA* — Gammon Ranges National Park; Italowie Gorge; Balcanoona Creek; Arkaroola area; Flinders Ranges National Park; Brachina Gorge. *NT* — MacDonnell Ranges; Simpsons Gap; Ellery Gap; Ormiston Gorge; Finke Gorge; Hugh River; Trephina Gorge; Ross River; Olga Gorge outflow; Valley of the Winds; Kings Creek; Hamersley Gorge; Python Pool.

Sounds: The rattle of dry gum leaves; noisy corellas squabbling around rock holes.

Smells: Sweet corkwood nectar.

Sensations: Cool shade.

Above, top to bottom: Immense rocky monoliths, such as Uluṟu, Kata Tjuṯa and granite monoliths in Western and South Australia, are such effective catchments that run-off often produces outwash woodland; Ghost Gums are common in the woodlands of the MacDonnell Ranges, NT; the entrance to Windjana Gorge, out of which wild wet-season waters rush, spreading water, seed and nutrients to outwash woodland.

The ephemeral, arid-zone Big John Creek (a tribute to explorer and surveyor John McKinlay) rises here in the Gammon Ranges, where its headwaters wrap around the resistant quartzite of Mount McKinlay (1051 metres). Over millions of years and through wildly variable climates, this creek has moved huge masses of boulders, gravels, sands and clays out through the Italowie Gorge and onto the plains that lead to Lake Frome. When the madly rushing creek slowed out on the plain, the heaviest boulders rolled to a halt. Soon, others, also sorted by weight, ceased their motion further out, forming a vast delta of graded sediment.

Only with the heaviest rains do the waters of Big John Creek, enriched with their dissolved salts, reach Lake Frome. During drenching downpours, little water soaks into the steep, rocky mountain slopes, which shed the rain down numerous impervious faces and undermining gullies. On the dry hillslopes, only spinifex, Mulga, other acacias, mallee, Caustic Vine and copperburrs thrive. In the less arid gullies, damp pockets of soil nourish Lemon Grass, Kangaroo Grass and Couch Grass under occasionally struggling River Red Gums. Where the creek sweeps off the rocky country onto a gravelly, boulder-strewn bed just before the gorge end, several deep, water-filled holes are routinely topped up by seepage from between the quartzite strata. This seepage encourages a scrub of paperbarks and sedges. Beyond the lip of quartzite there is no trace of water.

Yet the above description is too static in its portrayal of this wonderful outwash country. Towards the end of the big drought of 1983, I camped not far from where Reginald Murray Williams and his mate had carved their first leather-cutting bench out of a River Red Gum log. Fortunately, we set up tent on a high, grassy terrace, for there had been a build-up of threatening cumulus cloud over Mount McKinlay and the Gammons. On the precipitous slopes of the 600 metre Hawker Hill, opposite our campsite, only gaunt Mulga skeletons punctuated the brick-red field of gravel — blackened reminders of a bushfire that swept through just months earlier. By mid-afternoon, rain drenched the mountains in a 40-minute downpour during which thunder echoed and reverberated through the chasms of the gorge and the wind lashed at the grey ghosts of deluged trees. Then, behind the surging storm noises came a higher-pitched, rising roar. At first, just a watery few centimetres trickled over the lip, but this soon swelled rapidly to become three

Above: A lush oasis in Lawn Hill (Boodjamulla) National Park, Queensland, is divided by a limestone lip in the gorge.

Above, top: Valleys around the Finke River, with the MacDonnell Ranges beyond, are filled with outwash swept down by powerful but irregular floods. *Above, bottom left to right:* Ghost Gum; Cypress Pine; River Red Gum.

Flora of the Outwash Woodlands

Irrigated by flash floods that run off hard, dry catchments, this habitat is a major drought refuge. The well-watered pasture and cover provides shelter and sustenance for arid zone fauna, including herbivorous, insectivorous and carnivorous vertebrates and invertebrates. The key to this drought haven is its water overflow, and the capacity of the sandy, gravelly, boulder-strewn ground to absorb and retain water. At its outer perimeters, where the finest sediment is washed, it grades into savanna of Woollybutt, Wallaby Grass, Kangaroo Grass, Mulga Grass, Tall Oat Grass and Neverfail Grass, and finally sandy arid grasslands.

Classic Plants: River Red Gum; Coolibah; Ghost Gum; Beefwood; Needlewood; Corkwood; ironwood; Mulga; Desert Bloodwood; Royal Acacia; other *Acacia* spp.; Early Nancy; Cypress Pine; *Solanum* spp; Hop Bush; Spearwood; Lemon Grass; Kangaroo Grass; Neverfail; Woollybutt; Wallaby Grass; Mulga Grass; Wonga Vine; various daisies.

Above: The Northern Burrowing-frog is one of the continent's many "water-holding" amphibians; all are supremely adapted to inland habitats with infrequent rainfall.

Frogs and Reptiles of the Outwash Woodlands

This flash-flood-prone environment has significant areas that experience pooling, or ephemeral, waters — constituting ideal habitat for numerous insects. In turn, the abundance of insects coupled with water availability that ranges from permanent waterholes to muddy patches and areas with plenty of retained underground moisture, makes it excellent habitat for frogs. Due to lengthy periods of drought, the ability to burrow into damp soil and reserve water in body cavities is an admirable adaptation. Reptiles also find outwash communities to be happy hunting grounds, benefiting as they do from the availability of frog and invertebrate food and the dense ground cover created by flood debris. Dragons, monitor lizards, insectivorous skinks and geckoes are especially well represented.

Classic Frogs and Reptiles: Water-holding Frog; Spencer's Burrowing-frog; Spotted Grass-frog; Trilling Frog; Orange-crowned Toadlet; Desert Tree-frog; Spiny-tailed Gecko; Fat-tailed Gecko; Jewelled Gecko; Tessellated Gecko; Wood Gecko; Tree Dtella; Bynoe's Gecko; Beaded Gecko; Marbled Velvet Gecko; Beaked Gecko; Thick-tailed Gecko; *Delma tincta*; Hooded Scaly-foot; Ring-tailed Dragon; Mallee Dragon; Military Dragon; Dwarf Bearded Dragon; Central Netted Dragon; Western Netted Dragon; Painted Dragon; Gilbert's Dragon; Long-nosed Dragon; Thorny Devil; Perentie; Pygmy Mulga Monitor; Gould's Monitor; Black-headed Monitor; Pygmy Spiny-tailed Skink; Desert Skink; Tree Skink; Fire-tailed Skink; Centralian Blue-tongue; Western Blue-tongue; Eastern Blue-tongue; Shingleback; Woma; Children's Python; Carpet Python; Desert Death Adder; Yellow-faced Whipsnake; Red-naped Snake; Small-scaled Snake; King Brown Snake; Ringed Brown Snake; Western Brown Snake; Eastern Brown Snake; Myall Snake; Black-headed Snake; Bandy Bandy.

metres of raging chocolate water beneath a seething, foaming turbulent froth. A River Red Gum was uprooted and propelled along, dragging others with it before being jammed against the opposite wall. The obstruction caused the torrent to sweep sideways, eating into the opposite bank, where it ripped boulders from their base and rolled them off downstream. The storm swept on, moving southwards along the range and leaving only the hissing, clattering stream and the rumble of dying thunder to interrupt the eerie, atmospheric calm. Within hours, even the stream had vanished — all that remained was a high-water mark of debris and a clearing dribble running over the quartzite lip.

While the flood raged, the volume of water amounted to as much as a swimming pool every few seconds; where, then, did it all go? With some trepidation we noted that the main road in the gorge had been remade. Our four-wheel-drive negotiated boulders a metre wide that littered the track and a gully that now cleft the road. A number of centuries-old roadside gums had lost their bark to rolling logs. Beyond the gorge, Big John Creek divides into a number of channels to braid its course through the rubble and silt washed down by thousands of similar floods. Each course is lined by River Red Gums, which mingle with a woodland of Beefwoods, acacias, Hill Coolibah, Mulga, Rosewoods, Cypress Pines and Wild Orange beyond. On the floor, opportunistic saltbushes, grasses and many herbaceous species burst into life after rain.

We soon climbed onto a 100 metre high tabletop composed of water-rounded boulders and sands left by storms millions of years past. From its height we could look down over the many wandering courses heading towards Lake Frome. About 3–4 kilometres ahead there was a moving edge of flowing water. As we watched, it slowed, with one channel leading off, coming to a standstill and being "leapfrogged" by another channel. Slowly, all of the meandering channels died. There, written in the creek bed was our flash flood — now a mere 6 kilometres of wet mud and some shining pools! When we reached the place of the water's demise, we found that it had been 50% mud and too turbid to roll further. There was a further surprise. On the torrent's surface hundreds of tonnes of Common Wallaroo, Red and Grey Kangaroo and Yellow-footed Rock-wallaby dung had floated, swept up by the waters. In some places, dung was banked up 30–120 centimetres deep and piled around acacias and any other obstacle in the

Above: The King Brown has a wide range across most of Central–northern Australia, predominantly in arid woodlands.

path of the channels. Here was the fertility secret of the outwash communities! Herbivorous marsupials, grazing over perhaps 25–30 square kilometres of natural ground crops during the previous year, had created the faecal fertiliser that, gathered and concentrated by the floodwaters, would reinvigorate the woodlands by decomposing into a rich bank of plant nutrients.

FAUNA OF THE LANDS OF FLOOD AND FAMINE

The see-sawing climate of the past 2.5 million years required an evolutional fine-tuning process for flora and fauna. Those that have passed the test of boom and bust have become adapted to living with little water, waiting for the flood. Core resources in their survival are rock holes where the mountains meet the splayed, damp sediments of the outwash, such as the waterholes at the MacDonnell Ranges' gaps or at Italowie. The truly arid communities of spinifex and Mulga take up positions high in the hills, with enriched woodlands below. Common Wallaroos, rock-wallabies, Perenties, finches, Mulga Parrots, Spinifex Pigeons and other successful animals of the dry, mountainous country, come to water at these holes before returning to their specialist habitats in the barren aridlands. If droughts are long and food is scarce, they must move into the sustaining woodland, which they will share with its usual residents, some of which diurnally occupy drier habitat.

Outwash woodlands support possums, rodents, numerous reptile species, many birds — particularly parrots, cockatoos, honeyeaters and birds of prey — and a multitude of invertebrate species. Sap suckers and nectarivores are particularly well provided for. Perennial plants sink their deep roots in a retained, underground water resource. This reserve of water gives them reliable flowering seasons and, combined with abundant sunshine and nutrients, allows them to produce plenty of carbohydrates in the form of nectar, sap and sweet, succulent fruit. According to research conducted by the Commonwealth Scientific and Industrial Research Organisation on Australian arid communities, only four of the 95 mammal species, 25 of the 230 bird species, and none of the 210 reptile species or the many invertebrates depend on open water! Instead they conserve energy and their water needs are met by the vegetation. Many invertebrate herbivores (such as Witchetty Grubs) are active only after rain, spending drought periods as eggs or in passive, immature phases.

Above: Dingoes are successful predators of the outwash woodlands, where females often make their dens in hollows in undermined channel banks.

Mammals of the Outwash Woodlands

While the arid plains produce rapid, short-lived responses to rain, the irrigated floodouts in the ranges retain their crop of grasses for much longer. The lingering green pick is highly attractive to Red and Grey Kangaroos, Common Wallaroos and other macropods. Rock-wallabies nocturnally visit the grassy areas closest to their terraced cliffs. Permanent waterholes are home to the Water-rat, which feeds on yabbies and mussels. The many trees are fine homes for brushtail possums, and sometimes Sugar Gliders visit this usually too-arid area. Numerous small bat species find accommodation in the woodlands, along with a rich insect fauna. Unfortunately, southern areas of this habitat also appeal to the feral cat and fox, and these beasts have driven many small native mammals and rodents to extinction. The Central Rock Rat, particularly, struggles to survive and is little known.

Classic Mammals: Short-beaked Echidna; Red Kangaroo; Common Wallaroo; Black-flanked Rock-wallaby; Yellow-footed Rock-wallaby; Eastern and Western Grey Kangaroos; Fat-tailed Antechinus; Fat-tailed Dunnart; Common Brushtail Possum; Dingo; Common and Yellow-bellied Sheathtail-bats; White-striped Mastiff-bat; Little Mastiff-bat; Lesser Long-eared Bat; Gould's Wattled Bat; Little Broad-nosed and Western Broad-nosed Bats; Little Forest Bat; Sandy Inland Mouse; Long-haired Rat; donkey; camel; brumby.

Above: A Common Wallaroo quenches its thirst at a winding, rocky stream in outwash woodland.

Above: A Water-rat prepares to feast on a freshwater crayfish.

Above: A Budgerigar's natural plumage is vivid green and gold.

Classic Birds: Emu; Pacific Black Duck; Australasian Grebe; Little Black and Little Pied Cormorants; Great Egret; White-faced Heron; White-necked Heron; Black Kite; Wedge-tailed Eagle; Letter-winged Kite; Collared Sparrowhawk; Brown Goshawk; Australian Hobby; Peregrine Falcon; Brown Falcon; Black Falcon; Australian Bustard; Little Button-quail; Banded Lapwing; Crested Pigeon; Spinifex Pigeon; Common Bronzewing; Peaceful Dove; Diamond Dove; Red-tailed Black-Cockatoo; Galah; Little Corella; Cockatiel; Major Mitchell's Cockatoo (race: *mollis*); Princess Parrot; Adelaide Rosella; Mulga Parrot; Australian Ringneck; Red-rumped Parrot; Blue Bonnet; Bourke's Parrot; Budgerigar; Blue-winged Parrot; Scarlet-chested Parrot; Elegant Parrot; Pallid Cuckoo; Black-eared Cuckoo; Horsfield's Bronze-Cuckoo; Southern Boobook (race: *ocellata*); Barn Owl; Tawny Frogmouth (race: *brachypterus*); Spotted Nightjar; Australian Owlet-nightjar; Red-backed Kingfisher; Sacred Kingfisher; Rainbow Bee-eater; Splendid Fairy-wren; Variegated Fairy-wren (race: *assimilis*); Red-browed Pardalote; Striated Pardalote (race: *striatus*); Redthroat; Weebill (race: *flavescens*); Yellow-rumped Thornbill; Chestnut-rumped Thornbill; Inland Thornbill; Southern Whiteface (both races); Spiny-cheeked Honeyeater; Yellow-throated Miner; Singing Honeyeater; Grey-fronted Honeyeater; Grey-headed Honeyeater; White-plumed Honeyeater (race: *leilavalensis*); Brown Honeyeater; White-fronted Honeyeater; Mistletoebird; Crimson Chat; Hooded Robin; Red-capped Robin; Jacky Winter; White-browed Babbler; Grey-crowned Babbler (race: *rubeculus*); Chestnut Quail-thrush; Crested Bellbird; Rufous Whistler; Grey Shrike-thrush; Restless Flycatcher (race: *inquieta*); Grey Fantail; Willie Wagtail; Magpie-lark; White-winged Triller; Black-faced and Ground Cuckoo-shrikes; White-breasted, Masked, Black-faced and Little Woodswallows; Grey and Pied Butcherbirds; Australian Magpie (race: White-backed; *leuconota*); Australian Raven; Little Crow; Little Raven; Torresian Crow; White-winged Chough; Apostlebird; Western Bowerbird; Singing Bushlark; Australian Pipit; Zebra Finch; Painted Finch; Welcome Swallow; Tree Martin; Fairy Martin; White-backed Swallow; Rufous Songlark; Brown Songlark.

Above: The beautiful, proud Brown Falcon regularly sweeps the woodland for prey.

Birds of the Outwash Woodlands

Tongues of outwash woodland sweep from the ranges out onto the dry, grassy or scrubby plains, providing a more complex mosaic of habitat than birds based in the richer woodland require. Hence the favourite camping and nesting sites for flocks of splendid Red-tailed Black-Cockatoos, Galahs, Major Mitchell's Cockatoos, corellas and sprightly Budgerigars are in the woodlands. Other grass eaters are the finches, which lack the mobility of the larger birds and so do not stray too far from the outwash waterholes. Back in the woodland, patches of dense shrub offer sanctuary for Variegated and Superb Fairy-wrens and the stunning male White-winged Fairy-wren is often seen in saltbush on the woodland's periphery. Sometimes one hears the melancholy call of the Red-backed Kingfisher (on holiday from its usual abode in the drier country), which is easily distinguished from the clear, ringing call of the more common Brown Treecreeper.

Clockwise from top left: Galahs are clown-like characters of the bush; Western Corellas use their bills to dig for succulent underground stems and roots; the Sacred Kingfisher hunts frogs and unwary small fishes in the waterholes; Southern Boobooks can be heard serenading the evening with their low, melodic "book-book" calls; there are four known races of the Australian Ringneck, which some believe are four separate species — all prefer woodland habitat where they find nesting sites in tree hollows.

Scrublands and Shrublands

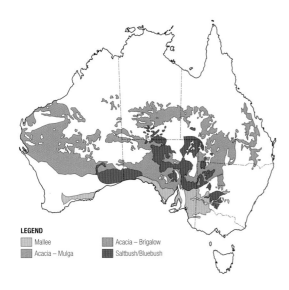

LEGEND

☐ Mallee   ☐ Acacia – Brigalow
☐ Acacia – Mulga   ☐ Saltbush/Bluebush

Above: Habitat vegetation map showing scrublands and shrublands.

Previous pages: Shrubs blaze in saffron beauty around Murchison River Gorge in Kalbarri National Park, WA.

Above: Sparse scrubland covers the Hamersley Ranges, Western Australia.

Scrublands and Shrublands

Just as Tartary is characterised by its steppes, America by its prairies, and Africa by its deserts, so Australia has one feature peculiar to itself, and that is its "scrubs" … One of the most common terms used by explorers is "Mallee" scrub, so called from its being composed of dwarf species of Eucalyptus called the "Mallee" by the Natives … Still more dreaded by the explorer is the "Mulga" scrub, consisting chiefly of dwarf acacias.

A.R. Wallace, in *Australasia* (1893), Volume 1, p. 46.

Scrublands and shrublands comprise some of the most extensive and important plant communities and animal habitats in Australia. Until quite recently they were considered intractable wastelands — a perception that arose from Australia's European history, inextricably linked, as it was, to the "mother country" and the "green and shaded lanes" of England. "Scrub" became the derogatory term for land that was considered of little value. As recently as 1981 a misguided British professor described the tropical woodlands of Kakadu as "mongrel scrub"! Even today, after 150 years of habitat destruction by sheep and the subsequent loss of millions of tonnes of topsoil in the land north of Cobar, New South Wales, species of semi-arid stabilising plants that are unpalatable to sheep have come to the rescue of the land, only to be described frequently as woody weed or "scrubbed-up" country only suitable for goats.

Scrub has always been tough. It is, by nature, a hindrance to "development". Its chief role, however, is to hold together a belt of country that runs right across the continent and is truly marginal as a cash-creating resource. Over the aeons these natural plant and animal communities evolved together with the land, developing relationships and survival strategies that incorporate built-in shock absorbers and enable them to resist life-threatening drought, fire and flood — all crises that occur in the extreme across this belt of land.

Above: Red Kangaroos shelter in Gidgee scrub in Sturt National Park, New South Wales, moving out to feed on nearby plains. *Right:* Shrubland and scrub meet, blending eucalypt and acacia on the mallee edge, western Victoria.

Above, top and centre: Eucalypt scrub, Dundas Nature Reserve, near Norseman, Western Australia; Brigalow scrub, near Yetman, central north-west New South Wales. Many such habitats have been severely affected by sheep grazing. *Above, bottom:* Mulga scrub in Yathong Nature Reserve, near Mount Hope, central New South Wales.

Rather than being tracts of worthless land written off under the general "scrub" title, the continent's scrub and shrublands include four distinct communities, each characterised by their own mix of vegetative species.

Covering southern Australia (and forming a mosaic with the western areas of New South Wales' temperate eucalypt woodlands as far north as Bourke and Gilgandra) is the mallee community. More than 130 eucalypt species make up the mallee scrublands, which occupy a band of country that experiences wet winters, hot, dry summers and 250–500 millimetres of rain annually — a truly Mediterranean climate. Southern South Australia, north-western Victoria and part of South-West Western Australia exhibit such prime communities. Typically, mallee is composed of numerous thin stems that rise up to 6 metres from a heavy, woody lignotuber (*Ligno* meaning woody; *tuber* meaning storage root) — creating famous, very hot campfire fuel. The density of these plants determines just how impenetrable the tangled, inter-meshed lateral stems become. Some mallee species, such as the White Mallee (*Eucalyptus dumosa*), are very similar to woodland trees, developing a main trunk. The Mallee community has evolved a very rich accompanying fauna.

Unlike the incredible diversity of species that populate the mallee genus, another scrub community is dominated by a single *Acacia* species, the eponymous Brigalow (*Acacia harpophylla*). More than 30 Aboriginal tribes lived across the Brigalow country, and while John Gould introduced "brigaloe scrub" to the English lexicon in 1839, no-one really knows which Aboriginal language the word sprang from, although it is probably Kamileroi in origin. Leichhardt, who spent a couple of months battling Brigalow on his epic trip to Port Essington in 1846, developed a warm appreciation of "the silver bricklow which formed a very pleasing picture". Brigalow grows as a 9–20 metre tall, rather spindly tree when locked into a scrub community. As a woodland tree it reaches heights of up to 25 metres and is resplendent with silvery-grey-green, scimitar-shaped leaves (phyllodes) and dense clusters of yellow, ball-shaped flowers growing from its leaf axils. Brigalow is often associated with Myall and Yarran (in the south) or Boree, Gidyea and Georgina Gidyea in the monsoon-affected north. Bottle Tree, a kurrajong, is also often found in this type of scrub. Brigalow thrives in a distinct bio-climatic belt that experiences from 500 to 750 millimetres of rainfall a year and requires 60–80% rain in the summer months. The closest similar climate is in north-west Argentina, Madagascar, on the Texas–Mexico border or in northern India — the environmental sources for most of the weeds that dot the Brigalow belt.

Aside from loosely labelling them as the much-maligned scrub, one might call the various Mulga communities the heartlands of Australia. Mulga (*Acacia aneura*) can be found from Griffith to Broome, from Longreach to Shark Bay and from Whyalla to the Victoria River. Such a huge geographic area is, of course, very diverse, including high, arid mountain ranges, silcrete tablelands, vast dune fields and sand plains, ancient river systems, gibber plains, salt lakes and a western rim adjacent to the Indian Ocean. Clearly this highly successful and adaptable plant can occur across a variety of community patterns and remain rather variable throughout its range. Dense scrubs of Mulga form, as well as communities where the most common plant will be the "hummock" spinifex grasses or saltbushes among chenopods, cassias, grevilleas and other shrubs. However, the most common identifier of the arid interior is usually Mulga. In most of the Mulga's arid environment, episodic rain is so highly variable in volume and timing that it is difficult, and perhaps meaningless, to ascertain average rainfall. It is estimated that during a dry period any rainfall less than 6 millimetres does not penetrate as far as the roots. In general, the acceptable average for Mulga is 150–200 millimetres per annum. Beautifully formed tall Mulga have upturned fingers of branches bearing wispy foliage. The leaf form varies across the range of Mulga habitat, with trees west of Tibooburra (NSW) having long, almost cylindrical needle-like phyllodes that give way to silvery, downy phyllodes near Dirranbandi (Qld) and become quite green, broad, short phyllodes on 10 metre trees north-west of Griffith (Qld). One exquisite variety, usually not found in scrub formations, stands vertically, with a strata of horizontal branches, and can be seen on the Valley of the Winds walk at Kata Tjuṯa in the Northern Territory.

Anyone travelling by road or rail to Alice Springs (NT), Broken Hill (NSW) or past Woomera, along the Stuart Highway (before irrigation began to change the face of the Hay Plain), or over the Nullarbor (SA) will have experienced the incredible feeling of space across the saltbush- or bluebush-speckled plains. This is the fourth group of this habitat type, the shrublands — home to the Red Kangaroo, White-backed Fairy-wren, butterfly-like Crimson Chat and Shingleback lizard. Shrublands are an eclectic mix of dense shrub precincts and wide, warm, pebbly or sandy soils that harbour animals of many different mobilities. Shrubland country probably has the least surface water of any other community, even less than that of the Mulga! Low rainfall and high temperatures render them harsh, specialist habitats, which is reflected in their Lilliputian dimensions — canopy height reaches only about a metre. By day, the mercury hovers between 17 and 22°C and summer days consecutively swelter at over 38°C, without the relief of any shade trees. Nights are humid, with approximately 80% humidity for six hours each night year-round in the southern shrublands. Like the mallee, the shrublands' evolution is inextricably linked with the evolution of its specialist fauna.

Above, top to bottom: Somewhat thinned bluebush shrubland covers a limestone floor on the side of the Eyre Highway, near Yalata, South Australia; acacia shrubland in a period of regeneration after rain near Bourke, New South Wales.

Below: Mixed arid scrub blankets the perched dunes of Zuytdorp Cliffs, east of Shark Bay, Western Australia.

Above, top to bottom: Fuschia Mallee, an attractive Western Australian wildflower that grows north of Esperance; White Mallee thrives north of Broken Hill, New South Wales.

Where Are They? Temperate Australia between the 250–500 millimetre rainfall isohyets in hot, dry Mediterranean climates. They grow on light soils and dune areas between Cocklebiddy, Merredin and Gnowangerup (WA); from Emu Junction to Whyalla, around the Yorke Peninsula to Adelaide then east of the Mount Lofty Ranges, north to Danggali Conservation Park and south-east to Mount Gambier (SA); east to Oxley, Swan Hill and Dimboola (Vic). Major outlying stands in woodland north of Hillston to Cobar and across to Condobolin and Dubbo (NSW).

What Do They Look Like? Large undulating dune and plain areas of low, open and closed, multi-stemmed eucalypts with understorey ranging from low mixed heath to spinifex and *Melaleuca* scrub.

Critical Conditions: Damp, cool winters; hot, dry summers; light-phosphate and nitrate-deficient soil.

Best Examples: *NSW* — Round Hill; Yathong Nature Reserve; Mungo National Park. *Vic* — Hattah–Kulkyne National Park; Wyperfield National Park; Little Desert National Park. *SA* — Flinders Chase National Park; Hincks and Danggali Conservation Parks; Ngarkat and Pinkawillinie Conservation Parks. *WA* — Balladonia to Esperance via Cape Arid National Park; Lake Magenta to Lake King; Frank Hann and Peak Charles National Parks.

Sounds: Malleefowl grunts; parrots screeching.

Smells: Dry dust; eucalyptus.

Sensations: Dry midday heat; cold, clear dawns.

The Mallee

Mr. Cunningham named those thick brushes of eucalyptus that spread in every direction around us Eucalyptus dumosa, *or the dwarf gum, as they never exceed twenty feet in height, and are generally from twelve to fifteen feet [4–5 metres], spreading out into a bushy circle from their roots in such a manner that it is impossible to see farther than from one bush to another; and these are very often united by a species of vine [cassyta], and the intermediate space covered by prickly wire-grass, rendering a passage through them equally painful and tedious … These ranges abound with native dogs; their howlings are incessant, day as well as night: as we saw no game, their principal prey must be rats, which have almost undermined this loose sandy country.*

Description of land west of the Cocoparra Range, NSW, from John Oxley's Journal of 7 and 10 June 1815.

John Oxley undertook the first great inland expedition beyond the Bathurst–Cowra area. His objective was to head south-west to describe the country between Bathurst and Cape Northumberland, near the South Australian–Victorian border. By 10 June 1817, John Oxley had crossed the Lachlan River, becoming the first European to tangle with mallee scrub during a very severe drought. His perception of mallee was greatly influenced by his fear of perishing in the boundless, waterless scrub — despite some relief from the heat, given that it was winter. Coincidentally enough, Oxley was perhaps only a few kilometres from what is now the Pulletop Nature Reserve near Griffith — the place where Dr Harry Frith conducted his famous research on the Malleefowl, and the place where, in 1954, he introduced me to mallee. Harry, the true integrative naturalist, learned to love the mallee, which proved to have so many hidden attributes:

As one travels along the earth roads of the mallee in a cloud of red dust, it is easy to be deceived by the seemingly endless avenues of thin grey stems and to imagine all this to be uniformly dead and uninteresting. The illusion is heightened if you walk in the scrub on a summer's day. The air is hot, still, and dust laden, and the heat radiates upward from the bare red soil. The scrub is silent and breathless; nothing moves: the only signs of life are a few shingleback lizards lying in the sun. Even the small red

Above: White Mallee begins its gradual renewal following a bushfire. Note the multiple stems growing from the lignotuber (underground woody tuber-like root head), which has buds that are protected from fire below ground level. When external leaves are scorched or destroyed, these buds shoot anew.

ants are still. Perhaps a bronzewing pigeon will explode from a shrub, or a heath-wren scuttle from under your feet — though even they usually sit tight and will not move. It is strange to reflect that, somewhere nearby, the mallee-fowl, alone active of all inhabitants of the scrub, are purposefully digging the sand of the mounds, in the blazing sun, while every other creature is silent and unseen.

Towards dusk, as the heat lessens, the scrub becomes alive. Bronzewing pigeons begin to boom and trot along the tracks, the "ban-ban-balele" of the crested bellbirds rings out, and chattering bands of honeyeaters move in the top of the scrub. If you sit still, the scrub-robins pipe around you and come bouncing up to look, emus can be heard drumming in the pine, and kangaroos are seen moving towards the nearest wheat; and if you are lucky you may hear a mallee-fowl bellowing his challenge near by … The mallee scrub is really a complex and interesting environment that contains many distinct plant and animal communities.

While Emus first invaded the wheat crops from the mallee country, eventually the wheat and irrigation invaded the mallee and left the tiny Pulletop Nature Reserve as the only surviving example of what Frith defined as the richest of mallee habitats. Surrounded, as it is, by a sea of wheat, even this rich "island" sample of habitat was too small to sustain its widest ranging animals throughout all climatic possibilities — there are now no Malleefowl in Pulletop Nature Reserve.

LIFE IN THE MALLEE — A RESIDENT'S TALE

The Malleefowl's close adaptation to mallee scrub means that the life history of this mound-incubating bird tells us much about its habitat. From Lake Grace (WA) to Eumungerie (NSW), mallee superficially looks the same. It has a low canopy that is closed over, to broken with winding open avenues. The patterning of understorey plants (dependent upon soil texture, alkalinity or acidity, available water and fertility) gives mallee scrub its variety and, as far as Malleefowl are concerned, its capacity to support their food and shelter requirements (particularly where acacias, legumes, cassias, lilies, Ruby Saltbush, sefton bushes, *Beyeria* species and *Portulacca* species grow). As for water, Frith showed that these birds need not drink at all. Instead, they derive moisture from fresh plant material and invertebrates such as grasshoppers, centipedes and spiders (of which the mallee has plenty) and drink only occasionally from rare, ephemeral puddles. So, in the

Above: Mallee, typically short of stature, growing in sandy, mineral soil in the Victorian Wimmera. Note the heavy understorey of *Acacia*, legumes and *Senna*. Across large areas of mallee the understorey of these plants and a great variety of other species have been eaten out by sheep, largely destroying most of the Malleefowl's food supply.

Above, top to bottom: Sand Mallee; the Mottlecah; Red-flowered Mallee; eucalypts flower profusely and, with more than 700 species, fill almost every environmental niche. Flowering often occurs en masse across a single species. The flowers are rich nectar producers and certain honeyeating birds have adapted brush-like tongues and migratory patterns that fit these flowering waves. Lorikeets are the most obvious, but many other, better camouflaged, non-parrot honeyeaters hide among gum leaves while they feed.

Above: Major Mitchell's Cockatoos feast on acacia seeds in mallee near Lake Mungo, New South Wales.

Birds of the Mallee

Apart from the turkey-sized mound-building Malleefowl, many other mallee birds are striking. Flashy Mallee Ringneck Parrots (sometimes known as Twenty-Eight Parrots, such being the sound of their call) are spectacular, flitting through the scrub. In the early morning comes a cacophonous choir of honeyeaters (particularly the Spiny-cheeked Honeyeater) singing as they collect nectar from flowering mallees, which are rich honey producers. When least expected on a hot, still day, an iridescent blue flash signifies the disturbance of a Splendid Fairy-wren. The gathering, evening silence is interrupted by the unforgettably mellifluous, ventriloquial call of the Crested Bellbird, drawing one into the dusky mallee. Ground-foraging Common Bronzewings stop and scratch the litter for invertebrates and seed.

Classic Birds: Malleefowl; Common Bronzewing; Emu; Budgerigar; Mulga Parrot; Mallee Ringneck; Galah; Blue Bonnet; Scrub-robin; Zebra Finch; Crested Bellbird; Wedge-tailed Eagle; Black Kite; Brown Goshawk; Brown Falcon; Australian Bustard; Little Button-quail; Painted Button-quail; Major Mitchell's Cockatoo; Red-rumped Parrot; Elegant Parrot; Little Corella; Cockatiel; Southern Boobook; Barn Owl; Tawny Frogmouth; Spotted Nightjar; Splendid Fairy-wren; Variegated Fairy-wren (race: *assimilis*); Mallee Emu-wren; Shy Heathwren; Redthroat; Western Gerygone; Weebill; Yellow-rumped Thornbill; Chestnut-rumped Thornbill; Southern Whiteface; Red Wattlebird; Spiny-cheeked Honeyeater; Striped Honeyeater; Yellow-throated Miner; Singing Honeyeater; White-eared Honeyeater; Purple-gaped Honeyeater; Yellow-plumed Honeyeater; Grey-fronted Honeyeater; Fuscous Honeyeater; White-plumed Honeyeater; Brown-headed Honeyeater; Pied Honeyeater; Mistletoebird; Hooded Robin; Red-capped Robin; Eastern Yellow Robin; Jacky Winter; White-browed Babbler; Chestnut-crowned Babbler; Chestnut Quail-thrush; Varied Sittella; Crested Shrike-tit; Rufous Whistler; Golden Whistler; Gilbert's Whistler; Grey Shrike-thrush; Grey Fantail; Willie Wagtail; Olive-backed Oriole; Dusky Woodswallow; Grey Butcherbird; Australian Magpie; Grey Currawong; Little Crow; White-winged Chough; Apostlebird; Diamond Firetail.

mallee one finds at Mungo and other arid areas, where spinifex dominates the floor, Malleefowl populations are low, while in the more humid areas where there is a far more diverse heath-like understorey (such as the Little Desert of Victoria and remaining pockets about the Coorong), population capacity is much higher. Eyre Peninsula and Norseman mallee sit somewhere in the middle as Malleefowl habitat. Principal mallee country lies in the winter rainfall belt. Sheep grazing through the uncleared mallee reduced the very fecund seed and fruit producers and ultimately greatly reduced the wildlife-carrying capacity of this habitat, particularly for the Malleefowl, which requires a lot of food. Of the millions of hectares of mallee habitat in the south-west of New South Wales, researchers have shown that barely 75 hectares of the most wildlife-productive type remained by the 1960s.

NESTING THE MALLEEFOWL WAY

Harry Frith, along with introducing me to mallee, introduced me to "Joe", one of his male Malleefowl study subjects. On hot, dry late-autumn days, Joe begins the task of seeking out a desirable place for a nest — soft, sandy soil on a fairly level floor located under a break in the eucalypt canopy, with much loose litter for at least 100 metres around. Scratching with his powerful, muscular legs, he begins to excavate a large hollow, loosening the sand over an area about 5 metres wide. He then digs a crater about 4 metres wide and 75 centimetres high, with a hollow up to 1 metre deep. Joe then begins to scrape up the dry litter from around his work area, piling it up into a number of arms that radiate 50 metres or more from the crater, before scraping them into the crater. With this monumental work complete, Joe can begin his lifelong romance with Josephine.

June usually brings the first cold showers of winter. Joe visits the couple's nest daily until the crater's contents are thoroughly soaked, when he begins to seal the wet litter under some 30 centimetres of sand. The nest mound is complete and now approximately 1 metre high. For now, it is a waiting game, allowing fungi and bacteria to begin the heating, fermenting process of decay in the heart of the mound. Meanwhile, another critical job remains — Joe must find Josephine and mate. Soon after, Josephine begins to worry the mound, her egg chain and hormone systems are calling. Joe steps up his work about the mound. First he digs a portal into the hot litter. Shoving his bill and head into the warmth, he determines the temperature — at 32–34°C the nest is ready to receive its first

Above: "Joe" the Malleefowl excavating his nest, perhaps to modify the temperature of the egg chamber.

egg. At sunrise, Josephine lays a delicate pink egg in the large nest hole dug by Joe, then walks away to feed. If the hole doesn't suit Josephine, Joe must carry out renovations. The male bird repairs the nest and maintains it continuously throughout the day, rarely moving outside of his work area. He regularly conducts his temperature test. In the early days, the temperature can get too high. If so, he opens the mound and mixes in sand, dropping the temperature to 33°C before closing it again. He remains totally in control. If opening the nest will jeopardise the incubating eggs, he even drives Josephine away until the next egg is due 6–8 days later. She then moves away, digs a small hole and lays the next egg.

A long nesting period beginning in early winter and extending into summer far outlasts the heat provided by fermentation. Joe's solution is to regularly monitor the temperature. When late winter arrives, he exposes the mound to the heat of the day to warm its interior. If necessary, he will drag sand from sunlit areas to keep the interior at 33°C, scraping a thick layer of sand over the top to hold the temperature overnight. At sunrise his vigil begins anew. While Josephine assists for half an hour before wandering off to feed for about seven hours each day, Joe rarely feeds for more than three hours. Summer comes and Joe continues his constant temperature testing. He waits for the coolest hours before exposing the contents to the cool air until 33°C is reached, then once again covering the nest with a great depth of insulating sand. While the nest is active, the couple are never far away. Joe remains on watch, alert to the slightest possible danger from marauding foxes, Sand Monitors or carnivorous marsupials. Protective colouration, a camouflage covering of red mallee dust and slow, strutting movements with regular lengthy freezes render the birds almost invisible at times. If they are suddenly disturbed, they half leap and fly into the canopy. The parents receive little thanks for their protection. When the precocious chick digs itself out of the sand, using part of its shell as a helmet, it neither recognises its parents nor remains nearby.

The remarkable Malleefowl is battling for survival. Grazing has reduced its quality habitat to such a small area and since 1870 increased predation by introduced foxes has proved particularly problematic. An increase in bushfires and lit "fuel reduction" blazes is exacerbating the problem. Wildlife management agencies at Yathong Nature Reserve (NSW), François Peron National Park (WA), Little Desert (Vic) and Danggali Conservation Park (SA) are helping in the search to find ways to conserve this unique mallee habitat species.

Above: Wallowa (*Acacia calamifolia*) is a favoured food of the endangered Malleefowl.

Above, top to bottom: Emu Bush; Coneflower (*Isopogon* sp.).

Flora of the Mallee

Dense stands of mallee in semi-arid country produces highly flammable litter. Fire-adapted strategies include: many seeds; hard-shelled seeds (as with acacias and oaks); need for heat to dry and open woody capsules to release seed; protection of buds for future growth (as in the mallee lignotubers); flowering, fruiting and seeding initiated by fire, for example, by compounds in the smoke; corky bark to insulate buds buried beneath (as in bloodwoods) and use of underground stems, tubers, corms and bulbs. Over generations, plants with fire survival strategies gain an advantage.

Classic Plants: Dwyer's Mallee Gum; Grey, Lerp, Congoo, Pointed, Red, Curly and Gooseberry Mallee; Yorrell; Slender-leaf, Green, Blue, Quorn and Bull Mallee; Ridge-fruited Mallee; Kangaroo Island Ash; Bell-fruited, Burdett's and Sand Mallee; Scarlet Pear Gum; Long-fruited Marlock; Crowned, Coarse-leaved and Fluted Horn Mallee; Upside-down Pea; Small-leaved Mintbush; Rose Darwinia; Bottlebrush Grevillea; Prickly and Black Toothbrushes; Round-leaf Pigface; Blue Pea; Yellow Starflower; Painted Featherflower; Wiry Honey Myrtle; Kondrung; Long-leaved, Spinifex and Mallee Wattles; Red Pokers; Emu Tree; *Caladenia* orchids; Broom Bush; Desert Geebung; Mallee and Murray Pines; Sefton Bush; Ruby and Bladder Saltbushes; Burr and Emu Bushes; Iron Grass; Dianella; *Cassia* spp.; bluebush.

Above: Western Grey Kangaroos favour the semi-arid mallee scrub habitat in southern Australia, west of the Great Dividing Range, leading to them becoming known as "scrubbers" in some parts. They are generally slightly smaller and darker in colouring than their Eastern Grey counterparts.

Above: The Fat-tailed Dunnart is a widespread semi-aridland mammal found across most of central and southern Australia. In lean times, fat stored in the tail provides the dunnart with reserves of energy.

Classic Mammals: Short-beaked Echidna; Western Grey Kangaroo; Eastern Grey Kangaroo; Red Kangaroo (sometimes sheltering); Common Wallaroo; Mulgara; Brush-tailed Phascogale; Common Dunnart; Ooldea Dunnart; Fat-tailed Dunnart; Hairy-footed Dunnart; Common Ringtail Possum; Common Brushtail Possum; Western Pygmy-possum; Little Pygmy-possum; Feathertail Glider; Tammar Wallaby; White-striped Mastiff-bat; Little Mastiff-bat; Greater Long-eared Bat; Lesser Long-eared Bat; Gould's Wattled Bat; Chocolate Wattled Bat; Little Broad-nosed Bat; Western Broad-nosed Bat; Little Forest Bat; Sandy Inland Mouse; Silky Mouse; Mitchell's Hopping-mouse; House Mouse; Dingo; Red Fox; feral cats; rabbits.

Above: Brush-tailed Phascogales are voracious predators of small mammals, reptiles, birds and eggs in woodlands and some humid mallee areas. They are common in northern parts of Western Australia, but vulnerable in Victoria.

Mammals of the Mallee

Mallee scrubland habitat has been hard hit by European settlement. Much of the mallee has been cleared for wheat production, and most of the remainder for range-grazing sheep, compounding the problem of lack of shelter and food, which the native animals had evolved with. What they had not evolved to counter was the new, efficient predator, the fox, which now had easy access to native species.

Western Quolls, the Plains Mouse, Gould's Mouse, Desert Mouse, Crescent Nailtail Wallaby, Bridled Nailtail Wallaby, Eastern Hare-wallaby, Brush-tailed Bettong, Burrowing Bettong, Pig-footed Bandicoot, Western Barred Bandicoot and Numbat were all lost from the mallee habitat. Some species still survive in adjacent habitats, but the changes to the mallee community, unfortunately, appear to be irreversible.

Left, top: The Western Barred Bandicoot once roamed the mallee scrubland habitat but is now locally extinct and found only on Bernier and Dorre Islands off the coast of Western Australia.

Left, centre: From the city to the centre of Australia, Red Foxes have proved themselves fast and efficient predators that are disastrous for smaller mammals and reptiles of temperate and semi-arid habitats.

Left, bottom: Mallee and other eucalypt scrublands are included in the wide distribution range of the Common Brushtail Possum.

Frogs and Reptiles of the Mallee

Mallee country is usually on sandy soils and dunes and is very dry country, with the exception being just after rain. Shrublands, in contrast, grow on soils that comprise much more clay, so water can pool for a time. In the mallee, amphibian life is restricted to those frogs that can hold water and live in the protection of burrows or those with rapid breeding cycles, which then retire to the protection of litter, stones or tree hollows.

Much of the bluebush and saltbush habitat lies on cracking clay soils, where deep fissures and "crabholes" offer a moist refuge. A number of spectacular reptilian representatives reside in these habitats, such as the Dugite, King Brown and other brown snakes, Netted Dragon, Thorny Devil, Sand Monitor and the Perentie — Australia's 2.4 metre giant lizard, the second-largest in the world after the Komodo Dragon. The more common Lace Monitor also dwells in the eastern habitats as far south as South Australia.

Classic Frogs and Reptiles: Trilling Frog;
Peron's Tree-frog; Jewelled Gecko; Eastern Spiny-tailed Gecko; Main's Ground Gecko; Box-patterned Gecko; Tessellated Gecko; Wood Gecko; Tree Dtella; Bynoe's Gecko; Beaded Gecko; Beaked Gecko; Thick-tailed Gecko; Mallee Worm Lizard; Marble-faced Delma; Patternless Delma; Sharp-snouted Delma; Burton's Snake-lizard; Common Scaly-foot; Hooded Scaly-foot; Bearded Dragon; Crested Dragon; Mallee Dragon; Western Bearded Dragon; Nobbi; Painted Dragon; Western Netted Dragon; Thorny Devil; Earless Dragon; Gould's Monitor; Lace Monitor; *Cryptoblepharus boutonii* complex; Southern Mallee Ctenotus; Robust Ctenotus; Barred Wedgesnout Ctenotus; Eastern Barred Wedgesnout Ctenotus; Desert Skink; Tree Skink; Peron's Skink; Wood Mulch-slider; Eastern Robust Slider; Grey's Skink; South-eastern Morethia Skink; Narrow-banded Sand-swimmer; Spinifex Slender Blue-tongue; Western and Eastern Blue-tongues; Shingleback; seven species of blind, burrowing snake; Carpet Python; Children's Python; Common Death Adder; Yellow-faced Whipsnake; Bardick; Red-naped Snake; Western Black-naped Snake; Eastern Tiger Snake; King Brown Snake; Dugite; Western and Eastern Brown Snakes; Coral Snake; Desert Banded Snake; Half-girdled Snake; Myall or Curl Snake; Black-headed Snake; Hooded Snake; Bandy Bandy.

Left, top: Living in a burrow helps the nocturnal Smooth Knob-tailed Gecko escape the heat of the sand country.

Left, centre: The Western Bearded Dragon (*Pogona minor minor*) lives in mallee coutnry near Norseman, south Western Australia.

Left, bottom: Although smaller and more slender than other death adder species, like the others the Desert Death Adder hunts by ambush, using its dark-tipped, worm-like tail as a lure. These dangerous, venomous snakes are common in Western Australia and across Central Australia where they prefer to live entirely nocturnal lives, hiding under thick vegetation or in burrows during the day.

Where Are They? Mulga scrublands are generally within the 250 millimetre per annum rainfall belt; however, on nutrient deficient soils (particularly those lacking in phosphorous) they do extend to 400 millimetres of rainfall under tropical influences.

What Do They Look Like? Varied landforms, usually reddish with silvery grey-green tall shrubs that cast little shadow even when growing closely together. Understorey ranges from bare red surfaces, through blond hummocky spinifex to dense, low shrubs.

Critical Conditions: Low rainfall with high to extreme summer temperatures; low-fertility soils.

Best Examples: *NSW* — 6 kilometres west of Cobar; Yathong Nature Reserve; Byrock to Bourke; Mutawintji National Park; Silver City Highway. *Qld* — south of Cunnamulla on the Matilda Highway. *SA* — Stuart Highway north of Marla; about Kingoonya; Oodnadatta area. *NT* — east of Kata Tjuṯa for 200 kilometres on Lasseter Highway; Mereenie Loop Road; Burt Plain; Plenty Highway; West MacDonnell National Park. *WA* — Great Central Road, Laverton to Uluṟu; Wiluna area; Meekatharra to Newman; Mount Augustus area

Sounds: Wind whispering through Mulga trees.

Smells: Dust; wet earth soaked with rain.

Sensations: Space; silence; loneliness and isolation.

Above: Feral goats have done some damage to this patch of Mulga (*Acacia aneura*) growing on the slopes of the Merrimerriwa Range in Yathong Nature Reserve, central New South Wales. The species name *aneura* refers to the lack of the typical tiny nerve usually along the edge of *Acacia* leaves.

Right: The Mulga-covered ridges of Mount Sonder in the West MacDonnell Ranges, made famous by artist Albert Namatjira, whose opalescent-blue mountain images of the "Pregnant Lady" of Aboriginal folklore drew worldwide acclaim.

Acacia Scrublands — Mulga

Cattle and sheep browse on the twigs of this, and some allied species, even in the presence of plentiful grass; and are much sustained by such acacias in seasons of protracted drought. Dromedaries in Australia crave for mulga as food. Wood excessively hard, dark brown; used, preferentially, by the natives for boomerangs, digging sticks and shafts of spears, wommerahs, nulla-nullas, and jagged spear ends.

Ernest Giles, *Australia Twice Traversed*, on his five desert explorations in 1889.

Mulga country is Giles's country. It is also the arid heart of Australia — red country populated by opportunistic plants and animals that genetically and instinctively wait for the abundance that follows infrequent rains. These species also know how to wait out the inevitable drought or fire. Sixty percent of this vast continent is marked as Mulga country. Rather than exist only in homogenous environmental conditions, Mulga covers such an immense area of the inland that this habitat is composed of a mosaic of soil types, altitudes, landforms, nutrient levels and available water. These variable environmental factors also change the mix of species, suiting Mulga as well as various mixes of xeromorphic plants (*xero* meaning dry; *morph* meaning form), such as the hummock grasses of the spinifex group, other *Acacia* species, *Calytrix*, *Micromyrtus* and *Cassia* species, Desert Oaks, Cypress Pine, Quandong and Sandalwood (Bush Plum).

THE NATURE OF MULGA

That Mulga is so prevalent across inland Australia is testimony to the effectiveness of its adaptations. Let's chronicle the story of a single Mulga plant at Preservation Creek, Milparinka (NSW) — the Depot Glen campsite of Charles Sturt in 1845 and a sheep station since the 1860s. One century later, in the midst of drought,

near-vertical slates above the creek retained little soil. However, just to the east of a larger slab, a dust drift formed and buried half a dozen shiny, black, hard-shelled acacia seeds, which had blown in the dust eddies for months before being carried to the creek by sugar-seeking ants, attracted by the seeds' white, sugary arils. Most of the mature Mulga plants by the creek were a gaunt reminder of better days — their surface roots exposed by thousands of trampling cloven hoofs and many of them having been lopped as drought fodder. Those that remained suffered the indignity of being stripped of their remaining leaves by desperate rabbits. The drought finally broke in 1973 and was followed by wet years, before drought inevitably returned. Ephemeral herbs, vast meadows of *Stipa*, *Aristida* and *Danthonia* grasses, along with some of the Mulga seeds, grew across the hills with renewed burr bush and saltbush growth. Nourished by such fresh green feed, female Red Kangaroos produce a joey every 8–10 months. While the time of plenty persists, each female carries a fertilised embryo (delayed implant) on her uterus wall. The buried Mulga seeds, too, were delayed — even after three damp years water had not been able to penetrate their impermeable shells.

The release of the Mulga seeds came in early summer, 1977. Dry weather had returned, turning the ephemeral herbs and grasses into fine, dry fuel for a summer storm. The initial conflagration lasted only minutes, consuming the paper-dry grasses and herbs, but long enough to ignite thousands of dead Mulga, which burnt thoroughly into stark white ash. The heat did its work, cracking the acacia seed cases, which had been less than a centimetre below the ashy surface. Weeks later, storm waters penetrated the heat-cracked seeds, triggering germination. Deeper seeds lay dormant and would remain so — dormant but alive (for 100 years if necessary) until they gained a similar freedom.

Having germinated, the Mulga seeds now faced a difficult post-fire period where they were at the mercy of flourishing invertebrates and small vertebrate herbivores feeding on the green pick. Fortunately, myxomatosis greatly reduced the young Mulga's main herbivorous enemy, the rabbit. Sheep, too, were not at liberty to feed on the young trees, having been fenced off from this part of the catchment.

Above: The intriguing nest of the Mulga Ant, covered with a thatch of Mulga leaves, resembles a small, peculiar crater on the hard clay soil that tops the deep sand Mulga habitat.

Above: Remains of Mulga scrub that has been battered by the constant grazing of sheep north of Broken Hill, NSW.

Above: Smoky, blue-tinted canopies are characteristic of Mulga scrub. This scrub in Mutawintji National Park, NSW, also shows the typical distribution of trees per hectare.

Above: Umbrella Mulga scrub on dunes near Finke and out to Chambers Pillar, Northern Territory. *Below:* The broad wilderness of Mulga scrub on the plain west of Kata Tjuṯa (Mount Olga) was never grazed by exotic stock, but feral camels now cause considerable damage.

Insect attack by locusts, some beetles and insect larvae was the most likely problem as bilbies, Burrowing Bettongs, Yellow-footed Rock-wallabies and native rodent herbivores had recently become extinct in the Milparinka area. Common Wallaroos also posed a threat, but luckily plenty of other regrowth sustenance, in the form of germinating seeds and root stock shoots, kept them occupied.

The Mulga seedling rapidly drove a tap root deep into the splitting "leaves" of slate, where residual water was stored. Simultaneously, a wide net of surface roots (ultimately stretching 15 metres) was extended in order to soak up rain. The developing branches and stiff leaves, arranged like a blown-out umbrella, acted as a catchment to channel water onto the furrowed trunk, which led directly to the base of the Mulga. Under these conditions, the young Mulga quickly drives upwards. It must depend upon rapid growth and the increasing stiffness of its "bony" branches to protect its leading shoots. Giles described this spiny barrier:

These scrubs are really dreadful, and one's skin and clothes get torn and ripped in all directions … It is so dense that in it we cannot see a third of the horses at once.

Mulga leaves are a miracle of design, especially for water conservation. The reflective, silvery grey-green, thick, leathery leaves are covered by fine hairs and numerous oil glands. The stomates, or breathing pores, are deeply bedded and few in number, and the leaves are vertically aligned, avoiding direct sunlight. Leaf length varies between 1 and 25 millimetres over the Mulga's widespread distribution. Leaf width is also variable, between 1 and 12 millimetres, depending on conditions. These xeromorphic traits are a result of nutrient-deficient soils, particularly those lacking phosphorous — typical of Mulga environments. As compensation, Mulga drops significant volumes of litter, which may add some humus. More importantly, Mulga is a nitrogen fixer, having symbiotic bacterial root nodules. The densest scrubs (300–5000 stems per hectare) occur on plains of deep sands composed of sediments that have run off ancient land surfaces, from which nutrients have been leached during intense rains.

Mature Mulga trees support an interesting group of animals. Ants lead the way — over 100 species may be represented in a 25 square metre area. The Australian Honey-pot Ant (*Camponotus inflatus*) is particularly fascinating, delighting as it does in free carbohydrate, which Mulgas exude as a white, powdery material. This solidly built black ant establishes a nest a couple of metres deep in the cracked soil below a large Mulga tree, excavating a shaft and tunnel system with numerous roomy horizontal chambers that are concealed beneath trees' litter fall.

Above, clockwise from top left: The Ornate Burrowing-frog inhabits the eastern and northern parts of the Mulga scrublands, where it seeks shelter from desiccation by burrowing; spectacular, coppery King Brown or Mulga Snakes are dangerous predators that grow up to 2 metres long and feed on small mammals, other snakes and frogs; beautifully patterned Central Netted Dragons are frequently seen sunning themselves on logs and on scrub limbs; the Centralian Blue-tongue is mainly herbivorous and delights in sandy country.

Frogs and Reptiles of the Mulga

Above all other habitats, Mulga is a reptile's paradise and is home to a tremendous range of skinks and dragons. Winter, however, presents a problem, with temperatures on clear nights regularly dropping to near zero. Reptiles counter this by going into hibernation, usually from the beginning of May through to late August. During hibernation their reserves of fat are well used, so, when they emerge, a hunting spree is necessary. They hunt during warmer parts of the day, lying in the sun when it is at its zenith. In mid-summer, Mulga's sandy surfaces can become scorching, skyrocketing to 150°C — a temperature that will kill a reptile and drive its prey to shelter. Consequently, most animals become nocturnal during summer in these aridlands, as the tracks and scats on sand dunes testify. Wandering the live dune surfaces will reveal animal movements in the desert, from the small insects (such as lacewing larvae) to the small mammals and even the Perentie. Careful observers will be surprised at the number of tracks and the bustle of activity.

Classic Frogs: Water-holding Frog; Spencer's Burrowing-frog; Trilling Frog; Shoemaker Frog; Desert Spadefoot Toad; Peron's Tree-frog; Desert Tree-frog.

Classic Lizards: Clawless Gecko; Spiny-tailed Gecko; Fat-tailed *Diplodactylus*; Jewelled Gecko; several Western Australian *Diplodactylus* species; Crowned Gecko; Tessellated Gecko; Northern Dtella; Tree Dtella; Bynoe's Gecko; Beaded Gecko; Rough Knob-tailed, Smooth Knob-tailed, Three-lined Knob-tailed Gecko; Marbled Velvet Gecko; Beaked Gecko; Marble-faced Delma; Rusty-topped Delma; Sharp-snouted Delma; Excitable Delma; Burton's Snake-lizard; Hooded Scaly-foot; Ring-tailed Dragon; Bearded Dragon; Military Dragon; Dwarf Bearded Dragon; Central Netted Dragon; Painted Dragon; Western Netted Dragon; Lally's Two-line Dragon; Winnecke's Dragon; Gilbert's Dragon; Thorny Devil; Earless Dragon; Long-nosed Dragon; Lined Earless Dragon; Eyrean Earless Dragon; Ridge-tailed Monitor; Short-tailed Pygmy Monitor; Pygmy Desert Monitor; Perentie; Pygmy Mulga Monitor; Sand Monitor; Black-headed Monitor; Callose-palmed Shinning-Skink; numerous *Ctenotus* spp.; Pygmy Spiny-tailed Skink; Desert Skink; Great Desert Skink; Gidgee Skink; Nocturnal Desert-skink; Southern Slider; Wood Mulch-slider; Grey's Skink; South-eastern Morethia Skink; Fire-tailed Skink; Narrow-banded and Broad-banded Sand-swimmers; Centralian Blue-tongue; Western Blue-tongue; Eastern Blue-tongue; Shingleback.

Classic Snakes: The Aborigines of Uluṟu have stories of great mythical snakes that relate to major features on the face of the rock. *Kuniya* is the ancestral python who migrated to Uluṟu with its eggs. Once the eggs hatched, she moved over the top to near the Mutitujulu waterhole, making great furrows en route. Here are found various *Typhlina* blind snakes; Woma; Children's Python; Carpet Python; Desert Death Adder; Common Death Adder; Yellow-faced Whipsnake; Rosen's Snake; Little Spotted Snake; Red-naped Snake; Mulga or King Brown Snake; Ringed Brown Snake; Gwardar or Western Brown Snake; Eastern Brown Snake; Desert Banded Snake; Narrow-banded Snake; Half-girdled Snake; Myall or Curl Snake; Bandy Bandy.

Mammals of the Mulga

Mammals that require a lot of food and choose to inhabit these lands, typified by drought with accidental rain, must be mobile and able to follow the storms that produce a green pick. Red Kangaroos, whose breeding cycles are timed by access to green feed, must sometimes travel great distances to find food, following the aridland rainfall patterns. Common Wallaroos are not so dependent on rainfall, as they can survive for 50 or more days without water. They do, however, depend upon shelter, resting under banks or in rocky caverns, where high humidity helps them conserve body moisture. Small mammals tend to live underground in tunnels and are active mainly at night.

Above, top to bottom: Now found only on Franklin Islands (SA), the Greater Stick-nest Rat was once widespread from western New South Wales to Shark Bay (WA). Old nests, 1 metre high communal interwoven stick piles with grassy central nests around a shrub foundation or rocky shelf, can still be seen at Mutawintji (NSW); Dingoes prey on mammals in the Mulga.

Classic Mammals: Short-beaked Echidna; Red Kangaroo; Common Wallaroo; Western Grey Kangaroo; Yellow-footed Rock-wallaby; Black-footed Rock-wallaby; Rufous Hare-wallaby; Kowari; Mulgara; Fat-tailed Antechinus; Common Dunnart; Ooldea Dunnart; Fat-tailed Dunnart; Hairy-footed Dunnart; Wongai Ningaui; Kultarr; Marsupial Mole; Bilby; Common Sheathtail-bat; Hill's Sheathtail Bat; White-striped Mastiff-bat; Greater and Lesser Long-eared Bats; Gould's Wattled Bat; Little and Western Broad-nosed Bats; Little Cave and Little Forest Bats; Plains Rat; Desert Mouse; Sandy Inland Mouse; Forrest's Mouse; Spinifex Hopping-mouse; Long-haired Rat; House Mouse.

Female workers wander over the tree, collecting the sugary powder and "milking" the sweet "dew" from species of scale insects, which had previously collected a concentrate from the sap. Returning to their cool underground storage chambers, these "worker" ants find a queue of numerous other females clinging to the chamber ceiling — these are "tankers" that have inflated abdomens. The workers regurgitate the amber, honey-like fluid, feeding it to the tankers, who store it in their grape-sized abdomens. In dry times, when ant food becomes scarce, the stored "honey" is rationed out — that is, of course, if Aboriginal women with their Mulga digging sticks and Desert Bloodwood scoops have not discovered the nest and taken the prized "sugar bag" first.

Another interesting ant is the architect of fascinating constructions. Out on the bare, red-clay "pavement" of the Mulga, in the groves of acacia, are scattered large, 40 centimetre wide, hair-covered doughnuts. Closer inspection reveals them to be Mulga Ant nests — small craters with rounded 10–15 centimetre earth walls that have been carefully covered with a mat of Mulga leaves. In the crater's centre is a large entrance to a tunnel system. The mat-protected wall is thought to be a dyke, because these bare clay surfaces are swept by sheets of water during storms. The mat helps save the levee from wash. However, some of these levees appear to be honeycombed with holes, leading some researchers to suggest the mat may be insulation from the scorching sun. Whatever they are, these are beautifully intriguing structures and the vastly populated, diverse desert-ant societies beguile with their sheer variety in insect form, nest construction and behaviour.

Fascinating mammals also reside in Mulga communities. The Greater Stick-nest Rat, now extinct on the mainland and surviving only on the Franklin Islands in South Australia, particularly impressed Giles:

They form their nests with twigs and sticks to the height of four feet [1 metre], the circumference being fifteen to twenty [5–6 metres]. The sticks are all up to three feet [1 metre], and up to an inch [24 millimetres] in diameter. Inside are chambers and galleries, while in the ground underneath are tunnels, which are carried to some distance

Above: Red Kangaroos are the largest of Australia's macropod species. These crepuscular marsupials are found across most of Central and Western Australia, particularly on plains skirting scrublands and open grasslands.

from their citadel … As a general rule, they frequent the country inhabited by the black oak [Casuarina]. They can live without water … Their flesh is very good eating.

More common species are the Red Kangaroo, rock-wallabies and the Common Wallaroo. It is often difficult to pinpoint the boundary of Mulga communities because *Acacia aneura* regularly has outliers far from the large Mulga scrubs, due to its ability to grow over such a variety of topography, from floodplains, deep sand areas, sand dunes, tablelands and stony hills to mountain ranges. Mulga also has a number of closely related acacias, some of which also form scrubs, such as the Umbrella Mulga, Red Mulga, Shrubby Mulga, Turpentine Mulga, Bastard Mulga and Witchetty Bush. For these reasons, Mulga will be discussed again later in this book, particularly when we reach the spinifex hummock grasslands.

Above: Male Variegated Fairy-wren with chicks.

Birds of the Mulga

Mulga alone does not prove an irresistible attractant for birds, with the exception being the Mulga-associated Crested Pigeons, Mulga Parrots and Blue Bonnet Parrots. However, a large proportion of Mulga country is in stony hills or out on deep sandy lands. Creeks running from the hills are usually lined with River Red Gums, greatly enhancing the habitat by providing numerous nesting sites for parrots and cockatoos. Dense shrubs also create nesting and feeding sites for Variegated Fairy-wrens, and sites for bower construction by Western Bowerbirds, as well as a home for busily social White-browed Babblers. In the understorey, nectar-producing *Eremophila* species (or "native fuschia" shrubs) attract honeyeaters.

Classic Birds: Emu; Wedge-tailed Eagle; Black Kite; Australian Kestrel; Black-breasted Buzzard; Whistling Kite; Little Eagle; Collared Sparrowhawk; Australian Hobby; Brown Falcon; Grey Falcon; Red-tailed Black-Cockatoo; Little Corella; Cockatiel; Major Mitchell's Cockatoo; Galah; Australian Ringneck; Mulga Parrot; Blue Bonnet; Bourke's Parrot; Budgerigar; Scarlet-chested Parrot; Pallid Cuckoo; Black-eared Cuckoo; Horsfield's Bronze-cuckoo; Crested Pigeon; Spinifex Pigeon; Common Bronzewing; Diamond Dove; Peaceful Dove; Red-backed Kingfisher; Rainbow Bee-eater; Splendid Fairy-wren; Variegated Fairy-wren (race: *assimilis*); Red-browed Pardalote; Striated Pardalote; Western Gerygone; Redthroat; Chestnut-rumped Thornbill; Inland Thornbill; Slaty-backed Thornbill; Southern Whiteface (all races); Banded Whiteface; Spiny-cheeked Honeyeater; Yellow-throated Miner; Singing Honeyeater; Grey-headed Honeyeater; Grey-fronted Honeyeater; Brown Honeyeater; Grey Honeyeater; White-fronted Honeyeater; Pied Honeyeater; Mistletoebird; Crimson Chat; Red-capped Robin; White-browed Babbler; Chiming Wedgebill; Chestnut-breasted Quail-thrush; Varied Sittella; Crested Bellbird; Rufous Whistler; Grey Shrike-thrush; Willie Wagtail; Magpie-lark; White-winged Triller; Masked, White-browed, Black-faced and Little Woodswallows; Grey Butcherbird; Pied Butcherbird; Australian Magpie; Australian Raven; Little Crow; Torresian Crow; Western Bowerbird; Australian Pipit; Zebra Finch; White-backed Swallow; Rufous Songlark; Barn Owl; Tawny Frogmouth; Spotted Nightjar; Australian Owlet-nightjar; Southern Boobook (race: *ocellata*).

Above, top to bottom: A Wedge-tailed Eagle swoops in to investigate a Common Wallaroo, which these eagles will take as prey if small enough; the Spotted Nightjar favours nesting on pebbly ridges, as here at Mutawintji, NSW.

Flora of the Mulga

Unmistakable, layered fire scars seen on satellite photographs of the great Australian deserts show just how much fire has affected the inland — and particularly the Mulga and spinifex country. Aboriginal people used fire as a hunting strategy and to make country more accessible. Graziers used fire even more enthusiastically in order to clear country and to gain a "green pick" for stock. Prior to human fire-lighting activity, lightning probably initiated many very large wildfires. There is a real danger that the timing and regularity of fire has now changed, increasing the threat to long-evolved patterns of existence. Global warming and the increase of severe weather systems will probably exacerbate the problem, giving rise to ever more serious wind and water erosion and loss of plant species (which are potentially valuable for pharmacological and other purposes), not to mention the loss of dependent wildlife species.

Right, top: Sturt's Desert Pea, Parakeelya and everlasting daisies, frequently associated with Mulga communities, burst into life after rains.

Right, centre: Mulga often shares its location with dense hummocks of spinifex, which crowds out many herbaceous plants in the understorey. Following fire, the dense spinifex gives way for a time to sequences of beautiful daisies, Sturt's Desert Pea, Parakeelya and other flowering plants.

Right, bottom: Everlasting daisies respond rapidly after fire. Mulga, as a plant, cannot survive these fires, however its seeds — buried in the soil where they may enjoy a longevity of more than 100 years — require fire to crack the shell and begin germination.

Below: Desert Heath Myrtle (*Thryptomene maisonneuvii*) seen here in Uluṟu–Kata Tjuṯa National Park, Northern Territory.

Classic Plants: *Acacia* species, particularly Mulga (*Acacia aneura*); Ironwood; Leopard Wood; *Cassia* spp.; Wild Orange; Warrior Bush; Butterbush; *Eremophila* spp.; White Cypress; Bimble Box; Desert Bloodwood; Wilga; Rosewood; Desert Kurrajong; Corkwood; Needlewood; Honey Grevillea; Yellow Flame Grevillea (*Grevillea eriostachya*); Rattle-pod Grevillea (*Grevillea stenobotrya*); Holly Grevillea; Desert Poplar; Desert Oak; Hop Bush; Desert Rose; *Abutilon* spp.; *Solanum* spp.; Native Pear or Bush Banana; spinifex, spear, wire and wallaby grasses; Sandalwood, Quandong, Woollybutt, Bottlewasher and Soft Spinifex grasses; various copperburrs; various saltbushes and the Ruby Saltbush; masses of Mulla Mulla (*Ptilotus* spp.); daisies; numerous ephemeral, annual and perennial herbs, including Desert Pea, Pigface, Parakeelyas of *Calandrinia* species; *Crotalaria* species; Caustic Weeds; various *Sida* species.; Paddy Melon; Grey Mistletoe; Harlequin Mistletoe; *Desert Poplar* (*Codonocarpus cotinifolius*); Camel Poison Bush; Weeping Pittosporum; Desert Lantern (*Abutilon* species); Blue Mallee (*Eucalyptus gamophylla*); Greenbird Flower (*Crotolaria cunninghamii*).

Clockwise from top left: Pink Mulla Mulla; Yellow Flame Grevillea is a prolific nectar producer used by Aborigines (who call it "sugar bag") and honeyeaters as a food source; following a light fire and rain, wildflowers are scattered below the Mulga trees, some of which have retained a canopy of leaves; the Varnish Bush (*Eremophila viscida*) is common throughout south-western semi-arid areas; Silver Cassia, one of a large variety of desert cassias; the Greenbird Flower, a member of the pea family, is also known as the Rattlepod because of the sound made by its hard seeds.

Above, top to bottom: Posy Starflower; Honeysuckle Spider Grevillea, a honeyeater attractant; Spotted Emu Bush has the scientific name *Eremophila maculata* (*Eremea* meaning desert, *phila* love and *maculata* spotted) — the desert spotted lover.

Where Are They? Between Goondiwindi and Collinsvale north-west of Mackay (Qld), with outliers as far south as the Culgoa River floodplain and the northern Pilliga (NSW).

What Do They Look Like? Dense, silver-green acacia scrub with a closed canopy 9–15 metres high. Outliers are more open and are lower southwards, taller in the north. There are eleven different communities dependent upon associated species, such as Bottle Trees, Yellow-wood, Wilga, casuarinas, eremophilas, and bauhinias. May also be classed as forest and woodland.

Critical Conditions: Require 0–750 millimetres of rainfall; winter and summer rain; clay, fertile soils; hot, humid summers.

Above, top to bottom: The Australian Brush-turkey was frequently reported by Leichhardt; dense blady grass-covered groves and hilltops are prime Whiptail Wallaby habitat.

Brigalow Lands

Travelling north-west we came to a Cypress-pine thicket, which formed the outside of a Bricklow [sic] scrub. This scrub was, at first, unusually open, and I thought that it would be of little extent; I was, however, very much mistaken: the Bricklow, Acacias, Casuarinas and a stunted tea-tree, formed so an impervious thicket, that the bullocks, in forcing their way through it, tore the flour bags, upset their loads, broke their straps. Having travelled five miles [8.5 kilometres] into it, and finding no prospect of its termination, I resolved upon returning to our last camp, which, however, I was enabled to effect without experiencing great difficulty, delay and loss ...

Ludwig Leichhardt, battling the "Bricklow" [Brigalow], from October to December, 1844.

Leichhardt was the first European to explore this "Bricklow", which is, in its extent, perhaps the most dependent on its "scrub" community habit. At the heart of these lands is Brigalow itself (*Acacia harpophylla*) — *harpo* meaning harp-shaped and *phylla* leaves. Along with Brigalow and Mulga, a number of the 900 *Acacia* species grow in massed stands or scrubs, such as Myall, Gidgee and Spearwood (*Acacia doratoxylon*). Unique Brigalow environment provides a phosphate-rich nutrient base of clay soils in a climatic system of extremes — neither desert nor tropical or temperate, but a mix of the three. Dominant Brigalow scrub is easily nourished by the fertile soils, and, as a dense scrub, can protect individual trees from the rigorous environment. For Brigalow, there is strength in numbers! While phosphates from the soil are recycled within the system, nitrogen, which can be depleted, is replaced by the acacia's nitrogen-fixing root bacteria. Some of the soils on the lower, flatter country are as deep as 3–4.5 metres, the surface being alkaline, with acidic deeper soil. These flatter areas are also gilgai country, with a surface dimpled with depressions 60–90 centimetres deep and 5–8 metres wide, which are colder in winter and retain water and surface growth for longer.

Climatic challenges that plants of the Brigalow lands must live with include rainfall of 500–750 millmetres a year, with 40% falling in winter and 60% in summer, which is usually intense when it comes — up to 20% can fall in one day. Droughts lasting three to four months are common, as are summer heat waves when extreme temperatures rapidly dehydrate the soils and vegetation. At Roma, records

Above: Thick Brigalow scrub south of the Queensland border, near the town of Texas. Leichhardt found Brigalow very difficult country to traverse on horseback.

Above: Sparse Brigalow scrub north of Goondiwindi, near the Queensland–New South Wales border.

show that a week-long heat wave exceeding 38°C usually occurs sixteen times a year! Fortunately, clay soils hold water better than adjacent sandier soils (where only open eucalypt woodland grows) and those further north (where grasslands dominate). Even so, evaporation accounts for a potential loss of 1651 millimetres per year over most of the region — a huge deficit that means very efficient water collection and respiration by plants is necessary for successful living. Uneven catchment run-off concentrates water in certain areas, allowing the community to structure itself accordingly. Frosts are common between April and October when temperature can plummet 15°C in two hours after 3 a.m., dropping to −5° to −8°C.

Apart from some small, recently protected reserves, much of the Brigalow has been "rolled" and burned for crop growing or cattle grazing, severely reducing this habitat's area. In Leichhardt's day, the pristine scrub thrived, although similarities in floral and faunal species remain:

*The Bottle-tree [*Sterculia, *remarkable for an enlargement of the stem, about three feet above the ground] was observed within the scrub. Many pigeons were seen: the Black-Cockatoo of Leach [*Calyptorhynchus leachii*] was shot; we passed several nests of the brush-turkey [*Alectura lathami*]. Charley got probably a new species of bandicoot, with longer ears than the common one, and with white paws. We distinguished during the rain, three different frogs, which made a very inharmonious concert. [14 Oct] ... We tried to obtain opossums, during the clear moonlight night, but only caught the common rabbit-rat. Pigeons, mutton-birds [*Struthidea], *are frequent, and provided us with several messes; iguanas are considered great delicacies; several black kangaroos were seen today. [22 Oct] ... Here water was very scarce; the banks of the creek were covered with Bricklow scrub; and a bush-fire, which had recently swept down the valley, had left very little food for our cattle: the bladey-grass, however, had begun to shew [sic] its young shoots, and the vegetation, on some patches of less recent burnings, looked green ... After having contended with scrubs, with swamps and with mountains, we were again doomed to grapple with our old enemy, the silver-leaved Bricklow, and a prickly acacia. ... The most remarkable feature in the vegetation, however, was an arborescent Zamia. ... In consequence of the prevalence of this plant, I called the creek Zamia Creek ... I was surprised to find Erythrina, which I had been accustomed to meet with only on the creeks, and at the outskirts of mountain brushes. [2 Dec, south-east of Rolleston, Qld]*

Flora and Fauna of the Brigalow Lands

As Leichhardt's journal implies, a great complexity of fauna and vegetation comprises the Brigalow lands, diversity that is enhanced by frequent interweaving with adjacent open habitats. Brigalow provides admirable shelter, and deep creek and drainage channels in its heavy alluvial soils create safe "highways" for fauna. It is heavy scrub interspersed with grassland, woodland and lagoons, so fauna of those habitats use it for shelter. The below faunal list is of those that use it for more than shelter.

Classic Flora: Brigalow; Bottle Tree; Belah; Wilga; Sandalwood; Dawson Gum; Yellow-wood; Bimble Box; Gidgee; Coolibah; Yarran; Queensland Bluegrass; Kangaroo Grass; flora of tropical woodland and savanna.

Classic Mammals: Short-beaked Echidna; Spotted-tailed Quoll; Yellow-footed Antechinus; Common Planigale; Northern Brown and Long-nosed Bandicoots; Common Ringtail and Common Brushtail Possums; Bridled Nailtail Wallaby; Black-striped Wallaby; Eastern Grey Kangaroo; Common Wallaroo; Swamp Wallaby; Little Red Flying-fox; Beccari's Mastiff-bat; Lesser Long-eared Bat; Little Bent-wing Bat; Gould's Wattled Bat.

Classic Birds: Emu; Brush-turkey; Black Kite; Wedge-tailed Eagle; Pacific Baza; Brown Goshawk; Crested Pigeon; Common Bronzewing; Wonga Pigeon; Bar-shouldered Dove; Red-tailed Black-Cockatoo; Red-winged Parrot; Shining Bronze-Cuckoo; Channel-billed Cuckoo; Pheasant Coucal; Barking Owl; Tawny Frogmouth; Laughing Kookaburra; White-throated Treecreeper; Yellow Thornbill; Apostlebird; Grey Shrike-thrush; Golden Whistler; Grey Fantail; Black-faced Cuckoo-shrike; Olive-backed Oriole; Grey Butcherbird; Torresian Crow; Spotted Bowerbird.

Classic Frogs and Reptiles: Striped Burrowing-frog; Ornate Burrowing-frog; Brown Toadlet; Red-groined Toadlet; Green Tree-frog; Bynoe's Gecko; Robust Velvet Gecko; Thick-tailed Gecko; Burton's Snake-lizard; Bearded Dragon; Gould's Monitor; *Cryptoblepharus boutonii*; Robust Ctenotus; Yakka Skink; Tree Skink; Grey's Skink; Eastern Blue-tongue Lizard; Shingleback; Blind Snakes; Children's Python; Carpet Python; Common Death Adder; Yellow-faced Whipsnake; Collared Whipsnake; Red-naped Snake; Grey Snake; Pale-headed Snake; King Brown Snake; Spotted Black Snake; Eastern Brown Snake; Curl Snake; Bandy Bandy.

Above: A male Common Wallaroo, a regular in Brigalow lands.

Where Are They? On exposed, temperate sandy and rocky coastlines and shorelines, usually where there are strong prevailing winds blowing across saltwater.

What Do They Look Like? Wind-streamlined, tightly packed, closed, mid-green canopies rising a metre or so (at the community edge) to 8 metres high on densely growing trunks. The upper branches are very finely divided, supporting a thin, but extremely dense band of small-leafed foliage. They frequently have a dry litter-covered floor.

Best Examples: *Qld* — Cooloola National Park. *NSW* — Wallis and Myall Lakes; Port Stephens; Jervis Bay; Green Cape; Nadgee Nature Reserve. *Vic* — Croajingolong National Park; Point Hicks; Gippsland Lakes; Wilsons Promontory (Tidal River); Western Port, Discovery Bay National Park. *Tas* — Macquarie Harbour; Mount William National Park; Mount Cameron west; the north-west corner and islands. *SA* — Flinders Island; Coorong National Park and Princes Highway to Kingston; Kangaroo Island; Flinders Chase National Park; Fowlers Bay area. *WA* — Cape Arid National Park; Cape Le Grand National Park; Fitzgerald River National Park; Walpole–Nornalup National Park; D'Entrecasteaux National Park; Dongarra to Lancelin.

Sounds: Wind across the canopy; whipbirds.

Smells: Sea air spiced with *Melaleuca* species.

Sensations: The itch of sharp twigs.

Above, top to bottom: Dune scrub behind Cape Howe Beach in Nadgee Nature Reserve is mainly of paperbarks, Coast Banksia and tea-tree, with a typical swampy lead running deep into the scrub; coastal scrub, mainly Banksia and tea-tree, on headland near Point Hicks, NSW, Captain Cook's first landfall.

Coastal Scrublands

The country here is in general low, sandy, and not without lagoons, yet in figure hilly, but the hills are little else than sand; they have indeed a patched covering which might deceive the eye at a distance, but the usual sterility of the soil still prevails … The general productions are short deformed gum-trees, tea tree, some small shrubs and patches of an almost impenetrable underwood of small brush, ground fern, and vines. A luxuriant crop of grass may occasionally be found in places where the underwood has thinned off.

George Bass, behind the western headland (Rame Head) of Wingan Inlet beach for twelve days during 1797.

Earlier, Cook had noted "lawns" as part of the vegetation along the continent's south-east coast; in the same frame of mind, Bass, too, had named Green Cape after "lawns" he observed from the sea. Anyone fortunate enough to sail this stretch of coast can forgive sailors for misinterpreting those smoothly rounded, clipped-looking, very dense, bright green canopies of coastal paperbark scrub. When Bass, in a whaleboat, was forced to seek shelter from the south-west Bass Strait gales, he busied himself by landing and undertaking the above exploration — in the process demystifying those "lawns" described by earlier seafarers.

Bass's description perfectly depicts coastal scrub, much of which I have battled through many times around Nadgee Nature Reserve, Green Cape, Point Hicks and many other places along the Australian temperate coast, right around to Geraldton in Western Australia. The wonderful back-beach drive to Point Hicks Lighthouse leads through that "impenetrable" brush of Coast Banksia, lily pilly, tea-tree and paperbark, bound together by Sarsaparilla Vine (*Smilax glyciphylla*), Clematis and Dodder. Immediately rising beside the road are incredible, scrub-bound, 60-degree sloping giant dunes. Where ancient banksias have fallen and dragged the roof in, masses of bracken, grasses and herbs make the most of the available light to complete their life cycles. A lyrebird and Swamp Wallaby flee in a ripple of brown shadows, while fat, white waistcoated Wonga Pigeons inspect the scrub floor. Without a track, travel through this dense, wind-pruned scrub is very slow, at about 400 metres an hour!

Coastal scrub not only grows on dunes. Rocky headlands exposed to salt-laden winds all generally have a broad fringe of streamlined, wind-sculpted tea-tree and paperbark, which protects the more sensitive inland woodlands and forests. Fire, or other disturbance to the scrub, sees the previously protected inland communities retreat before the persistent wind. However, due to a lack of understorey fuel, muffled air-flow, and scrub density, unless conditions are extremely dry (as they were at Nadgee in 1970–71) fire is very difficult to start and maintain in the coastal scrublands. Under very dry, hot and windy (westerly) conditions, the finely divided branches and oil-charged leaves of *Leptospermum* and *Melaleuca* species explode when ignited.

Other very dense coastal scrubs develop around lagoons, as at the back of the Gippsland Lakes, Western Port, Macquarie Harbour, Port Stephens, Myall Lakes, Kangaroo Island, the Coorong, and as far north as Fraser Island in Queensland. In Western Australia, a great number of southern saltwater lakes inland produce similar environments to those of the coast, and have shoreline areas densely covered with similar scrubs, particularly *Melaleuca* paperbarks.

Flora of the Coastal Scrublands

Sand, wind, salt, water and landform all play an important role in determining what plants grow where. Sand and wind give the land its shape. Water and landform decide the available nutrients. Sand remains unstable until covered with vegetation to hold it in place. Wind heaps the sand into dunes and sheltered swales that provide an environment similar to a hot-house. A succession of plant types invade the sandy mass or the exposed rocky headland, but only those that can accept a continuous coating of sea salt survive. Most plants have water drained from them by salt. Paperbarks (*Melaleuca* spp.) and tea-trees, with their tiny leaves, are ideal. Most can still intercept much rainwater and are protected by a waxy surface coating. In the canopy, the wind prunes tiny shoots that interfere with its flow, a process aided by the sea salt. Beneath the canopy, sand becomes covered in litter, dampness is maintained and the warm, sheltered conditions favour soft, dim-light-seeking plants (such as ground orchids) and climbing vines (such as Clematis and Sarsaparilla). Coastal scrub also has some rainforest species (Tuckeroo and lilly pilly).

Classic Plants: Yellow, Black, Inland Grey, White, Red and Bimble Boxes; Yellow, Scribbly and White Gums; Red and Yellow Bloodwoods; Sydney Red Gum; Black Oak; Belah; Rosewood; River Red, Dwyer's Red and Grey Gums; Coastal Ash; Myall; Kurrajong; White Cypress Pine; Wilga; Budda; Brown Mallet; York and Salmon Gums; Wandoo; Gimlet; WA Flooded Gum; Redwood; kangaroo and wallaby grasses; spear, wire and snow grasses; NSW Waratah; boronias; Heath-leafed and Old Man Banksias; hakeas; Showy and Golden Dryandras; Wellington, Cootamundra and other wattles; Pingle; Painted Featherflowers; Common Cauliflower; Flat-leafed Wattle; Firewood, Bull and Acorn Banksias; *Grevillea* spp.; Striking Hovea; Starflower; *Diplolaena* spp.; *Isopogon* Coneflowers; cat's paws; *Daviesia, Gastrolobium, Templetonia, Gompholobium* and *Urodon* peas; Gungurru.

Above, top to bottom: Lagoons, estuaries, beaches and headlands are prime settings for coastal scrubland, seen here at Mimosa Rocks National Park, north of Merimbula in New South Wales; wind-pruned coastal scrub of *Banksia, Casuarina* and rainforest trees on Cape Byron. *Right, top to bottom:* The nectar-rich blossoms of a Broad-leafed Paperbark bloom in late spring; Cowslip Orchids adorn some coastal thickets in south-western Australia.

Above: The Eastern Pygmy-possum lives on nectar, flowers and invertebrates and also eats the fruit of the lilly pilly.

Mammals of the Coastal Scrublands

Coastal scrub habitat is perfect for those arboreal beasts that can climb amid the canopy and nest there, including ringtail possums and pygmy-possums. Excavators of soft, damp soil, such as the Southern Brown and Long-nosed Bandicoots, feed on invertebrates and plant roots in these environments, and small wallabies can negotiate the cramped spaces. Numerous other species make use of the very fine shelter provided by the dense vegetation, although those that do must also be immune to the Paralysis Tick, which also thrives in the coastal thickets.

Classic Mammals: Short-beaked Echidna; Spotted-tailed Quoll; Eastern Quoll (Tas only); Western Quoll (WA); Tasmanian Devil; Brush-tailed Phascogale; Yellow-footed Antechinus; Brown Antechinus; Swamp Antechinus; Common Dunnart; Southern Brown and Long-nosed Bandicoots; Common Wombat; Common Ringtail Possum (high populations); Eastern and Western Pygmy-possums; Long-nosed Potoroo; Western Brush Wallaby; Tammar Wallaby; Tasmanian Pademelon; Red-necked Wallaby; Eastern Grey and Western Grey Kangaroos; Swamp Wallaby; Lesser Long-eared Bat; Gould's Wattled Bat; Chocolate Wattled Bat; Eastern Chestnut Mouse; Ash-grey Mouse; Bush Rat; Swamp Rat.

Birds of the Coastal Scrublands

Surges of heavy flowering in these scrubs attract honeyeaters from adjoining coastal heath, particularly New Holland and Tawny-crowned Honeyeaters. On the floor, Wonga, Common and Brush Bronzewing Pigeons are frequently seen scratching away; however, none are as industrious as the Superb Lyrebird. The sharp crack of the male Eastern Whipbird (and the female response) gives away a bird that is notoriously difficult to spot. Coastal scrub is one of the Eastern Whipbird's choice habitats. Grey Fantails, too, are always diverting the eye during these excursions. The heavy canopy of coastal scrub assists more-secretive birds, which are able to conceal themselves easily thanks to the subdued light, very dense twigs and small, tightly packed leaves of the canopy.

Above, top to bottom: The Southern Brown Bandicoot forages for insects and other invertebrates, fungi and tubers; in the Tasmanian scrub, the Eastern Quoll is free from fox predation, but this is its last refuge and it is now considered extinct on the mainland; a well-fed Quokka is protected by Juncus while it feeds on a grassy clearing.

Above, left to right: New Holland Honeyeaters build a cup-shaped nest, where the female will sit on one to three small, pink eggs for around a fortnight; Blue-faced Honeyeaters frequent the coastal scrub around Byron Bay, NSW.

Classic Birds: Superb Lyrebird; Wonga Pigeon; Osprey; White-bellied Sea-Eagle; Square-tailed Kite; Whistling Kite; Brown Falcon; Buff-banded Rail; Brush Bronzewing; Yellow-tailed Black-Cockatoo; Short-billed Black-Cockatoo; Rainbow Lorikeet; Scaly-breasted Lorikeet, Crimson Rosella; Red-capped Parrot; Blue-winged Parrot; Rock Parrot; Oriental Cuckoo; Brush Cuckoo; Pheasant Coucal; Southern Boobook; Tawny Frogmouth; Sacred Kingfisher; Eastern Bristlebird; Western Bristlebird; Rufous Bristlebird; Noisy Scrub-bird; Superb Fairy-wren (races: *leggei* and *cyaneus*); Variegated Fairy-wren (race: *lamberti*); Red-winged Fairy-wren; Chestnut-rumped Heathwren; Shy Heathwren; Striated Fieldwren; Yellow Thornbill; Buff-rumped Thornbill; Western Thornbill; Brown Thornbill; Little Wattlebird; Red Wattlebird; Spiny-cheeked Honeyeater; Noisy Friarbird; migratory honeyeaters when *Melaleuca* and *Banksia* species are in flower; New Holland Honeyeater; White-cheeked Honeyeater; Spinebills; Crescent Honeyeater; Southern Scrub-robin; Eastern Yellow Robin; Olive Whistler; Satin Flycatcher; Grey Fantail (various races); Figbird; Grey Butcherbird; Black Currawong (Tas); Pied Currawong; Grey Currawong; Forest Raven; Regent Bowerbird; Beautiful Firetail; Western and Eastern Whipbirds.

Above: The courtship ritual of the Satin Bowerbird is one of the most interesting of all birds. To entice a female to mate, glossy-blue males create an elaborate bower adorned with blue objects. The bower is not a nest — the female will build her own plate-shaped nest when she is ready to lay her eggs — it is a "performance" stage for the male.

Frogs and Reptiles of the Coastal Scrublands

Several factors make dune and coastal scrub good habitat for many species. Soft, sandy soils suit burrowing animals, such as the snake-lizards, while grey, textured trunks and plant stems are perfect camouflage for geckoes. The tight canopy conceals Common Tree Snakes and Diamond Pythons, which are attracted by numerous bird nests and ringtail possums. Damp, sandy soils are the perfect substrate for burrowing and litter-living invertebrates, including centipedes, cockroaches and spiders. Often, behind the dunes are swampy areas or central soaks at water table level. Spike Rushes and aquatic plants in these areas offer shelter and special space needs for frogs, which, in turn, attract Red-bellied Black Snakes, tiger snakes and others. Always on the lookout for prey are the opportunistic, predatory Lace Monitors.

Classic Frogs and Reptiles: Common Eastern and Wallum Froglets; Moaning Frog; Spotted Grass-frog; Southern Toadlet; Slender, Bleating, Peron's and Leaf Green Tree-frogs; Alpine Tree-frog; Lesueur's Frog; Western Spiny-tailed, Marbled and Thick-tailed Geckoes; Burton's Snake-lizard; Common Scaly-foot; Western Heath, Bearded, Spotted, Western Bearded and Painted Dragons; Jacky Lizard; Eastern Water Dragon; Gould's Monitor; Lace Monitor; *Cryptoblepharus boutonii*; Tussock Rainbow-skink; Copper-tailed, Weasel, Delicate, Cunningham's, Lowlands Earless and Metallic Skinks; Robust Ctenotus; Tussock Cool-skink; *Lerista* spp.; Oak Skink; Pink-tongued Lizard; Blotched Blue-tongue; Western and Eastern Blue-tongues; Diamond Python; Common Tree Snake; Eastern Small-eyed Snake; Common Death Adder; Bardick; Red-naped Snake; Black-bellied Swamp Snake; Copperhead; Dugite, Yellow-faced Whipsnake; Black Tiger Snake; Red-bellied Black Snake; Eastern Brown Snake; Bandy Bandy.

Above, top to bottom: Leaf Green Tree-frogs live in coastal swamps and lagoons in eastern parts of Victoria, New South Wales and Queensland; Yellow-faced Whipsnake.

Saltbush and Bluebush

"I'd like to see green grass again, And watch clear water run,
Away from this unholy plain, And flies, and dust, and sun."

Such are the hopes of an outback character in A.B. "Banjo" Paterson's famous *Saltbush Bill J.P.* verse.

The above description, although a very negative impression of this shrubby environment, gives a good sense of the seemingly bare isolation of the saltbush habitat. Although sparse, saltbush and bluebush are far from barren. A few kilometres east of Yanga Creek bridge, near Balranald in New South Wales, the highway swings through a rare stand of bluish Old Man Saltbush. Early in the morning or at late afternoon (about 4 p.m. or later) this area is visited by one of Australia's most exquisite birds, the White-winged Fairy-wren, with its deep blue and snowy white livery. Male birds flutter among the 2–3 metre densely leafed bushes and perch briefly on the highest points, all the time making their undulating, metallic, sewing-machine-like, "chirirrit-chirrrr-chirirrit-chirrrr …" Quite often, too, on warm sunny mornings, dragons can be seen sunning themselves on the very peak of saltbushes and bluebushes.

Tens of thousands of square kilometres of the Riverina were once covered by a dense scrub of Myall with an understorey of Old Man Saltbush. Today, this saltbush species is rather rare, mostly because sheep and cattle find its highly nourishing leaves delectable. As the name implies, the leaves have a bitter, salty taste to humans. Two major droughts in the nineteenth century, saw saltbush eaten out by sheep (in the first), and edible Myall cut to feed animals (in the second). There are many saltbush species in the family Chenopodiaceae (*Chen* meaning goose; *pod*, foot, in reference to the leaf shape of some early described species), including *Atriplex* and other genera. Many species are perennial, but some are annuals and others ephemeral, appearing for a few months after rain.

Most of the shrublands are on landscapes formed on, or from, the products of deeply weathered land surfaces. Those of the western Riverina are on almost-level alluvial deposits of clays, sands and loams, with the clay-based deposits being deeply cracked. Weathered areas with alkaline soils produce rolling downs of scattered bluebush, some species with small, succulent, pale blue-grey leaves (such as Pearl Bluebush) and others of a deeper green (Black Bluebush); still others bear a silvery fuzz and spines. Another product of the ancient deep-weathering processes has been the development of soil duricrusts (duri being durable; crust, a layer). Some 40 million years ago, groundwater with dissolved iron and silicates, moved down slopes into broad, shallow valleys, where the minerals cemented the soil into porcelain-like crusts. Over millions of years, erosion removed softer layers above the duricrusts and, in places where the new surface was not protected by these resistant layers, went much deeper, leaving the crusts perched as a cap on tablelands or mesas. Ultimately, these tough layers begin to break up into boulders, gibbers, pebbles and gravel on the surface. Added to these are more stones, which are squeezed to the surface because particular clays below seasonally dry out and shrink, later expanding again when they become seasonally wet. Vast gibber plains such as these stretch across much of inland Australia and, where there is winter rain on this gibber country, such as around Woomera, Coober Pedy, White Cliffs, Broken Hill and Rawlinna, great saltbush and bluebush plains arise.

Where Are They? In the winter-rainfall, southern arid zone on texture contrast soils — much of them gibber covered with considerable areas of micro-relief from gilgais and "crabholes". Rainfall of less than 350 millimetres per year.

What Do They Look Like? Dense perennial shrubs to 2 metres high with numerous lower perennial, annual and ephemeral shrubs and grasses in between. Shrubs are often grey-green and, after rain particularly, the common Bladder Saltbush can be a lush green. Pale gibbers are seen in the Tibooburra region and reddish shimmering, "desert varnished" gibbers near Woomera, Oodnadatta and Coober Pedy on plains' downs, plateaus and low hills. Saltbush and bluebush also often form understoreys in woodlands.

Critical Conditions: Cool winters with winter rain; texture-contrast soils; riverine plains and calcareous earths with gilgais and other micro-relief.

Best Examples: *NSW* — Mungo National Park; Hay Plain; Booligal area; north-east of Wentworth and northern Lake Victoria; Milparinka. *SA* — North of Port Augusta; Woomera; Coober Pedy; Oodnadatta; Witjirra National Park; Nullarbor Plain west to Rawlinna (WA).

Sounds: Clattering pebbles; wrens chittering.

Smells: Crushed succulents.

Sensations: Sheer space interrupted only by spiky shrubs.

Frogs and Reptiles of the Saltbush and Bluebush

On the vast saltbush and bluebush lands there are few shelters larger than the bushes. Most fauna is exposed to the weather and to predation. Dense, succulent bluebush and Old Man Saltbush become islands of shade and cover. Bearded Dragons and others utilise the bushes as bases, around which their lives are lived. On cool spring mornings, they perch in the sun on the apex of the bush. On hot summer days they retire to the bush's shaded core. Similarly, smaller Jacky Lizards dart across the open spaces from bush to bush, tussock to tussock. These shrub islands are also secure areas for small mammals, invertebrates, fairy-wrens and other birds, so they act as pantries for roaming insectivorous and carnivorous skinks, dragons, goannas and snakes.

Classic Frogs and Reptiles: Water-holding Frog; Trilling Frog; Fat-tailed Diplodactylus; Eastern Spiny-tailed Gecko; Beaded Gecko; Bearded Dragon; Mallee Dragon; Military Dragon; Central Netted Dragon; Red-barred Dragon; Thorny Devil; Lined Earless Dragon; Perentie; Gould's Monitor; Pale-rumped Ctenotus; Desert Skink; Western Blue-tongue; Eastern Blue-tongue; Shingleback; Woma; Children's Python; Carpet Python; Common Death Adder; Desert Death Adder; Yellow-faced Whipsnake; Red-naped Snake; King Brown Snake; Small-scaled Snake; Ringed Brown Snake; Western and Eastern Brown Snakes; Myall Snake; Bandy Bandy.

Flora of the Saltbush and Bluebush

Scientific research at Kinchega National Park, east of Broken Hill, has shown that some ancient bluebushes are the true elders of Outback plant communities. Some were twice the age of River Red Gums and their incredible root systems plumbed water from the depths of the soil, with some roots sinking 15 metres into the deep, Darling River floodplain soils. Above, a dense covering of small but fat, succulent leaves are protected from evaporation by their smoky-white, powdery covering, which reflects the light and heat. Apart from the dominant bluebush, saltbush and copperburrs, these are the lands of a multitude of daisies. Completely bare spaces may sometimes exist between saltbushes but, after infrequent rains, annuals and ephemerals make their brief appearance, particularly small white Dwarf Sunray Daisies and magnificent pink Koonamore Daisies. Pearl and Black Bluebush and the Old Man, Bladder, Mealy, Pop and Cottony Saltbushes, along with the common nitrebush, are common chenopods.

Left, top to bottom: The Nullarbor limestone plateau is scattered with Pearl Bluebush and ephemeral herbs; a saltbush-covered sand plain in the Flinders Ranges, South Australia; starkly beautiful Breakaways Plain, north of Coober Pedy, South Australia, is saltbush land.

Birds of the Saltbush and Bluebush

My favourite stand of Old Man Saltbush is on a bend of the Sturt Highway near Yanga Lake, New South Wales. Here, on almost every occasion I visit, I hear the undulating, metallic voice of the White-winged Fairy-wren and, in a truly magical moment, presently a male bird dressed in immaculate deep blue and white perches on the crown of a bush to investigate the interloper. Flocks of Red-rumped Parrots also visit the area, as do Galahs and corellas.

Above: White-winged Fairy-wrens are commonly seen perched on termite mounds in saltbush and bluebush country.

Classic Birds: Wedge-tailed and Little Eagles; Black and Whistling Kites; Black–shouldered and Letter-winged Kites; Spotted Harrier; Brown Goshawk; Australian Hobby (both races); Nankeen Kestrel; Brown and Black Falcons; Australian Bustard; Plains Wanderer; Australian Pratincole; Inland Dotterel; Banded Lapwing; Common Bronzewing; Crested Pigeon; Diamond Dove; Bush Stone-curlew; Cockatiel; Galah; Mulga Parrot; Major Mitchell's Cockatoo; Budgerigar; Scarlet-chested Parrot; Black-eared Cuckoo; Spotted Nightjar; Fork-tailed Swift; White-winged Fairy-wren; Striated Pardalote (race: *substriatus*); Rufous Fieldwren; Redthroat; Slender-billed Thornbill; Barking Owl; Barn Owl; Southern Whiteface (race: *leucopsis*); Crimson Chat; Orange Chat; Gibberbird; Jacky Winter; Chestnut-crowned Babbler; Cinnamon Quail-thrush; Chirruping Wedgebill; Crested Bellbird; Willie Wagtail; Ground Cuckoo-shrike; Black-faced Woodswallow; White-backed Magpie; Australian and Little Ravens; Little Crow; Singing Bushlark; Australian Pipit; White-backed Swallow; Brown Songlark.

Unfortunately, in the drought of 1845, Charles Sturt foretold the future for saltbush and bluebush shrublands when he wrote of his campsite at Depot Glen, after just six months of his occupation with around 200 sheep and horses:

> *The vegetable kingdom was at a stand, and there was nothing either to engage the attention or attract the eye. Our animals had laid the ground bare for miles around the camp, and never came towards it but to drink … The axe had made a broad gap in the line of gum-trees which ornamented the creek, and had destroyed its appearance.*

Thirty-six River Red Gum trees had been cut to roof over a huge creek-bank dugout, their protection against the incredible 57.5°C daytime heat in the shade. However, for at least another century few savvy readers had enough environmental knowledge to heed Sturt's warning!

RED KANGAROOS — MASTERS OF DROUGHT

Australia's shrublands and grasslands are the preferred habitat of the world's largest macropod, the elegantly adapted, highly mobile Red Kangaroo. After measuring more than a million Red Kangaroos in the late 1960s to early 1970s, I found the oldest "Big Red" was more than 20 years old and weighed 98 kilograms. In normal times, these highly social kangaroos avoid disturbance, staying close to their favoured grasses, such as Woollybutt and Danthonia, which grow, among other places, on the saltbush/bluebush speckled plains within 5–10 kilometres of a water source. While there is a source of green feed, 15–24-month-old females undertake their breeding cycles (oestrus) over a 35-day sequence until after 33 days a tiny, immature jelly-bean-sized joey is born and attaches itself to a teat. With two days of oestrus still to go, she mates once again and a miniscule 0.25 millimetre, 25-cell fertilised embryo (called a blastocyst) remains attached to her uterus wall in a state of suspended growth. With all of her breeding options accounted for, the female Red Kangaroo then goes out of oestrus for eight months while she suckles her joey.

Remarkably enough, if for some reason the pouch young is lost and suckling ceases, the female immediately comes back into oestrus if there is green feed around. The blastocyst commences to grow and, after its gestation of another 30 days or so, is born and makes its way to the pouch. In her remaining few days of oestrus, the female mates again — again taking out an insurance policy by attaching a spare embryo to her uterus wall. She knows well enough that when the inevitable drought comes and local feed disappears, her pouch young may be lost. When there is no green feed, hormones suppress her oestrus cycle and development of the blastocyst does not begin until the drought breaks or until she begins a long-distance movement to green feed somewhere else.

Incredibly, the blastocyst's state of suspended animation can last for almost a year. For 330 days (and very possibly more) it waits, attached to the uterus wall, until green feed presses its mother's reproductive trigger and it fires into development and life. With such uniquely adapted breeding and birth control, coupled with the ability to travel long distances to find food if necessary, Red Kangaroos are truly the masters of food scarcity by drought. However, in good times they are rather sedentary, only becoming semi-nomadic if needs be. If there is a critical limiting factor to their survival, it is water supply. When natural waters dry out, they must move away. The wool industry largely removed this environmental constraint by providing tens of thousands of dams and bores. Red Kangaroo populations rocketed and these large marsupials remained longer on drought- and sheep-decimated pasture, further worsening habitat destruction.

Mammals of the Saltbush and Bluebush

Apart from Red Kangaroos, which are easy to spot from the air on sunny spring days as they lie with their pale stomachs and legs out on the lee side of bushes, the list is small. A number of small and medium-sized mammals have been lost from these communities because of radical changes to cover and food — eaten out by sheep, which find the shrub communities very much to their taste. Stick-nest rats, Western Barred Bandicoots, Burrowing Bettongs, Woylies, Eastern Hare-wallabies and nailtail wallabies have suffered local extinction in much of this habitat. Planigales survive living in the protection of deep fissures in cracked soil. With human management to protect habitat, the Southern Hairy-nosed Wombat survives in reserves in South Australia.

Above, top to bottom: Southern Hairy-nosed Wombat; the Kultarr, a nocturnal insect- and spider-eating marsupial, occupies this habitat. *Left:* Male Red Kangaroos can grow very large and are often heavily muscled and extremely strong.

Classic Mammals: Red Kangaroos; Short-beaked Echidna; Common Dunnart; Fat-tailed Dunnart; Striped-faced Dunnart; Kultarr; Narrow-nosed Planigale; Southern Hairy-nosed Wombat; Common Wallaroo; Gould's Wattled Bat; Little Broad-nosed Bat; Plains Rat; Forrest's Mouse; Fawn Hopping-mouse.

Heathlands

LEGEND
■ Wallum
■ Temperate

Above: This plant community map shows only Australia's largest heathlands; however, there are many that are too small for the map scale but are nevertheless absolutely crucial for the survival of some species, such as the Ground Parrot and the Eastern Bristlebird.

Previous pages: Low heath covers rocky terrain that sweeps down to the sea at Two People's Bay near Albany, Western Australia.

Heathlands

Australia's heathlands (at less than 2 metres high) can almost be considered miniature, stunted rainforests! Their dense, closed, layered canopies thrive with a diversity of flowering plant species. Yet unlike rainforest, heath is a tough community suited to life in tough places. Rainforest contains a number of storeys, but heath is usually only a dense canopy above a low herbaceous layer of grasses, sedges, herbs and ground-hugging ferns. The components of the soil, whether of country rock or wind-blown sand, determine the distribution and type of heath. Formidable conditions with thin, sandy, infertile soils — sometimes overloaded with minerals such as sea salt and frequently in drought — coupled with usually windy locations, combine to stunt these communities. Some heaths must survive in very cold places; others in hot environments — yet others are frequently scorched by fire. Heath plant species must be adapted to preserve moisture, to be fireproof or to rise phoenix-like from the ashes. The mix of plants and animals in heath communities heavily depends upon the timing of the last fire.

Despite harsh environmental conditions, heathlands produce brilliant flowers and sufficient shelter and food to nourish a dynamic community of small animals, especially nectar-eating mammals, birds, reptiles and insects. Beneath the dense canopy of heathland flora, some small animals construct "animal expressways" that link feeding areas with nesting areas. Small stands or thickets of taller shrub, such as mallee or banksia thicket, greatly increase the variety of animals that inhabit the heathland ecosystem. Just as nutrients can be deficient in dry areas, some wet areas pose similar problems. A different suite of heath plants have evolved to effectively build "wet heath" communities in such places. In subtropical and tropical areas, particularly on infertile or trace-element-deficient coastal sands, a form of tall heath called Wallum grows. Limiting environmental factors such as drought, saturation, fire, infertile soils, chemical contamination (salt) and exposure to strong winds have all selected out only those plants (and associated animals) that are able to resist these environmental problems and go on to reproduce a similarly well-suited next generation. This is the true meaning of adaptation

Above, top to bottom: Short coastal heath grows on sand dunes on the granite coast near Remarkable Rocks, Kangaroo Island, South Australia; dense, low heathlands spread across the plains surrounding the Devils Backbone, Hartz Mountain National Park, Tasmania.

— once adaptation has taken place, the "new" plant no longer only fits the old environment. A new species has been born, a heathland organism. There is usually no return to the place from whence its ancestors came, certainly not without undergoing generations of further environmental testing and genetic change in order to suit the ancestral environment once again.

Heathland plant adaptations produce communities that are highly distinctive, and their differences are much more obvious than the differences between forests and woodlands, for example. Under severe environmental duress, heath plants survive as diminutive structures with hard, small leaves that, in order to reduce water loss, are sometimes little more than needles, such as those of needlebushes and some paperbarks. To further resist desiccation these leaves are packed with green chlorophyll below a surface of thick transparent waxes. The "breathing" stomates under the leaves are protected by cells that almost close the pores if dehydration threatens. Many species have leaves rich in aromatic oils (for example, tea-tree oil).

Because many heathland soils are acidic, very low in phosphates and nitrogen and cover sandstone surfaces or a shallow pan layer, root systems must spread wide and shallow to absorb the required goodness from the soil. Species of banksia, hakea, grevillea, mallee and some peas have knotty root stock, from which the adventitious roots spread. Under the buried root stock bark are many dormant buds — plant insurance policies against wildfire, which is highly damaging to these flammable leaves with their protective waxes, oils and masses of small leaves borne on fine twigs. Beneath the fireproof corky bark of banksias, some needlebushes and mallee-form angophoras lie protected buds that can flourish after fire. Other herbaceous plants, such as many ground orchids, burst into flower a season or two after fire and shower numerous tiny seeds, ensuring that some will fall down into cracks in the ground and germinate some years before the next fire. Acacias have another trick — their seeds are covered with a hard skin, known as a testa, which requires a blazing fire or an extensive period of weathering or abrasion to break through the skin and allow water to start the germination process. In a further act of defence, a sweet, ant-attracting addition to acacia seeds encourages ants to collect them and store them underground.

Western Australia is by far the richest State for heathland floral species, with 1875 heath plant species in one exemplary national park alone. South Australia is home to 403 species; a Victorian lowland heathlands park, 477; Tasmania, 406; a south-east corner park including highland heath, 541; Hawkesbury sandstone national parks, such as Brisbane Waters north of Sydney, 745; subtropical Queensland Wallum coast and granite belt heathlands, 468; tropical Queensland, 165; the Top End of the Northern Territory, 146; and the Western Australian Kimberley, 98. From these statistics of species composition, and from the abundance of similar South African flora, it becomes clear that heathland has strong ancestral links with Gondwana and was later enriched by tropical flora from Asia. Today, there is intense competition between species for a place in the heathland community. Such competition, especially to attract insect and bird pollinators, has led to the evolution of a striking variety of floral and faunal counterparts that are wholly or significantly dependent upon heathland. While we revel in brilliant wildflower displays during springtime walks, it is even more fascinating to delve deeper — to search for pollinating animals and to sift through the intricate evidence of recently burned areas, to see for ourselves exactly why heathland plants are such successful survivors. However, first let us discover what we can about the short "wet" and "dry" heaths and the taller, warmer Wallum country.

Above, top to bottom: Verdant coastal heath on the granite Cape Le Grand National Park, near Esperance, Western Australia; mountain heath swathes the sandstone tops at Kanangra–Boyd National Park, south of Katoomba, New South Wales; short coastal heath covers the sandstone foundation around Marley Lagoon, Royal National Park, New South Wales.

Where Are They? Mainly exposed coastal slopes and sand plains with low soil fertility (including micronutrients) and/or low moisture levels. Also found on exposed mountain tops with thin, low-fertility soils, from Ballina (NSW) to Port Lincoln (SA) and Tasmania and in south Western Australia from Cape Arid to Albany, Kalbarri and Jurien/Eneabba. Wet heath grows on seasonally waterlogged soils, where tree seedlings fail to survive periods of poor aeration. When they do, there is a shortage or imbalance of soil nutrients.

What Do They Look Like? Dense, low (less than 2 metre high) communities with scattered higher thickets. Heath leaves are usually small, often stiff, waxy surfaced, spiky and flammable. There is a spectacular variety of colour and form in flowering species. Trees occur only where there is a sudden change in ground geology and/or surface geography.

Critical Conditions: Low soil nutrients, particularly phosphorous; seasonally droughty or seasonally waterlogged soil; some areas under influence of excessive cyclic salt; some lack of trace elements.

Best Examples: *Qld* — Moreton and Stradbroke Islands; Girraween National Park. *NSW* — Bundjalung National Park; Yuraygir National Park; Crowdy Bay National Park; Myall Lakes National Park; Brisbane Water National Park; Ku-ring-gai Chase National Park; Blue Mountains National Park; Sydney Harbour National Park; Kanangra–Boyd National Park; Royal National Park; Barren Grounds Nature Reserve; Morton National Park; Jervis Bay National Park; Ben Boyd National Park; Kosciuszko National Park; Nadgee Nature Reserve. *Vic* — Croajingolong National Park; Port Campbell National Park; Wilsons Promontory National Park; Grampians National Park. *Tas* — Mount William National Park; Freycinet National Park; Southwest National Park; Frenchmans Cap; Cradle Mountain–Lake St Clair National Park; Mount Field National Park; Walls of Jerusalem National Park. *WA* — Cape Le Grand National Park; Fitzgerald River National Park; Cape Arid National Park; Kalbarri National Park; Nambung National Park; Badgingarra National Park; Wongan Hills area, Stirling Range National Park.

Sounds: Wind in the bushes; bird calls.

Smells: Floral, sweet and spicy leaves.

Sensations: Wind on the face; spacious freedom.

Short Heathlands

The country we had traversed in our route still consisted of the same sandy plains and undulations, covered with low shrubs, heathy plants, grass and cabbage trees, with here and there elevations of granite … very little wood was to be met with anywhere, and nothing that deserved the appellation of trees … Deep gorges or valleys are met with, through which flow brackish or salt-water streams.

Edward John Eyre, traversing what is now Australia's finest heathland, Fitzgerald River National Park, in June 1840.

Eyre, the first European to experience this astounding heathland with its 1800 plant species, unfortunately missed seeing it in all its flourishing glory because he walked through it in mid-winter (somewhat ironically trudging along in the freezing rain after spending four months struggling across the Great Australian Bight on the brink of death from dehydration). Fitzgerald River country heathlands are arguably the richest heathlands on the planet. Remarkably, their incredible floral diversity grows on extremely thin, droughty soils, many of them affected by salination. Southern exposure to the cold westerlies results in a later spring than that experienced on the east coast (or for that matter 1000 kilometres north at Kalbarri — the site of another great Western Australian heathland national park). Acacias flower first, in July, followed by such spectacular oddities as kangaroo and cat's paws, Royal Hakea, crimson Beaufortias, Yellow Trumpets, exquisite ground orchids, some 25 or more *Grevillea* species and approximately 208 species of the Myrtaceae family, blooming in waves right through to December. The combined effect of droughty soil and salt places most of the area into a "dry heath" category. However, environmental factors are never homogenous, so heath communities will always be a mosaic of heath types. There will be wetter places, more fertile pockets and areas located where they are less affected by fire. If one visits an area often, one comes to recognise these different types of blended heath communities.

LIVING THE SWEET LIFE

A habitat that produces such a profusion of nectar-producing, flowering plants must also entice an abundance of nectarivores. Heathlands draw in honeyeating birds, many of which are races of "nomadic" eastern birds that follow the successive seasonal flowering from the heaths of Kalbarri National Park to later-flowering southern coast heathland, such as that of Fitzgerald River. The slender, curved beaks of these specialist honeyeaters are designed to fit certain floral forms, such as banksia flower spikes. For the Western Spinebill, an exquisite curved bill and hummingbird-like hovering allow it to sip grevillea nectar from more than 25 species of these plants at Fitzgerald River. The Purple-crowned Lorikeet is another heathland regular, equipped with a narrow bill and a brush-tipped tongue perfect for lapping nectar from the mallees on the heath.

Also reliant on a diet of pollen and nectar is the uniquely specialised Honey Possum, which inhabits the short Western Australian heaths. So different is it from its marsupial cousins that the Honey Possum is the sole surviving member of the Tarsipedidae family, the last branch of a long-extinct family tree. A little shorter and lighter in body weight than the House Mouse, the Honey Possum uses its long, prehensile tail and monkey-like toes, which have expanded pads on the

Above, clockwise from top: Typical short coastal heath with low Old Man Banksia, grevilleas and grass-trees and a dense, vibrant ground cover of bush peas, Boronia, Guinea Flowers, sedges, grasses, ground orchids, Necklace Fern and numerous other low plants; coastal heath at Nadgee Nature Reserve in New South Wales is dominated by hakea following very severe bushfires sixteen years before; heathland wildflowers bloom in a riot of colour at Walpole–Nornalup National Park, Western Australia; mixed heath and sedgeland on Barren Grounds Nature Reserve, behind Kiama, New South Wales. *Opposite, top left:* Short heath on sandy soil fringes the blue arc of Two Peoples Bay Nature Reserve, Western Australia.

Above, top to bottom: Fire plays a significant role in renewing short heathlands, especially because many wildlife species rely on food plants that flourish many years after a fire; heath on the Nadgee Nature Reserve, New South Wales, in July 1972; the same tract of land in Nadgee is burned to mineral soil following a devastating wildfire in December 1972.

last phalange of the toes and a small upper nail (similar to the feet of the Tarsier) to grip leaves and twigs. Like many of the small heathland mammals, it makes spasmodic movements, leaping about the banksia spikes. Its eyes are situated towards the top of its long, pointed and narrow head, and its mouth is armed with rudimentary pegs for teeth and a long, brush-tipped tongue. A nocturnal animal, it sleeps by day in disused birds' nests and hollows, such as in broken-down grass-trees. This exquisite little animal breeds up to twice a year, carrying two or three young in the pouch for eight weeks. Similar to kangaroos, it can also carry a delayed implant (a dormant, fertilised embryo attached to the uterus wall). However, a penalty of becoming so superbly adapted to its environment is that it now finds few places in which to live. This "square peg" can now only fit into square holes! A serious threat to the vitality of its heathland community, such as root rot disease, could suddenly eliminate such a dependent, specialised species.

FIRE — DISASTER OR SPECIES DIVERSIFIER?

As for most habitats, fire plays a significant role in maintaining the complex composition of the heath. Long-term studies, as conducted on the south-eastern Australian heaths at Nadgee and Barren Grounds Nature Reserves, have demonstrated that these communities pass through a series of continuous phases or successions, and at each stage various mixes of plant species (at various ages) supply food and shelter for dependent mixes of animals, also at various stages in their life cycle. At any time, a dynamic balance is achieved (and then altered) by changing the mix of species as they age. Thus the endangered Ground Parrot finds the short heath habitat at its most favourable about nine years after a fire, when there is cover but also a plentiful supply of its sedge seed food (*Leptocarpus* spp.). Similarly, a number of native rodent populations respond best when particular mixes of plants combine to form the optimum density of shelter and food. As each of these herbivores build their biomass, so too predators build their populations on this expanding food supply. Initially, birds such as the Nankeen Kestrel thrive while cover is light. Harriers build later, particularly where there is adjacent swamp or taller wet heath. Soon after fire, when young, protein-rich regrowth shoots and the short-lived grassland phase begins, grey kangaroos and wallabies benefit and their populations increase prolifically.

At Fitzgerald River National Park, one small cross-section measured before a fire registered 23 species. A year later that same plot registered 45! Individual fires initiate radical habitat change. If an area is burned too often and the surviving vegetation is repeatedly burned at an immature stage, the species that comprise later-phase ecosystems could well face extinction. The opposite, although unlikely, scenario occurs when fires do not eventuate. Then a few dominant plants such as casuarinas ultimately crowd other species, depleting the soil seed store, which dies before it can germinate. The best fire practice in heaths seems to be those that allow various ages of vegetation across the community. However, the habitat must be large enough to nourish such a blend of organisms — size of habitat is also extremely important in preserving the special spaces required by fauna.

Despite its superficial similarities, each section of short heath has differing environmental factors that are revealed on closer inspection. One heathland studied at Nadgee showed no less than four "types" of heath; another at Marley Lagoon in Royal National Park had three types, each with its own suite of plants and animals. Like the flourishing, specialised ecosystems of the rainforest, these most abundant "dryland" heaths are very complex structures indeed.

Above, clockwise from top left: Red-browed Finch; New Holland Honeyeaters follow the flowering coastal heath; Scarlet Robin; White-eared Honeyeaters. *Top right:* A tiny Honey Possum uses its elongated nose and tongue to probe a banksia flower for nectar. *Bottom right:* Mainland tiger snake.

Birds of the Short Heathlands

The sheer variety of flowering heathland plants results in a long flowering season, which produces nectar over an extended period in this habitat and in adjacent woodlands. Banksias, in particular, flower heavily, and most of the Proteaceae family depend upon birds for cross-pollination. For this reason, short heathland is alive with joyous birdsong, as New Holland, Tawny Crowned and Yellow-faced Honeyeaters, Friarbirds and Little and Red Wattlebirds forage for nectar. Many of the species also nest in dense heath shrubs. Delicate Southern Emu-wrens stay close to the ground as they dart through the heath. The green-and-yellow-speckled Ground Parrot sometimes surprises bushwalkers when it dashes out of undergrowth and rapidly flies low across the canopy before dropping to the ground and fleeing — a retreat behaviour not unlike that of Stubble and Brown Quails, which also inhabit the heaths. Emus once also dwelt in the coastal heathlands, but they have long since retreated, except for in areas south of Evans Head in New South Wales. The main predatory birds are the Brown Falcon and Australia's smallest falcon, the Nankeen Kestrel.

Classic Birds: Noisy Scrub-bird; Western Bristlebird; Ground Parrot; Crimson Rosella; Eastern Rosella; Yellow-tailed and Short-billed Black-Cockatoos; Rainbow and Purple-crowned Lorikeets; Red-capped Parrot; Rock Parrot; Eastern Bristlebird; White-eared Honeyeater; Brown Honeyeater; Brown-headed Honeyeater; Tawny-crowned Honeyeater; Little Wattlebird; Brown Quail; Striated Fieldwren; New Holland Honeyeater; White-cheeked Honeyeater; Eastern and Western Spinebills; Beautiful Firetail; Emu; Brown Hawk; Kestrel; harriers; Common and Brush Bronzewings; Horsfield's Bronze-Cuckoo; Superb Fairy-wren; Variegated Fairy-wren; White-winged Fairy-wren; Blue-breasted Fairy-wren; Southern Emu-wrens; Spotted Pardalote; Heathwrens; Inland Thornbill; Brown Thornbill; Pipit; Scarlet Robin; Eastern Yellow Robin; Eastern and Western Whipbirds; Olive Whistler; Willie Wagtail; Australian Raven; Forest Raven; Little Crow; Dusky Woodswallow; Chestnut-breasted Mannikin; Beautiful Firetail; Red-browed Finch; Silvereye.

Mammals of the Short Heathlands

The most successful mammals here survive on rich flower and nectar supplies, copious seeds of some sedges and grasses, and green leaves. The largest are Eastern Grey Kangaroos, Western Grey Kangaroos (in Kalbarri and Fitzgerald River National Parks), Red-necked Wallabies and Swamp Wallabies in south-eastern Australian heaths, and Bennett's Wallaby in Tasmania. The New Holland Mouse is the smallest.

Classic Mammals: Honey Possum (the only mammal that is totally confined to the heath); Swamp Rat; New Holland Mouse; House Mouse; Bush Rat; Eastern Pygmy-possum; Mosaic-tailed Rat; Broad-toothed Rat; Macleay's Marsupial Mouse; Dusky Marsupial Mouse; White-footed Marsupial Mouse; Potoroo; ringtail possums; Short-nosed and Long-nosed Bandicoots; Dingo; Eastern and Western Grey Kangaroos; Tammar Wallaby; Swamp and Red-necked (Bennett's) Wallaby; Red-bellied Pademelon; Common Wombat; Short-beaked Echidna.

Frogs and Reptiles of Short Heathlands

Short heathlands are dry places cut by swampy, or at least damp, drainage lines with resident frogs that move out onto the short heath in rainy weather. The reptiles tend to spend most of their lives in the warmer, drier heath, slithering into the marshy areas to prey on frogs and, in the case of tiger snakes, yabbies. Numerous skinks also live in the heath.

Classic Frogs and Reptiles: Red-bellied Black Snake; Haswell's Frog; Common Eastern Froglet; Turtle Frog; Lesueur's Frog; Leaf Green Tree-frog; Blue-tongues; Dwarf Litter Skink; Lace Monitor; Cunningham's Skink; Bearded Dragon; Ground Gecko; tiger snakes; Eastern Brown Snake; Copperhead; death adders; Diamond Python.

Above: A dramatic granite tor in Waychinicup National Park, Western Australia, is surrounded by heathlands in flower.

Above left, top to bottom: Boomerang Triggerplant (*Stylidium breviscapum* subsp. *erythocalyx*); Grass-leaf Triggerplant (*Stylidium graminifolium*); Slender Riceflower (*Pimelea linifolia*); Rosy Riceflower (*Pimelea ferruginea*). *Centre, top to bottom:* Southern Cross (*Xanthosia rotundiflora*); Cranbrook Bell (*Darwinia meeboldii*); Pink Rainbow (*Drosera menziesii*); Native Wisteria (*Hardenbergia comptoniana*). *Right, top to bottom:* King Spider Orchid (*Caladenia hueglii*); Wallflower Donkey Orchid (*Diuris corymbosa*); Zebra Orchid (*Caladenia cairnsiana*); Purple Enamel Orchid (*Elythranthera brunonis*).

Flora of the Short Heathlands

What may look like a fairly homogenous habitat is actually hiding a number of subtle environmental differences. These differences are not so much in the genera of plants from which the heath is constructed, but in the particular species. Distinguishing factors are soil moisture, subsoil depth, perched water table, soil nutrients and trace elements — even the nature of the wind and weather after the last wildfire. These things and more play a major role in the variety of plants present and their distribution. So numerous are the representatives of some plant families that the following list is mainly in family groups, rather than species. In a Sydney sandstone heath there could be 1000 or more species, while a heath in Fitzgerald River National Park in Western Australia has 2000.

Classic Plants: *Dry Heath:* Banksias; dryandras; isopogons; grevilleas; paperbarks; darwinias; Kangaroo and cat's paws; tea-tree; acacias; hakeas; bottlebrushes; grass-trees; Parrot Pea; daviesias; Pink Heath and other Epacrids; boronias; borreas; lomandras; Purple Flag; *Leptocarpus tenax;* ground orchids (post fire); Scrub She-oak; hoveas; pultenaeas; mallees; verticordias; kunzeas; beaufortias; starflowers. *Wet Heath:* Banksias; tea-trees; paperbarks; Coral Heath; Pink Swamp Heath; Conestick; Wax Plant; sedges; *Gahnia* spp.; rushes; Coral Fern; Bladder Wort.

Above left, top to bottom: Hood-leaved Hakea (*Hakea cucullata*); Many-flowered Fringe Lily (*Thysanotus multiflorus*); Emu Tree (*Hakea francisiana*); Prickly Dryandra (*Dryandra falcata*). *Centre, top to bottom:* Scarlet Banskia (*Banksia coccinea*); Rough Honey Myrtle (*Melaleuca scabra*); Milkmaids (*Burchardia umbellata*); Pink Fairy Orchid (*Caladenia latifolia*). *Right, top to bottom:* Albany Bottlebrush (*Calistemon glaucus*); Fine-leaved Darwinia (*Darwinia acerosa*); Acorn Banksia (*Banksia prionotes*); Red and Green Kangaroo Paw (*Anigozanthos manglesii*).

Above: The Basket Flower (*Adenanthos obovates*) flowers in heathlands from late autumn through to early summer.

Where Are They? From Taree (NSW) to Broad Sound (Qld) on coastal, sandy lowland areas and nearby wetter areas with a high water table.

What Do They Look Like? A ragged, tall heath with tall, emergent Wallum Banksias and a floor that is saturated, if not flooded, in the wet season.

Critical Conditions: Extremely infertile silica-rich soil; tropical coastal seasonal conditions; very high water tables that may flood in the wet season. A bumpy micro-relief of the soil surface allows plants unable to live in saturated soil to survive.

Best Examples: *Qld* — Eurimbula National Park; Teewah Coloured Sands; Great Sandy National Park; Noosa River and Lake Cooloola; Fraser Island; Moreton Island; Broadwater National Park; Bundjalung National Park.

Sounds: Chattering honeyeaters; the bell-like call of the Wallum Froglet.

Smells: Flying-foxes; musky banksia nectar.

Sensations: The rasp of the *Ghania* Saw Sedge; squelching ground; wet feet.

Above: New Holland Honeyeater on Wallum Bottlebrush.
Right: Typical Wallum heath on Fraser Island, Queensland.

Wallum

When one assesses the geological, climatic and soil nutrient factors that determine how heathland grows, it comes as no surprise to find that as we move north up Australia's east coast to a higher-rainfall climate, short heath grades into a wetter heath and then into a taller heath-like scrub about Broad Sound on the Queensland coast. This heath is given the name Wallum, the Aboriginal word for the ubiquitous banksia that characterises this habitat, *Banksia aemula*.

From Taree, in New South Wales, northwards, rainfall over the coastal low heaths increases to range from 1016–1778 millimetres per year. Heathland communities beyond Broad Sound in Queensland are more influenced by the tropical climate, which produces a dry season drought and a high-rainfall wet season. From Broad Sound, the coastal heaths become almost unrecognisable. Northwards of Lake Macquarie the nature of the land changes. South of the lake most heathland is on raised coastal land with a rocky base. Those who have visited the south coast will know that, until the Gippsland Lakes are reached and with the exception of Illawarra, the coast is characterised by short beaches, small estuarine lakes and magnificent, heathy headlands. The north coast from Newcastle onwards is quite different. It is a low coast with sweeping beaches, wide lakes, significant wetlands, large estuaries and spaced headlands — a coast that runs on to the deep sands of the Gold Coast, Moreton Bay, the Great Sandy Islands, Wide Bay and the lowlands of the Fitzroy delta.

The reason for all of this sand along the coast from northern New South Wales is that sea levels fluctuated on many occasions over the past million years, isolating hills and mountains, which became archipelagoes off the "new" north coast. This geological change is evident from the lookout on North Brother Mountain, near Laurieton (NSW), where a spectacular panorama of lakes, mountains, beaches and wetlands is laid out. Cape Hawke Lookout provides a similar view over the Wallis Lake area. During these sea level changes, huge volumes of current-carried sands were trapped in the sandspits and bars that linked the islands and cut off the lagoons beyond the now-enclosed bays. Sea sand becomes fertile only after long

Flora of the Wallum

Wallum develops in places with high water tables, summer flooding, warm weather and very acidic soils — areas that are usually on low, sandy coastal country near coastal lagoons and/or river systems. When sandy country rises from such areas (as in the Great Sandy Islands) and soils dry out, some moisture-loving species, such as Broad-leaved Banksias and callistemons, cannot survive — opening up the canopy to more light and increasing the dry land heath species, such as boronias and bush peas.

Classic Plants: Prickly-leafed Paperbarks; Thyme-leafed Honey Myrtles; Sweet-scented Hakea and other hakeas; Fern-leafed Grevilleas on drier soils; banksias; Christmas Bells; Wallum Boronias; Wallum and Green Wallum Bottlebrushes; Swamp May and other leptospermums; Epacrids; Wallum Waxflower; a number of tussocky grasses; sundews; *Gahnia* spp. and other sedges; and the Coastal Grass-tree.

Above, clockwise from top left: Yellow Flag; paperbark sp.; Dune Fan-flower; *Acacia lasiocalyx*; Golden Grevillea; *Dillwynia* sp.; *Leptospermum rotundifolium*; Swamp Banksia. *Left:* There are many areas of Wallum on Fraser Island. This area, near Boomerang Lake, is dominated by Wallum Banksia, Coastal Grass-tree, needlebush, kunzeas and melaleucas.

Above: A Scaly-breasted Lorikeet dines on the sweet nectar of a grevillea.

Birds of the Wallum

Like other forms of heath, Wallum is a rich producer of flowers and nectar. Spectacular Wallum plants are the Golden Parrot Tree (*Grevillea pteridifolia*), various paperbarks and bottlebrushes, all of which attract significant numbers of honeyeaters such as Noisy Friarbirds and the Little Wattlebird (especially on the Great Sandy Islands). Other birds attracted by the flowers are Rainbow and Scaly-breasted Lorikeets. Because there is swampy land and open water nearby, the Wallum provides nesting sites and shelter for waterbirds, such as White-faced Herons, Black Bitterns, Striated and Night Herons and Azure Kingfishers. Rainbow Bee-eaters are winter visitors.

Classic Birds: White-faced Heron; Rufous Night Herons (if creeks are nearby); Black Bittern; Little Bittern; Swamp Harrier; Black-shouldered Kite; Nankeen Kestrel; Brown Falcon; Lewin's Rail; Australian Spotted Crake; Common and Brush Bronzewings; Emerald Dove; Yellow-tailed Black-Cockatoo; Rainbow Lorikeet; Scaly-breasted Lorikeet; Little Lorikeet; Eastern and Pale-headed Rosellas; Ground Parrot; Brush Cuckoo; Fan-tailed Cuckoo; Little Bronze-Cuckoo; Pheasant Coucal; Grass Owl; Tawny Frogmouth; White-throated Nightjar; Azure Kingfisher (near creeks); kookaburras; Rainbow Bee-eater; Noisy Pitta (in wet areas); Eastern Bristlebird; Superb Fairy-wren; Variegated Fairy-wren (race: *lamberti*); Red-backed Fairy-wren; Southern Emu-wren; White-browed Scrubwren; Brown Thornbill; Little Wattlebird; Noisy Friarbird; Blue-faced Honeyeater; Noisy Miner; Lewin's Honeyeater; Yellow-faced Honeyeater; White-eared Honeyeater; Fuscous Honeyeater; Tawny-crowned Honeyeater; New Holland Honeyeater; White-cheeked Honeyeater; White-throated Honeyeater; Eastern Spinebill; Scarlet Honeyeater; Dusky Honeyeater; Eastern Yellow Robin; Eastern Whipbird; Grey Shrike-thrush; Leaden Flycatcher; Rufous Fantail; Grey Fantail; Willie Wagtail; Spangled Drongo; Varied Triller; Barred Cuckoo-shrike; Grey Butcherbird; Torresian Crow; Green Catbird; Regent Bowerbird; Chestnut-breasted Mannikin; Red-browed Finch; Tawny Grassbird; Silvereye.

periods, once plant successions and organic matter build up. Where sandy areas endure heavy seasonal rainfall, much of this "organic topsoil" is washed away. Thus coastal heath areas on these sandplains come under increased nutrient stress the further north one ventures. The soils are very high in silica but deficient in many elements such as nitrogen, phosphorous, potassium, calcium, sulfur, copper, zinc and molybdenum, the last three being essential trace elements. A direct result of the nutrient-deficient soil is that the number of species in the heath decreases. Only those species that can endure very low nutrient levels coupled with an annual drought of several months, followed by saturation for three or four months, are able to survive.

In this environment, even those species that are "survivors" require specialised adaptations. The eponymous Wallum Banksia grows on slightly raised sandbanks in the swampy heath and has large, leathery, 12–15 centimetre leaves that grow around green-coloured flower spikes, which when pollinated form hardy, massive seed follicles. In wetter areas, Wallum Banksia is replaced by a fairly similar plant — Swamp Banksia (*Banksia robur*). The Swamp Banksia has leaves up to 30 centimetres long and 8 centimetres wide, and its flower spikes are blue-green when immature, opening to a yellow-green when mature. Both species have deep brownish-red, heavy and finely figured wood with attractive, rusty-brown young growth. *Banksia robur* probably received its species name because the wood reminded the taxonomist of that of the English Oak (*Quercus robur*). English settlers were besotted with the English Oak, naming all of the casuarinas "Oaks", because of the perceived likeness of the wood.

The grotesque heavy trunks of these banksia species, covered as they are with corky bark, serve very useful purposes. They protect epicormic buds that allow these banksias to vigorously re-shoot from root stocks and the trunk if leaves are destroyed by fire. The bark also provides micro-relief — the bumpy, variable surface features that give many plants a secure seedbed high above the seasonally fluctuating water table — which is crucial in maintaining the diversity of Wallum habitat. Seeds are then protected in their environment until the time is right for them to flourish. And, when they do flourish, the results are truly magnificent. Prickly-leafed Paperbarks, Thyme-leafed Honey Myrtles, Sweet-scented Hakeas, Fern-leafed Grevilleas, banksias and more create a brilliantly coloured, cacophonous habitat where honeyeaters chatter and majestic Yellow-tailed Black-Cockatoos fly in to crack open the hard, wooden follicles of hakeas and banksias.

Above: Yellow-tailed Black-Cockatoos are frequently seen in this habitat when hakeas and banksias are seeding.

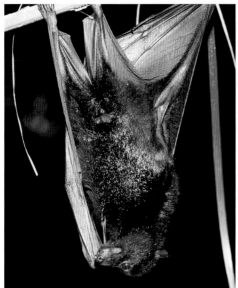 

Above, clockwise from top: Spotted-tailed Quolls appear to be making a comeback in some areas of South-East Queensland Wallum; Sugar Gliders feed on the sweet nectar and sap of grevilleas; Black Flying-foxes form large, noisy camps in paperbark trees surrounding Wallum heath.

Mammals of the Wallum

This prolific flower-producing habitat with sheltering vegetation attracts numerous honey-seeking mammals. Especially dominant are the large bats, the Least Blossom Bat, Eastern Blossom Bat and the Eastern Tube-nosed Bat. Sharing the trees with them are Sugar Gliders and Feathertail Gliders. The Delicate Mouse, the Eastern Chestnut Mouse and the Bush Rat work the ground floor and low branch levels, while the Water-rat fishes the swamp waters and pools for crustaceans, invertebrate larvae and fish. The voracious Yellow-footed Antechinus will take any small prey that crosses its path while Northern Brown and Long-nosed Bandicoots terrorise the subsurface invertebrates. Most southern Wallum areas also lie over the southern distribution of the delightful, carnivorous Spotted-tailed Quoll. Echidnas, which are surprisingly good swimmers, also don't mind this damp habitat.

Classic Mammals: Swamp Wallaby; Platypus (if streams pass through the Wallum); Short-beaked Echidna (in drier parts); Spotted-tailed Quoll; Northern Quoll (both quoll species are poisoned by the Cane Toad and may be considered locally extinct across much of this habitat); Yellow-footed Antechinus; Common Dunnart; Common Planigale; Northern Brown Bandicoot; Long-nosed Bandicoot; Common Ringtail Possum; Eastern Pygmy-possum; Feathertail Glider; Long-nosed Potoroo; Black Flying-fox (particularly if paperbarks form an emergent canopy); Queensland Tube-nosed Bat; Queensland Blossom Bat; Little Northern Mastiff Bat; Little Bent-wing Bat; Greater Broad-nosed Bat; Little Cave Bat; Water-rat; Fawn-footed Melomys; Grassland Melomys; Eastern Chestnut Mouse; Swamp Rat.

Frogs and Reptiles of the Wallum

Because these habitats are dominated seasonally by warm freshwater, rich with invertebrates, Wallum attracts many frogs, and even has its own frog, the Cooloola Tree-frog. In late winter, a "Tching … Tching … Tching", like the tinkling of a small bell, signifies that the Wallum Froglet is starting to breed. Of note is the Green and Golden Bell Frog, pictured below. Plenty of amphibians mean plenty of reptiles, including a number of dragons and the Lace Monitor, one of the most formidable lizards. Green Tree Snakes are common in the taller Wallum, searching out bird nests and preying on smaller bat camps. Keelback snakes prey on frogs, tadpoles, lizards and fishes; they can even successfully devour small Cane Toads without fatal consequences. Highly venomous Common Brown Snakes can be found in the Wallum, but the most prevalent reptiles are pythons such as the Eastern Carpet or Diamond Python and the Spotted Python, which luxuriate in the humid, wet and warm environment of the Wallum.

Classic Frogs and Reptiles: Tusked Frog; Common Eastern Froglet; Wallum Froglet; Fletcher's Frog; Eastern Banjo Frog; Ornate Burrowing-frog; Spotted Grass-frog; Great Barred Frog; Red-backed Toadlet; Green Tree-frog; Cooloola Tree-frog; Bleating Tree-frog; Lesueur's Frog; Leaf Green Tree-frog; Cane Toad; Thick-tailed Gecko; Common Scaly-foot; Bearded Dragon; Jacky Lizard; Two-lined Dragon; Eastern Water Dragon; Gould's Monitor; Lace Monitor; *Ctenotus robustus*; Copper-tailed Skink; White's Skink; Eastern Blue-tongue; Carpet or Diamond Python; Brown Tree Snake; Common Tree Snake; Eastern Small-eyed Snake; Black-bellied Swamp Snake; Eastern Tiger Snake, Red-bellied Black Snake.

Above, top to bottom: Green and Golden Bell Frog; Diamond Pythons find suitable humid habitat in the Wallum.

Grasslands and Herbfields

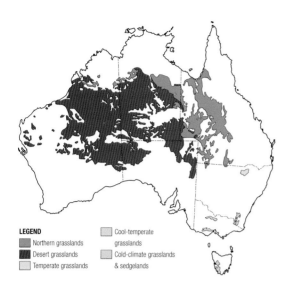

LEGEND
Northern grasslands
Desert grasslands
Temperate grasslands
Cool-temperate grasslands
Cold-climate grasslands & sedgelands

Previous pages: Tropical grassland of native sorghum or speargrass, bent over after a "knock-em-down" storm. Monsoon woodland adds a touch of greenery to the background.

Above: Bunch grasses, probably Flinders Grass, grow on the plains of western Queensland. *Right:* The haughty Australian Bustard is the camouflaged king of this grassy realm.

Grasslands and Herbfields

March 27, Camp 20: The whole country passed over today is excellent pastoral country … Sixteen and a half miles [26.5 kilometres], over beautifully grassed, very gently sloping, and undulating country; rising ground seen to the west, in the distance. [Next day] Beautiful weather; dews at night. At ten miles [16 kilometres], struck and crossed a box creek, where it empties itself into a flat; passed over splendid country. A quarter of a mile [0.4 kilometres] further on is another box creek. Any traveller caught here in rainy weather, such as has been lately deluging these vast plains, would to a certainty, be washed away — there is not a knoll six feet [2 metres] high within range of the eye. [Two weeks later] Rode over pretty thickly timbered spinifex rise of considerable length, and for the last five miles [8 kilometres] over plains with light belts of timber here and there … vast numbers of gulahs [sic], curellas [sic], macaws [sic], cockatoo parrots, hawks and crows here.

John McKinlay, near Diamantina Lakes National Park, Queensland, in 1861, during his incredible journey (twice the distance of that of Burke and Wills) to find Burke and Wills.

McKinlay's journey took him from Adelaide to the Gulf of Carpentaria and down to Rockhampton for fresh animals, before crossing back to Adelaide. On the way, he had the pleasure of encountering and describing the great tropical and arid grasslands of Australia. His Journal, and his detailed surveyor's annotated maps, show very clearly how the tropical and arid grasslands were being extensively fire-managed by Aborigines, even at the tail-end of the wet season in April. He also noted the preponderance of termites in the grasslands.

EMPIRES OF THE SUN

Grasslands have been called "empires of the sun". Long-term and seasonal drought over many thousands of years has filtered out certain unsuitable species and modified the survivors and their descendants. Ever since the continent drifted into the tropical, north-west monsoon regions, the yearly climate has been divided into the Wet and the Dry, and random cyclonic rain depressions bring torrential rains during the Wet (1861 was such a year). The Dry is just that: extremely dry, inhospitable and parched.

About 100 million years ago, the eastern edge of the continent began a slow wrinkling. Ultimately, this geological movement lifted the Great Divide (a north–south continental condensation trap), which drained the onshore, humid easterly winds of their water. With no high ranges in the interior, Australia has a heartland of drought. Sweltering summer heat and bountiful sunshine beats mercilessly down on desiccated and "tired" nutrient-deficient ancient soils, on some sweeping, moderately fertile alluvial plains, and on stony stumps of ancient ranges and endless dunefields. These environmental ingredients support tropical bunch grass, tussock grassland and arid hummock grasslands that provide habitat for the greatest diversity of reptiles on the planet. They also provide for other specially adapted animals, from invertebrates through to mammals.

Above: Mitchell grasses, of which there are four species in the genus *Astrebla,* are some of the most productive grasses of north-western New South Wales and south-west Queensland.

In temperate Australia, too, there are conditions that suit temperate tussock grasslands, including plains on the Monaro and western districts of Victoria, which were formed from large volcanic flows. Fertile, deep clay soils in these regions are cracking soils, which, when dried out, shrink and form wide, deep fissures. Such chasms would effectively rip apart the roots of large plants. High Country, which is too cold for effective tree growth, supports sod-tussock grasslands that are also found in wide valley frost hollows sometimes too wet for trees. Each of these grassland habitats encourages distinct suites of interdependent animals.

THE REALM OF RECYCLERS

All successful ecosystems must allow for members to be fed, and all food chain consumers depend on a critical source: producers. Primary producers are plants, which convert the sun's radiant energy, water, gases and minerals (the plant's food) into organic material. Water and atmospheric gases are in continuous circulation. Similarly, many of the minerals are moving in cycles, although this cycle occurs much more slowly, sometimes over aeons. If minerals are consumed or lost from the environment, replenishing them may take much longer than the life spans of many generations of plants. Living systems, like organisms, also have lifetimes. Over billions of years of evolving together, exquisite shortcuts in mineral recycling have appeared in the form of countless microbes, invertebrates and fungi. The living world above the litter on the floor is mirrored by a world of life below. Inhabitants of this "underworld" rely on consuming the used organic matter that drops from above. Organisms of this realm below the litter (such as protozoans, bacteria, fungi, algae, nematodes, worms, arthropod adults and larval stages) are also compulsive users of water and atmospheric gases in their warm environment. These are the living recyclers — critters that break down the dead organic litter raining down from above (as well as their own litter) and convert it into reusable minerals. The golden rule is that both worlds, and all creatures in them, depend on each other for life — the shunt between all species is the recycling process.

With such dependence on the tiny recyclers of the leaf litter, grasslands and other arid and semi-arid communities face a problem. One essential element for the creation of a happy underworld is scarce: water. Perpetual drought makes it all but impossible for many of the microbes and fungi to survive. Mineral recycling is almost at a standstill for much of this country most of the time. Even worse, very low available nutrient in these ancient land surfaces means they require more efficient recycling than most other lands. Despite these challenges, this land still supports grasslands and scrublands, and a tiny miracle worker that maintains the food supply of the "upper world" — the termite. Some years ago, while working in Kakadu National Park, we mowed the fast-growing speargrass on Cannon Hill airstrip and knocked down the fresh ant hills. By sunset the strip resembled a hay paddock. Later that night we returned. In the headlights, the flattened grass appeared to be shivering. Closer scrutiny revealed trillions of tiny, creamy-white bodies clipping the fallen grass into 1 centimetre lengths. Each then had a termite fastened to one end and was marched away. By morning these energetic mini-beasts had taken all of the cut grass underground, where, in the humid environment, fungi and bacteria (some in the gut of the termites themselves) would turn the grass into free nutrients. One way or another, this energy was going back into the ground, ultimately to grow more grass and give us some more work the next year!

Right, top to bottom: Typical of much habitat above the tree line, this valley near Club Lake in Kosciuszko National Park is a mosaic of sod-tussock grassland of snow grass, herbfield and Snow Daisy with low alpine shrubs; wire grass around Lake Dove in Cradle Mountain–Lake St Clair National Park, Tasmania.

Above: Bootlace Oak, a *Hakea* species, rises above tropical grassland on the western edge of the Barkly Tableland in the Northern Territory.

Below right: Tropical grassland bordered by green, spindly Pandanus trees near Fogg Dam Conservation Park in the Northern Territory.

Where Are They? In a broad belt of summer rainfall between the northern monsoon woodlands and forests from Derby, sweeping around to the Channel Country and the New South Wales border area, inland to the 500 millimetre isohyet. Especially on the floodplains of the Georgina, Diamantina, Thompson, Bulloo, Warrego, Culgoa, Flinders and Leichhardt Rivers.

What Do They Look Like? Grassy plains and downs to lightly timbered savanna and woodland. On the coast they can blend with open tropical woodlands.

Critical Conditions: Summer rainfall on medium–heavy textured soils on floodplains and undulating hills.

Best Examples: *NSW* — Moree Plains; Goodooga area; Sturt National Park. *Qld* — Bulloo Downs; Longreach; Winton; Diamantina Lakes National Park; Matilda Highway near Burke and Wills Roadhouse. *NT* — Barkly Tableland; Victoria River (Wave Hill). *WA* — Halls Creek area; middle Fitzroy River area.

Sounds: Galahs; Budgerigars; the "swish-sh-shing" of walking through grass.

Smells: Dry, hot hay.

Sensations: Space; distance; singular isolation.

Northern Grasslands

... a Spinifex hill or range close on the right, good open country travelled over; creek on the left, about two miles [3 kilometres] off, alluvial deposits on plain, over which we travelled for six and three-quarters miles [11 kilometres]... plenty of feed, and numerous traces of Emus ...

Typical of John McKinlay's 1861 journey across plains at the head of the Diamantina River, Qld.

It is difficult to tell where northern grasslands begin and end. Towards the coast they merge with open tropical woodlands, which often have a wet season understorey of dense, tall annual grasses (particularly on coarse soils). Speargrasses dominate in places where annual burning-off is common. In drier places Darwin Woollybutt and Stringybark, Smooth-barked and Long-fruited Bloodwoods, Darwin Box and Scarlet Gum become more scattered and the community becomes savanna. On the northern grasslands' arid zone edge, grass species mix with aridland Curly and Feathery Spinifex before being dominated by the spiny hummocks of "desert" spinifexes. These grasslands also cover medium-textured soils, as on major floodplains of the Georgina, Diamantina, Thompson, Bulloo, Warrego, Culgoa, Flinders and Leichhardt Rivers — the famed paradise lands of Bluegrass, Mitchell and Flinders Grasses, all prime fattening fodder for Red Kangaroos, Antilopine Wallabies and cattle. Grasslands, however, produce much more than mere stalks of grass. They are the granaries of the world and sustain vast populations of grain feeders. Weevils, ants, termites, parrots, cockatoos, finches, Emus, geese, pigeons and even humans rely on grains. However, seeds are very dry food and, wherever animals principally eat grain, there must be a

nearby water supply. Wherever you see finches, you can be certain there will be water in the vicinity. When water does come unexpectedly, it is often in torrents. Termites of the northern grasslands must construct their "cities" in such fashion to protect them from drowning during the wet season and from being roasted in the dry season. Mounds are fluted, towering, brick-hard structures composed of clay mixed with termite "saliva", and are impervious to water. With vertical corrugations and "blobby" eaves, much of the wall area is shaded. Another very effective shading technique is practised by the "magnetic anthill" species. At midday, its quite thin, sheet-like tower a couple of metres high and a metre or so wide is oriented due north–south, with its widest walls receiving only the most oblique rays at the hottest time of day. Later, in the arid hummock grasslands section, we will look at what happens inside the colony.

Flora of the Northern Grasslands

Northern, or tropical, grasslands have a double environmental advantage over the hummock spinifex grasslands of the arid interior. In the north, they receive a fairly regular annual replenishment of water and, for those on the floodplains of monsoon-flooded rivers, a layer of flood-borne silt to rejuvenate the topsoil. Apart from the Channel Country, with its incredible network of flooding rivers, billabongs and creeks that support Mitchell and Flinders Grasses, soils of the ancient arid zone land surfaces are in an exhausted condition and are very deficient in nutrients, particularly phosphates and nitrates. However, much of this country has experienced these environmental hardships for so long that there are many plants that have adapted to living under such conditions.

Classic Flora: Queensland Bluegrass; Curly Bluegrass; Mitchell Grass; Flinders Grass; kangaroo grasses; various native sorghums (such as *Sorghum australiense; S. stipoideum; S. plumosum; S. intrans*); various *Aristida* spp.; the wire grasses (such as Three Awn, Erect Kerosene and Northern Kerosene Grasses and Feathertop Wire Grass); Fine Armgrass; Buffel Grass; Ribbon Grass; Beetle Grass; Awnless Barnyard Grass; *Eragrostis* spp. such as Clustered Lovegrass, Sickle Lovegrass, Neverfail, Handsome Lovegrass; Wandarrie; Silky Browntop; Bunch Speargrass; Swamp Grass; Australian Wild Rice; Native Millet; Curly Spinifex; Rat's Tail Grass (declared); Australian Dropseed; Prairie Grass; Silky Heads; Cotton Panic Grass; Umbrella Grass; various bottlewashers; Umbrella Canegrass.

Above, top to bottom: The Brown Falcon hunts low over the grassy plains and frequently lands to catch large grasshoppers, lizards or small mammals such as the Long-haired Rat; termites are an essential recycling element in the grassland community and their tall mounds are frequently seen jutting from the plains. These are in Undara Volcanic National Park in Queensland.

Birds of the Northern Grasslands

Grasslands are the "empire of the sun", and if global warming persists we shall see a lot more of them before the century's end. That is, of course, if the instability created as the planet changes leaves enough soil behind! On these wide open lands shelter must be either underground or within the sward itself. Birds have a great advantage, being able to move by air from adjacent shelter and water to and from their grassland food source (primarily grass-seed). Small birds that burn off energy very rapidly, such as finches, cannot stray too far from water. Larger birds also supplement their diet of grain with juicy invertebrates and may stay away longer and cover greater distances. Even larger birds, those that can store even more energy (such as parrots and cockatoos) are airborne wanderers of the grasslands. Red-tailed Black-Cockatoos and corellas can climb to higher, windy altitudes and use the currents to help them in their travels. The largest bird of all, the Emu, mixes his diet with succulent berries and invertebrates and, like the Bustard, can stay grassland-bound the longest.

Classic Birds: Emu; Australian Bustard; Gouldian Finch; Stubble Quail; Great Egret; White-faced Heron; Straw-necked Ibis; Brolga; Black Kite; Black-breasted Buzzard; Wedge-tailed Eagle; Square-tailed Kite; Spotted Harrier; Black-shouldered Kite; Letter-winged Kite; Nankeen Kestrel; Brown Falcon; Black Falcon; Little Button-quail; Red-chested Button-quail; Plains Wanderer; Bush Stone-curlew; Australian Pratincole; Oriental Plover; Masked Lapwing (race: *miles*); Flock Bronzewing; Crested Pigeon; Diamond Dove; Little Corella; Cockatiel; Major Mitchell's Cockatoo (race: *mollis*); Galah (race: *roseicapilla* and *albiceps* in south-east); Red-winged Parrot; Northern Rosella; Cloncurry Ringneck; Budgerigar; Black-eared Cuckoo; Pheasant Coucal; Barn Owl; Grass Owl; Red-backed Kingfisher; Rainbow Bee-eater; Variegated Fairy-wren (race: *assimilis*); Red-backed Fairy-wren; Willie Wagtail; Australian Magpie; Australian Raven; Pied Butcherbird; Singing Bushlark; Australian Pipit; Zebra Finch; Double-barred Finch; Welcome Swallow; Fairy Martin; Rufous Songlark; Brown Songlark.

Above: Crested Pigeons, a species of bronzewing pigeon, are a true bird of temperate and arid grasslands.

Above, clockwise from top left: Pale-headed Rosella, the north Queensland form of the rosella parrot; Red-winged Parrots are at their most common in central Queensland, preferring habitat with a grassy understorey; Double-barred Finches inhabit grassland in an arc from the Victorian border northwards to the Kimberley, WA; in the 19th century, Brolgas were common on Victoria's Western District plains, now they are mostly seen dancing on grassy northern plains; the beautiful Gouldian Finch is a grass-seed-eating finch that has suffered a severe decline in numbers.

Frogs and Reptiles of the Northern Grasslands

In such dry areas, amphibians require special adaptations to help them conserve water. Water-holding frogs fill up with surface water before digging a shaft and covering themselves with mucus that dries into a waterproof sleeve, protecting them until further rain dampens the soil and the frog can return to the surface. For reptiles, this warm to hot habitat rich in small mammals and also the domain of vast numbers of insects and other invertebrates is paradise. Skinks, dragons and monitors are plentiful. Outstanding are the Centralian Blue-tongue, Western Blue-tongue and Common Blue-tongues, Shingleback, Thorny Devil, Military, Central Netted and Central Bearded Dragons. Pythons are well represented by a native Australian group, *Aspidites*, including the Black-headed Python and the Woma — both devour venomous snakes, which are common in grasslands, where the heavy cracking soils provide "crab holes" and large crevices as shelter from heat and cold.

Classic Frogs and Reptiles: Striped Burrowing-frog; Australian Burrowing-frog; Green Tree-frog; *Litoria inermis*; *L. latopalmata*; Desert Tree-frog; Spiny-tailed Gecko; Tessellated, Bynoe's and Beaked Geckoes; Burton's Snake-lizard; Hooded Scaly-foot; Ring-tailed, Central Netted and Gilbert's Dragons; Speckled Earless Dragon; Gould's Monitor; Storr's Monitor; Robust Skink; Chocolate Skink (*Ctenotus strauchii*); Grey's Skink; Woma; Eastern Blue-tongue; Shingleback; Stimson's Python; Olive Python; Carpet Python; Desert and Common Death Adders; Yellow-faced and Collared Whipsnakes; Red-naped Snake; Taipan; Small-scaled Snake; King Brown Snake; Ingram's Brown Snake; Ringed Brown Snake; Gwardar; Eastern Brown Snake; Half-girdled Snake; Myall Snake.

Above, top to bottom: Desert Death Adders are smaller and more brightly coloured than their temperate cousins; the Olive Python, one of Australia's largest snake species.

Above, clockwise from top left: During the day, the Spectacled Hare-wallaby stays in a grass-lined tunnel in grass hummocks, coming out to feed at night; male Red Kangaroos can live for about 24 years and, although usually fairly sedentary, can travel as far as 300 kilometres in a week in search of a fresh, green pick; the Rufous Bettong is a nocturnal feeder that shelters in nests of woven grass beneath a tussock by day, emerging to feast on fungi, tubers, seeds and invertebrates at night.

Mammals of the Northern Grasslands

Where there is water and green feed that stimulates their breeding cycle, kangaroos are clearly successful, as high populations attest. Grassland survivors must be protected from the elements and from keen-eyed predators, such as Wedge-tailed Eagles, Black-breasted Buzzards, Little Eagles, kites, falcons and others. Rodents and small marsupials of the grasslands provide these birds with prey. Most grassland mammals are nocturnal and dependent on a cover of darkness. Dingoes range the grasslands, eager to catch a meal at their ambush hideouts near permanent waterholes.

Classic Mammals: Short-beaked Echidna; Northern Quoll; Fat-tailed Antechinus; Fat-tailed Dunnart; Striped-faced Dunnart; Kultarr; Narrow-nosed Planigale; Paucident Planigale; Northern Brushtail Possum; Spectacled Hare-wallaby; Rufous Bettong; Northern Nailtail Wallaby; Agile Wallaby; Antilopine Wallaby; Red Kangaroo; Common Sheathtail-bat; Lesser Long-eared Bat; Little Broad-nosed Bat; Western Broad-nosed Bat; Little Forest Bat; Plains Rat; Western Chestnut Mouse; Long-haired Rat.

Where Are They? Desert grasslands occupy one-third of arid Australia, wherever there are red sands, red clay sands, red dunes and many rocky slopes.

What Do They Look Like? Endless tawny, tight, grassy hummocks about 75 centimetres deep but up to 2 metres when in seed; often with a loose overstorey of *Acacia* species, Desert Oak, mallee and other aridland eucalypts, with *Triodia* species and *Plectracne* species dominating.

Critical Conditions: Infertile, unstructured sandy soils, particularly low in phosphates; hot, arid climatic conditions.

Above: Tough hummocks of spinifex matt a rocky hillside at Ormiston Gorge in the Northern Territory.

Desert Grasslands

I do not know its right name, and have seen it described as "Spinifex", "Porcupine Grass", "Triodia", "Triodia pungens", and "Festuca irritans". Why such a wretched, useless plant should have so many names I cannot say. So often am I bound to refer to it that I might vary the monotony by using each in turn. Spinifex grows in round, isolated hummocks, one to three feet high [30–90 centimetres]; these hummocks are a dense mass of needle-like prickles, and from them grow tall blades of very coarse grass to a height of sometimes six feet [2 metres]. Occasionally the hummocks are not round (hemispherical) or isolated, but grow in crescent form or almost complete rings — however it grows it is most cursed vegetation to walk through, both for men and camels.

Hon. David Carnegie, in *Spinifex and Sand*, 1896 — a record of his explorations in the deserts of Western Australia.

Carnegie, like Giles twenty years before, was an explorer of vast distance in arid Australia. However, unlike Giles, who immigrated to Australia as a boy and saw South Australia as home, Carnegie was a British adventurer from an upper-class family, out in search of gold. While Giles could romanticise the sheer beauty of early sun striking the silvered, feathery crests of hillside spinifex, Carnegie saw it as a "wretched, useless plant", a barrier for both people and camels. Both explorers traversed thousands of kilometres of spinifex and began to realise the truth — that 60% of Australia was desert largely covered by the hummocks of spinifex and Mulga scrub. Value judgements aside (many of which unfortunately set later national perceptions of landscape), Carnegie's superficial description of spinifex — the basis for classifying these arid grasslands as desert, or hummock grasslands — is essentially correct. But let's build some more positive perceptions before we truly explore the desert grasslands.

Although many hummock grasses are commonly called spinifex, the only true species are those in the genus *Spinifex* and are scrambling coastal dune plants such

Above: Desert Spinifex is comprised of a dense clump of very hard, pointed leaves, which act as a protective fortress wall for small mammals and reptiles. The seed is also a valuable food resource.

as Beach Spinifex (*Spinifex hirsutus*). The 33 species in the genus *Triodia* are quite different grasses that apparently acquired the common name spinifex by error, simply because the word spinifex is derived from the Latin *spina*, meaning thorn, and *fex* from *facio*, meaning I make — a more obvious name for desert plants than *Triodia*, which refers to three sharp teeth on the seed. However, the great Carl Linnaeus (the father of binomial nomenclature in 1771), and the naming of the widespread beach plant came first, with Matthew Flinders' botanist, Robert Brown, giving *Triodia*'s description later, in 1810. *Triodia* has another closely related genus with very similar adaptations — *Plectrachne* (from the Greek *plektron*, meaning a spur), which is also commonly called spinifex. This spiny individual is known as Soft Spinifex.

Arid and semi-arid landscapes cover huge tracts of the continent and comprise a number of different plant environments, from sandy plains and dunes to stony ranges. Nutrient deficiency, water and evaporation have been problematic environmental factors for many thousands of years. Thus, many species of *Triodia* have evolved and now cover over 22% of the continent in their purest stands, more than doubling that area where spinifex grows as an understorey to mallee, Mulga, Desert Oak, *Grevillea* species and, in places, Cypress Pine. This being the case, what is the secret of spinifex's success? The plant itself is superbly adapted to an environment that starves plants of nutrients, either through deficient soils or a lack of moisture to carry nutrients to the roots. Spinifex has a lineage dating back to Gondwanan times, when ancestral *Triodia* and *Plectrachne* species lived around exposed arid verges. The best surviving ancestors were those that put down a deep root network of 3 metres or more; developed long, slender, rolled leaves that almost enclosed the narrow stomates; and stiffened with silica crystals and hard "woody" tissue with resin-coated stems and surfaces. Any water gained was not to be easily lost! In this arid environment dead tissue is not quickly removed by decomposition. Instead it dries out and builds up as dense, dry spindly litter locked into the hemispherical hummock of the plant's multitude of tangled stems and needle-pointed, stiffened leaves. The most widespread species, Soft Spinifex (*Triodia pungens*) and Feathertop Spinifex (*Plectrachne schinzii*), are particularly successful because they produce copious amounts of sticky toffee-like resin, used

Above: Dunes on the edge of the Simpson Desert, Queensland, separate wide belts of grassland. Here, near Birdsville, an overflow stream lined with Coolibah runs in from the north.

Above, top to bottom: Desert grasslands stretch before the red rock of Mount Connor, 80 kilometres east of Uluru; Aboriginal people burned spinifex hummocks to trap the food within; rain comes in violent downpours across this country, causing flash flooding and erosion; grassland along the road verges near Oodnadatta, South Australia, flourishes after rain, growing Darling Pea and other ephemeral herbs and grasses.

Above: Desert grasslands near Glen Helen Gorge in the Northern Territory.

Flora of the Desert Grasslands

Plants of the desert grasslands depend upon the volume and timing of the last rainfall. It is the nature of the desert to make use of water while it lasts. One day this habitat is bare, desolate red desert; a fortnight later it may be a paradise of surging, living variety. Just a month on it can flourish into a garden of flowers, carpeted with pink, blue, golden or white daisies, masses of soft, pink-petalled Parakeelya (with fleshy, water-filled leaves) and the crimson and ebony Sturt's Desert Pea. It could even be a rippling sea haze of pink, purple and greenish-golden grass heads moving in the surging wind. This is the desert's conception of life — the outcome of rain in the desert.

Classic Plants: Soft and Buck Spinifex and other *Triodia* spp.; Porcupine Grass; Feathertop Spinifex; wire grasses; Woollybutt; Parakeelya; Ribbon Grass; Blue, Red and Bull Mallee; Sandhill and Desert Bloodwoods; Desert Oak; Ghost Gum; Heath Myrtle; Hairy Mulla Mulla; Dead Finish Acacia; Mulga; Umbrella Bush; Black Gidgee; Witchetty Bush; Needlewood; Corkwood; Honey, Holly, Desert and Rattle-pod Grevilleas; Quandong; Bush Plum; Desert Poplar; Camel Poison Bush; Wallflower Poison Bush; Upside-down Plant; Desert Rose; Jockey's Caps; Desert Raisin; Wild Tomato; various emu bushes and desert fuchsias; various daisies and everlastings.

Invertebrates of the Desert Grasslands

Termites are the most vital recyclers of the arid zone. The desert gives life to the termite and the termite gives life to the desert: the perfect relationship.

Classic Invertebrates: Termites (the main recyclers of spinifex); Meat Ants (*Iridomyrmex purpureus*); Slit-nest Ants (*Rhytidoponera* sp.); Turret-nest Ant (*Polyrachis* sp.); Bull Ant; Scorpions (*Urodacus* spp. and *Isometroides* sp.); beetles, including Jewel and Carabids; Witchetty/ Witjuti Grub (*Endoxyla leucomochla*); Bloodwood Apple Gall Bugs (*Cystococcus echiniformis*); grasshoppers; Gibber Hopper; sand wasps; *Ametrus gryllacrididis*; cockroaches; centipedes; barking spiders.

as a source of glue, called *kiti*, by Pitjantjatjara Aborigines from Uluṟu. This resin was secreted from glands in the stem nodes, from which both leaves and roots grow. Many of the nodes, with their buds, become buried by wind-blown sand and each node can then produce a clone of the parent plant.

Each hummock — and there are millions dotting the sand plains and dunes — is highly flammable. Ignition by lightning or, as was common over the past 50,000 years, by human hand for hunting purposes, caused a very hot and rapidly burning bushfire with a high, sooty smoke cloud. Many of these fires were limited in extent. Now, in spinifex desert grasslands, satellite photographs show fire sometimes laid waste to hundreds of square kilometres. Grassfires are carried by spinifex through Mulga, Desert Oak, *Grevillea* and other associated plant stands, knocking out (or at least slowing) the spinifex's understorey competitors. Spinifex, with its buried nodes, rapidly regrows. Major associated species have lived with the spinifex problem for so long that they, too, have undergone evolutionary changes to protect themselves from fire — such as the thick, insulating corky bark of Desert Oak, Corkwood, Needlewood, Desert Bloodwood and some *Grevillea* species; the long-lasting, buried seed of the Mulga; and the buried buds in the lignotubers of mallees. Unfortunately, when environmental patterns change due to human intervention or climate change, the long-time adaptations that evolved under ancient regimes become outdated and the community faces dire consequences. Increased occurrences of fire mean many Mulga communities are reaching the end of their soil seed stores, and are therefore also reaching the end of the line, being burned again before they have time to flower and seed.

In some places, however, due to the geography of dunes and natural fire barriers (such as claypans), spinifex may remain unburned for very long periods. Desert grassland is naturally of low fertility, so the dense network of roots drains away the available minerals from below the plant. Rambling, subsurface grass stems soak up this moisture, so those buried nodes furthest away from the centre have access, via their new roots, to the most nutrition. Gradually, the starved centre begins to die out while the ever-expanding rim remains healthy, creating a ring of hummocky spinifex. Red Kangaroos and Common Wallaroos find these dense, circular spinifex barriers entirely satisfactory as shelters from cold winter winds, just as the Aboriginal people constructed their horseshoe-shaped windbreaks, or wiltjas, from Mulga branches packed with spinifex. Eventually, the grass edges become so large that they break up into perhaps a dozen circular hummocks.

Above, left to right: Like troops of science fiction "Daleks", the clay castles of the desert termites march across the spinifex-covered plains of the Tanami Desert, Northern Territory; the tiny architects and construction workers of these fortresses built from desert clay and insect digestive juices are billions of tiny termites.

Above: Greater Bilbies were once widespread from the west coast to New South Wales' western slopes, where they lived in long, deep burrow systems that, following their local demise, were later taken over by rabbits. Habitat destruction and the arrival of feral animals decimated the Greater Bilby's population and caused its nearest relative, the Lesser Bilby, to become extinct. The Greater Bilby now survives in the spinifex grasslands of the Tanami and Great Sandy Deserts, where there is a ready food supply of invertebrates, tubers and fungi.

Hummocks of spinifex are citadels for an astonishing diversity of desert life. After a few still days, invertebrate life is evidenced by the intricate patterns of tracks marking the dunes, resembling insect "roads" radiating from desert cities of spinifex or White Foxtails. Sand records the wanderings of centipedes, barking spiders, beetles, dragons, skinks, sand-swimmers, snakes, mole crickets, grasshoppers, birds, hopping-mice and many others, although some of the tinier invertebrates are too light to scar the surface. One such small creature is a tiny black ant that uses sticky resin to cement sand particles and constructs enclosed runways along leaves and stems of spinifex. After a fire, balls of black sandy resin are all that remain of past nests; Aborigines used this knowledge to locate a fine sources of hard, baked *kiti* — the burned resin excellent for tool construction.

HOPPING AMID THE HUMMOCKS

Those immense banks of sand were in truth marked over with their footprints as if an army of mice or rats had been running over them. They are not much larger than a mouse, have a beautiful full black eye, long ears, and tail feathered towards the end. The colour of the fur is a light red, in rising they hop on their hind legs, and when tired go on all four, holding their tail perfectly horizontal ...

Charles Sturt, fascinated by the numerous exquisite hopping-mice — his "Jerboas" — of the sandhill country west of Depot Glen (Milparinka), 1845.

Most dunes in desert grassland have a dry surface on which we can track the lives of desert inhabitants, but they also retain a life-sustaining damp core beneath. There are many intriguing desert adaptations, but in his studies of the hopping-mouse Sturt touched on one of the most common adaptations when he wrote of their burrows, "... tending like the radii of a wheel to a common centre, to which a hole is made from the top of the mound, so that there is communication from it to all the passages". Hopping-mice burrows are about 2 metres long and a metre deep with a 10 centimetre chamber below to accommodate a small community. Often with a central vertical shaft positioned in a spinifex hummock, they provide a humid, cool shelter that is "air-conditioned" and, wisely, has a number of escape routes. These cool burrows, coupled with a diet of green herbs, seeds and some "juicy" invertebrates, alleviate the hopping-mouse's water requirements — they do not need to drink. As in all habitats, animals must develop strategies to adapt to their changing environment in order to remain successful in that ecosystem.

Mammals of the Desert Grasslands

An array of small mammals live in and about dune spinifex and in the great cracks that form when clay soils dry out. Desert sand dunes are wonderful records of animal life. Written in the sands are the movements of nocturnal animals, night activity being one of the most common behavioural adaptations to help avoid dehydration. Regardless of the dunes' surface temperatures (which frequently exceed 50°C), many animals know that the core remains cool and damp. As Sturt discovered, Spinifex Hopping-mice build "air-conditioned" family burrows beneath hummocks, while incredible blind marsupial moles spend their entire lives digging in the sands beneath the surface. Red Kangaroos employ modified physiology. For 300 days or more, a blastocyst (a very young foetus) remains attached to the female Red Kangaroo's uterine wall. This "spare joey" is awaiting further development when rain falls and there is green pick to give the young joey a fighting chance at survival.

Classic Mammals: Short-beaked Echidna; Northern Quoll (marginal northwards); Kowari; Mulgara; Fat-tailed Antechinus; Little Red Antechinus; Ooldea, Long-tailed, Sandhill, Fat-tailed, Striped-faced and Hairy-footed Dunnarts; Ningaui; Pilbara Ningaui; Kultarr; marsupial mole; Greater Bilby; Spectacled Hare-wallaby; Rufous Hare-wallaby; Black-footed Rock-wallaby; Common Wallaroo; Red Kangaroo; Common, Yellow-bellied and Hill's Sheathtail-bats; White-striped and Little Mastiff-bats; Greater and Lesser Long-eared Bats; Gould's Wattled Bat; Little Pied Bat; Little Broad-nosed Bat; Little Cave Bat; Plains Rat; Sandy Inland Mouse; Pebble-mound Mouse; Forrest's Mouse; Spinifex Hopping-mouse; Dusky Hopping-mouse; Long-haired Rat; Dingo.

Above, top to bottom: The beautiful, endangered Bridled Nailtail Wallaby; Spinifex Hopping-mice construct "air-conditioned" burrows beneath spiky spinifex fortresses.

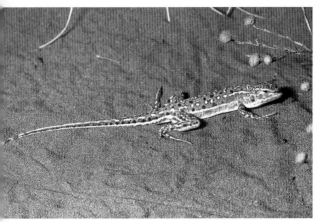

Above, top to bottom: Central Military Dragon; Variegated Dtella; the Trilling Frog is a burrowing species able to cool itself in the moist soil; Leopard Skink.

Above: A true desert dweller, the Thorny Devil can even change colour to fit its immediate environment and has unique body scales that act as a water catchment, with the grooves channelling water to the mouth. The Thorny Devil survives on a diet entirely made up of small black ants.

Frogs and Reptiles of the Desert Grasslands

The desert grassland has a most impressive list of reptiles and some authorities class its western area as the great ancestral region for many of the Australian reptile families. Spinifex habitat sustains some of the richest lizard fauna in the world, particularly geckoes, skinks and dragons, and the below list includes only those most likely to be seen. This habitat is also home to many very timid skink species, particularly *Ctenotus* species, which "swim" through the sand. Southern parts of the northern tropical grasslands merge with desert grasslands, so the two habitats share many species. Two reptiles well represented in the ancestral dreaming of the Pitjantjatjara Aboriginal people are the *Kuniya*, the large carpet snake (sometimes the Woma) and the *Liru*, a highly venomous snake, probably the King Brown. Both the Woma and the Black-headed Python eat other venomous snakes.

Classic Frogs and Reptiles: Trilling Frog (*Neobatrachus centralis*); Water-holding Frog (*Cyclorana platycephalus*); Desert Spadefoot Toad; Main's Water-holding Frog (*Cyclorana maini*); Spencer's Burrowing-frog; Shoemaker Frog (*Neobatrachus sutor*); Desert Tree-frog; Clawless Gecko; Spiny-tailed Gecko; Fat-tailed Gecko (*Diplodactylus conspicillatus*); Jewelled Gecko; *Diplodactylus taeniatus*; Sand Plain Gecko; Tessellated Gecko; Pilbara Gecko (in termite mounds); Bynoe's Gecko; Desert Cave Gecko, Beaded Gecko; Centralian Knob-tailed Gecko; Pale Knob-tailed Gecko (*Nephrurus laevissimus*); Smooth Knob-tailed Gecko (*N. levis*); Beaked Gecko; Thick-tailed Gecko; Marble-faced Delma; Northern Snake-lizard; Sharp-snouted Delma; Excitable Delma; Burton's Snake-lizard; Western Hooded Scaly-foot; Thorny Devil; Ring-tailed Dragon (among rocky, spinifex habitats); Black-collared Dragon; Bicycle Lizard; Mallee Dragon; Central Military Dragon; Dwarf Bearded Dragon; Central Netted Dragon; Painted Dragon; Rusty Dragon; Lozenge-marked Dragon; Blue-lined or Winnecke's Dragon; Pebble Earless Dragon; Gibber Earless Dragon; Eastern Lined Earless Dragon; Sand Monitor; Pygmy Monitor; Perentie; Ridge-tailed Monitor; Short-tailed Pygmy Monitor; Pygmy Mulga Monitor; Black-headed Monitor; Leopard Skink, Wedgesnout Ctenotus; Blue-tailed Finesnout Ctenotus; Buff-tailed Finesnout Ctenotus; *Ctenotus dux*; *C. grandis*; *C. helenae*; *C. leae*; *C. leonhardii*; *C. piankai*; Rock Striped Skink; Schomburgk's Striped Skink; Tanami Ctenotus; Desert Rainbow Skink; Desert Skink (*Egernia inornata*); Great Desert Skink; Night Skink (*Egernia striata*); various *Lerista* spp. (the second-largest group of lizards with reduced legs are sand-swimmers that eat termites and ants); Fire-tailed Skink; Narrow-banded Sand-swimmer; Broad-banded Sand-swimmer; Centralian Blue-tongue; Western Blue-tongue; Shingleback; a number of blind snake species; Woma; Children's Python; Carpet Python; Desert Death Adder; Yellow-faced Whipsnake; Orange-naped Snake; King Brown Snake; Ringed Brown Snake; Gwardar; Eastern Brown Snake; Desert Banded Snake; Narrow-banded Snake.

Birds of the Desert Grasslands

Desert grasslands cover hills, mountain ridges and plains; wherever they are, their sparsity of cover gives sky-borne predators a great advantage. Consequently, birds of prey come from on high, including soaring Wedge-tailed Eagles, Australian Black-breasted Buzzards, and flocks of aerial acrobats such as Black Kites, graceful Black-shouldered and Letter-winged Kites, and agile Nankeen Kestrels. A bird hide concealed near a waterhole repays over and over. My greatest delight is when Spinifex Pigeons gather just out of range then, as a mob, walk in to water. Individuals of the species acting as one body is their greatest defence, apart from sheer cunning. Often the eye is diverted by the flash of green "aerial bullets" — Budgerigars wheeling in a great flock towards water, where, to avoid the predators that always keep close to the water supply, they drop rapidly to the muddy edge for a quick sip. Near the water too are finches, which operate in a similar fashion, knowing that there is usually at least one feral cat (the curse of small birds and reptiles) living nearby.

Classic Birds: Emu; Crested Pigeon; Spinifex Pigeon; Common Bronzewing; Diamond Dove; Crested Bellbird; Striated Grasswren; Eyrean Grasswren; Dusky Grasswren; Rufous Fieldwren; Rufous-crowned Emu-wren; Spinifexbird; Red-backed Kingfisher; Wedge-tailed Eagle; Australian Kestrel; Black Kite; Letter-winged Kite; Black-breasted Buzzard; Spotted Harrier; Brown Falcon; Black Falcon; Australian Bustard; Little Button-quail; Inland Dotterel; Budgerigar; Major Mitchell's Cockatoo; Little Corella; Galah; Princess Parrot; Blue Bonnet; Port Lincoln Parrot; Scarlet-chested Parrot; Mulga Parrot; Night Parrot; Zebra Finch; Painted Finch; Crimson Chat; Black, Grey, Grey-headed, Grey-fronted, Pied, Singing and Spiny-cheeked Honeyeaters; Yellow-throated Miner; Gibberbird; White-winged Fairy-wren; Variegated Fairy-wren; Black-faced, White-browed and Little Woodswallows; Black-eared Cuckoo; Southern Boobook; Barn Owl; Spotted Nightjar; Australian Owlet-nightjar; Inland Thornbill; Banded Whiteface; Hooded Robin; Red-capped Robin; Grey-crowned and Chestnut-crowned Babblers (race: *rubeculus*); Chestnut-breasted Quail-thrush (race: *marginatum*); Rufous Whistler; Willie Wagtail; Ground Cuckoo-shrike; Australian Magpie; Australian Raven; Little Crow; Pied Butcherbird; Torresian Crow (northwards); Australian Pipit; Brown Songlark.

Above, clockwise from top left: Crimson Chats search the desert grassland for recently rained upon areas where they will begin to nest; Black-faced Woodswallows typically perch together in a group; Budgerigars have green plumage in the wild, helping them blend in with their woodland and grassland habitat; the bright-yellow Spinifex Pigeon spends most of its time strutting among the grasses, looking for seeds; small, buff-cheeked Zebra Finches, like other grass-seed eaters, stay in close proximity to water. They make their nests in prickly Dead Finish Acacias.

Above: Budgerigars form large flocks when food is plentiful.

Where Are They? Across small parts of the Darling Downs (Qld), Liverpool Plains and Monaro Gap (Vic), western districts of Victoria, and numerous small pockets of natural grassland set in woodlands and dry temperate forests. Often on human-created grassland.

What do they look like? Plains and undulating downs of knee-deep speargrasses and kangaroo and wallaby grass tussocks. Grazing, fertilising and "pasture improvement" have radically changed species composition.

Critical Conditions: Fine-textured soils; 400–700 millimetres of rainfall; subsoil moisture relatively inaccessible; frosty winters, warm to hot summers; fire tolerant.

Best Examples: *NSW* — Breeza Plain; Gunnedah area; Moree Plains; Cooma to Nimmitabel. *Vic* — Hamilton to Camperdown; Mount Napier.

Sounds: Whispering grasses; cheeky Galahs.

Smells: Fresh-cut to dry hay.

Sensations: Space; big skies; freedom and the bite of the sun.

Southern Temperate Grasslands

We were under no constraint now in selecting a camp, from any scarcity of water or grass; for all hollows in the plains contained some water, and grass grew everywhere. The strips of wood which diversified the country as seen from the hills, generally enclosed a depression with polygonum bushes [Lignum]…a fertile country, enclosed as this is by copious rivers … [June 30] the view was exceedingly beautiful over the surrounding plains … different from anything I had ever before witnessed … A land so inviting, and still without inhabitants! As I stood, the first European intruder on the sublime solitude of these verdant plains, as yet untouched by flocks or herds; I felt conscious of being the harbinger of mighty changes.

Major T.L. Mitchell, in *Australia Felix*, near Pyramid Hill, Victoria, 29–30 June 1836.

Grass is such a common plant that we hardly even notice it and yet, no matter whether we are vegetarian or carnivore, this group of plants maintains our lives. Scientists now believe that climate change in Africa, which changed the habitat of our forebears from forests and woodlands to savannas and grasslands, accelerated human evolution. These changes provided huge tracts of new habitat for herbivores, from tiny invertebrates to the fauna that graces Africa's Serengeti Plain today. Our human ancestors, when faced with the trials of this increasingly dominant and rich environment, over thousands of generations changed the way they moved about the country. Modifications occurred, first in locomotion and then in the DNA of individual genes, producing "genetic mutants" that could stand and walk vertically. These "freaks", our *Homo erectus* forebears, were more effective survivors who could out-distance, out-collect and out-hunt their quadruped, tree-climbing siblings. These highly effective bipeds mated and produced more of their kind, our ancestors. Grasslands, therefore, as part of our genealogical history, deserve our attention.

Above: A typical sample of temperate grasses east of the Flinders Ranges, South Australia — including wallaby grass, wire grass, Soft Brome, Golden-beard Grass and Short-haired Plume.

Above: Mitchell grassland between Goodooga and Brewarrina in New South Wales, growing on heavy grey floodplain soils of the Culgoa River near the end of winter. Mitchell Grass is one of the most important grasses for the grazing industry, and for the maintenance of Red Kangaroo populations. This hardy grass is long-lived, with seeds surviving buried in the soil for up to five years, their germination being dependent on rainfall.

Above: Mitchell Grass, one of Australia's most valued cattle-fodder grasses, covers a recently flooded plain on the overflow of the Warrego River, south of Cunnamulla, Queensland.

EXPLORATION OF THE GRASSLANDS

Aboriginal people survived and thrived on the Australian grasslands for thousands of years, utilising and managing all of the habitat's resources. Europeans, however, eked out a grim, hungry existence in the sandstone woodlands surrounding Port Jackson until they found the Wianamatta shale country on which domestic grasses and crops would flourish.

Three waves of European exploration took place. First came the surveyors — men such as Barallier, Bass, Blaxland, Lawson, Wentworth, Currie, Oxley, Evans, Sturt and Mitchell — who sought to understand where they were in an entirely strange land already peopled with resourceful Aborigines.

Following them were those with specific objectives: principally to find pastoral land and establish within Australia exotic lives for immigrant Britons. These men, such as Throsby, Hume and Hovell, the Henty brothers, Angas, Eyre, Stuart, McKinlay, Burke and Wills, Jardine, Forrest, Brodribb, the Gregory brothers, Baines, and the Duracks, often had an entourage of assistants and frequently had wealthy patrons and financiers — first the government itself and later the growing aristocracy, men such as Elder and Chambers.

The third group, which began with the interest of Joseph Banks and the Royal Society encouraging men such as Caley, Lhotsky, Strzelecki, Sturt, Leichhardt, Giles, Gosse, Kennedy, Spencer and Madigan, were interested in and supported by science. Often they undertook exploration with an additional pastoral or mining motivation (Carnegie, especially, epitomised exploration for mining interests), but they were largely encouraged by the desire to increase scientific knowledge of this continent. The most accurate, detailed observations of wild Australia appear to have been made by the "surveyors", the "scientists", and by Giles, Eyre and Sturt, who explored lands of little economic value. To them, grasslands (and indeed all of the land they traversed) were more than sheep or cattle pastures, but because of the grassland's potential economic value they were always recorded.

Above, top to bottom: Grassland over the north Flinders Ranges, near Leigh Creek, includes spinifex tussocks on the drier range top; cool tussock grassland in drought condition on the Monaro basalt soil south of Cooma, New South Wales; grasslands in northern Mutawintji National Park, New South Wales. Old Gnalta Station, now part of this park, was once owned by "Cattle King" Sir Sidney Kidman and was heavily overstocked. Speargrass is indicative of degraded pasture.

Above: The striking crimson and yellow Cowslip Orchid (*Caladenia flava*).

Flora of the Temperate Grasslands

These lands have distinct winter and summer seasons, with ameliorating spring and autumn. Inland, drought is the dominating influence on this living system, a problem that will increase as global warming increases. One can expect more drought-resistant species and more arid-adapted plants and animals if there is time enough for adaptation to occur. The temperate grasslands provide for a wide variety of plants other than grasses. How that will shift over the next 50 years will demand attention, particularly for agricultural industries reliant on the grasslands and on irrigation. Many species will probably require gene technology for survival. Of all grasslands, these temperate lands will be the ones that will suffer most.

Classic Plants: Kangaroo grasses; wallaby grasses; White-Top; Summer Grass; Hairy Panic; Pale Pigeon Grass; Parramatta Grass; Rough Speargrass; Plains Grass; Common Wheatgrass; Bluegrass; Barbed Wire Grass; Couch Grass; snow grass; Blackhead Grass; Shivery Grass; Silky Brome; Red Brome; Stink Grass; Barley Grass; Australian Bluebell; Tall Sedge; Common Spike Rush; Variable Sword Sedge; Early Nancy; Bulbine Lily; Flax Lily; Nodding Blue Lily; Common Fringe-lily; Wax-lip Orchid; Cowslip Orchid; Tawny Leek-orchid; Lignum; Slender Dock; Creeping Saltbush; Sandspurrey; Common Buttercup; River Buttercup; Native Poppy; Native Stock; Pale Sundew; Gold Dust Wattle; Showy Parrot Pea; Twining Glycine; Kneed Darling Pea; Hairy Geranium; Cat-head Burr; Caustic Weed; Narrow-leafed Hopbush; Wild Gooseberry; River Red Gum; Yellow Box; Red Box; Grey Box; White and Black Sallees; Slender Violet; Spike Centaury; Australian Bindweed; Black-berry Nightshade; *Brachycome* spp.; Cut-leaf Burr Daisy; Rough Burr Daisy; Common Cotula; Common Billy-button; Common Everlasting; Clustered Everlasting; Common Sunray; Scaly Button; Yam Daisy.

John Oxley described the Liverpool Plains, near Gunnedah, NSW, 26 August 1818:

To the east south-east and south-east, clear plains extended to the foot of very lofty forest hills, at a medium distance of from twenty-five to forty miles [40–65 kilometres]. … We found them to consist of a rich vegetable soil; and although, from their vast extent, they may, as a whole, be properly denominated plains, yet their surfaces were slightly broken into gentle eminences with occasional clumps, and lines of timber. Their white appearance was occasioned by the grass having been burnt early in the year, and the young growth killed by the frosts … the soil is a rich, loose loam, of a dark red approaching to black in colour, but of great apparent fertility and strength: some hundreds of kangaroos and emus were seen in the course of the day. We killed several, the dogs being absolutely fatigued with slaughter. The game was by no means shy … indeed I do not think they are much disturbed by the natives.

Major Mitchell describes Victoria's western districts, north-east of Penshurst on 21 September 1836:

We now travelled over a country quite open, slightly undulating, and well covered with tussocks of grass. To the westward the noble outline of the Grampians terminated a view extending over vast plains, fringed with forests and embellished with lakes … One feature peculiar to that country appeared on these open downs: it consisted of hollows, which being usually surrounded by a line of "yarra" gum trees [River Red Gums], seemed at a distance to contain lakes, but instead of water, I found only blocks of vesicular trap [volcanic flow rock]. Some of these hollows were of a winding character, as if they were the remains of ancient water courses [lava tubes]. The genial warmth of spring had begun to show its influence on the plants, and also brought the snakes from their holes, for on this day, it was ascertained that twenty-two had been killed.

Brodribb describes grasslands east of the Latrobe River, Gippsland, May 1842:

We continued our journey, about north-east for several days, over beautiful plains of fine rich land. The plains were intersected with belts of forest, not thickly timbered, and we saw numerous emus from day to day. The natives had burnt all the grass at Gippsland

Above: Western plains, south of Tibooburra, New South Wales — lands of recurrent drought. In the 1901–03 drought, properties in this area lost as many as 80,000 sheep. In 1845, Sturt was boxed into nearby Depot Glen for six months — there being no water within a week's travel.

late in the summer. Heavy rains must have fallen before we reached there ... The whole country was very green. It had here, the appearance of young cornfields, the young grass was about six inches [15 centimetres] high, and in places, very thick.

It is also clear from Brodribb's account that Aboriginal people traditionally burned the grasslands upon which they lived in order to encourage herbivorous game, to protect more sensitive habitats, to "clean-up" sites of religious significance and provide better access, and to farm certain fire-encouraged food species such as Bush Tomatoes (*Solanum* sp.).

ECOLOGY OF THE TEMPERATE GRASSLANDS

Many of the more extensive temperate grasslands occur on chocolate soils derived from volcanic rock. Ecologist Dr Alec Costin, in *A Study of the Ecosystems of the Monaro Region of New South Wales* for the State's Soil Conservation Service (1954), used the example of the Monaro grasslands to show the basic reasons that grass grows in places trees cannot.

The absence of forest communities from the chocolate soils and the dominance of grassland, or savanna woodland, is related to the subsoil constitution. Unlike surface-rooting grasses or the trees of savanna woodland communities, which also obtain much of their moisture from lateral roots near the surface, most of the trees in dense sclerophyll forests derive a large part of their moisture from the deeper subsoil. In coarse-to medium-textured soil, this deeper root penetration goes apparently unhindered by any property of the soil itself; but in fine textured soils such as the chocolate soils, the subsoil is typically so closed and compact that inadequate aeration inhibits deep root development. Even though the subsoil moisture content of chocolate soils in damper areas may be adequate for forest vegetation, its insufficient aeration renders this moisture inaccessible, so that in climates that are apparently suitable for forests, only savanna woodland and grassland can develop. (Note that saturation can also retard adequate aeration.)

Above: Eastern Grey Kangaroos, seen here feeding on southern tableland grasses near Canberra in winter, are commonly featured macropods on the southern temperate grasslands. The patriarch and matriarch of the mob lead them out from adjacent woodland to feed in the late afternoon or early morning.

Above, top to bottom: Eastern Barred Bandicoots survive only in Tasmania and in pockets of western Victoria where foxes are absent or controlled; the Common Planigale is a voracious, nocturnal hunter of invertebrates.

Mammals of the Temperate Grasslands

Grassland productivity can be gauged by the many stone-tool artefacts scattered across the inland claypans — campsites of Aboriginal people who were sustained by the many species that occupied this habitat. Over the past 150 years, these grasslands have fed tens of millions of sheep and near as many cattle. Dams have alleviated the lack of water — once kangaroos' greatest constraint, so some millions of these macropods have thrived. This has all been at tremendous cost to the soil. Birds such as corellas and Galahs benefited from the water as well, but rabbit-sized mammals suffered in competition with the kangaroo. Echidnas, except where grasslands have been replaced by irrigated cotton with heavy pesticide, still find plenty of ants, making grasslands a great place to raise their monotreme young. The role of now-rare small native mammals as food for reptiles and birds has been adopted by plagues of introduced House Mice, which thrive on wheat and grass crops.

Classic Mammals: Eastern Grey Kangaroo; Short-beaked Echidna; Eastern Quoll (Tas); Swamp Antechinus; Common and Fat-tailed Dunnarts; Southern Brown and Eastern Barred Bandicoots; Common Wombat; Tasmanian and Rufous Bettongs (near Pyramid Hill); Tasmanian Pademelon; Red-necked Wallaby (timbered edges); Gould's Long-eared and Gould's Wattled Bats; Lesser Long-eared, Chocolate Wattled, Little Broad-nosed and Little Forest Bats; Mitchell's Hopping-mouse; Swamp Rat; Dingo; hares; rabbits; Red Fox.

Reptiles of the Temperate Grasslands

With warm to hot summers, plenty of invertebrates and small mammals for food, and deeply cracked and broken earth for nests, grasslands suit the lifestyles of many reptiles. However, during cool, frosty winters from the end of April to late August, reptiles will rarely be seen, preferring to go into hibernation.

Eastern Browns, King Browns, Bardicks, tiger snakes and death adders are common, with copperheads present on the coolest edges of these grasslands. Apart from the comparatively short "growth" period, grasslands are usually a tawny colour, making these snakes effectively camouflaged. Visitors to grasslands must be alert and take care — these snakes are quite venomous and deliver strong neurotoxins with their bite. The Eastern Brown, because of its antagonistic behaviour, is particularly dangerous.

As the winter days warm up, some of the lizards will emerge in order to bask, including bearded dragons, which climb to the pinnacle of shrubs such as saltbush or bluebush to sun themselves. Meanwhile, smaller dragons, such as Jacky Lizards, busily scurry across the bare soil patches, darting from grass tussock to tussock.

Classic Reptiles: Eastern Long-necked Turtle; Thick-tailed Gecko; Patternless Delma; Burton's Snake-lizard; Common Scaly-foot; bearded dragons; Mountain Dragon; Jacky Lizard; Eastern Lined Earless Dragon; Mountain Heath Dragon; Gould's Monitor; Robust Striped Skink; Cunningham's Skink; White's Skink; *Leiolopisma entrecasteauxii*; *Leiolopisma guichenoti*; Red-throated Skink; Oak Skink; Blotched Blue-tongue; Eastern Blue-tongue; Carpet Python; Common Death Adder; copperheads; Eastern Small-eyed Snake; Yellow-faced Whipsnake; White-lipped Snake; Red-naped Snake; Black Tiger Snake; Eastern Tiger Snake; Spotted Black Snake (northern areas); Red-bellied Black Snake; Eastern Brown Snake.

Above: Jacky Lizard dragon — one of the reptile speedsters.

Above: Tiger snakes vary in colour slightly over their range, with some having very dark bars around the body.

As for all habitats, variations in country rock, soil quality, drainage, aspect, overall geography and fires shape the ecosystem. In many places, these factors have created mosaics of grassland between temperate woodlands and dry sclerophyll forests, with the grassland playing a vital role in the distribution of animal populations. Grassland areas within the woodlands and forests produce the significant ecological circumstance of "edge effect". An area of forest alone provides habitat for arboreal animals, such as possums, gliders, Koalas and Powerful Owls, but break that mass with patches and strips of grassland and — because of the greater variety of food and because the edge provides far greater security against predators — the area opens up to a greatly increased variety of animals. These patchworks of habitat attract numerous seed-eating parrots, doves, finches, rodents, species of macropods and the like. The majority of such grassland areas, while highly significant, are pockets too small to appear on most vegetation maps at the scale at which they are drawn.

HUMAN IMPACT ON TEMPERATE GRASSLANDS

So many of the temperate grasslands that have played such a significant role in human history in Australia are both the outcome of natural processes and also an artefact of human industry. Artificial grasslands, in the form of wheat, oats, and sorghum fields, are now one of the nation's largest plant communities — a fact that has resulted in vast population increases for many parrot species and almost total local extinction for a number of competing herbivorous marsupials that were better suited to the earlier "un-improved" pasture. Many of the most interesting temperate grassland animals are invertebrates or small vertebrates, such as the small Earless Dragons, which after devouring wolf spiders also usurp their burrows. Grasslands do not inspire the same dramatic attraction as other landscapes, such as the Blue Mountains or Kakadu, so they have not figured greatly as national parks. However, some more forward-thinking governments have established nature and conservation reserves specifically to maintain a level of natural diversity necessary to sustain evolution. The new Kuma Nature Reserve on the Monaro grasslands, a few kilometres south of Cooma in New South Wales, is such an example. While zoos and sanctuaries are the equivalent of unrelated still pictures, useful for protection and education purposes, nature reserves maintain interdependent life stories that are embedded within the habitat. Habitat restoration management is now one of the most difficult yet crucial occupations of the twenty-first century.

Above, clockwise from top: Although small for a bird of prey, the Black-shouldered Kite is a rapacious hunter that will aggressively defend its nest; Barn Owls feast on rodents in the grasslands; Emus wander the grasslands and most other dry habitats searching for a seed or fruit diet; the Long-billed Corella has a beak shape ideally suited to digging up tubers, roots, corns and bulbs. Once relatively widespread, its numbers have declined due to habitat loss.
Right, top: Major Mitchell's Cockatoo, seen here searching inside a Cypress Pine cone for seed, sometimes seeks out an invertebrate dietary supplement beneath bark, but is usually a seed or fruit eater that takes special delight in melons.

Birds of the Temperate Grasslands

Few spectacles in the Australian bush rival that of a snowy cloud of thousands of Little Corellas or chattering Galahs wheeling en masse, turning first into a pink blush then a wonderful pearl-grey haze and screeching all the while. When a River Red Gum is taken up as a perch by these hordes, the tree is often left almost leafless because the birds snip the leaves with their powerful bills. A special delight is to see the Galahs acting like the proverbial "galah", hanging and swinging on one leg while enjoying a sun-shower. In early summer, Old Man Emu can be seen shepherding his flock of up to a dozen brown and cream striped chicks across the plain. The female Emu will be sitting on another clutch of large, textured, deep-green eggs out on the plain. Parrots, cockatoos, finches, pigeons and Emus, with Wedge-tailed Eagles cruising high above, typify the temperate grasslands.

Classic Birds: Emu; Stubble and Brown Quails; Great, Intermediate and Cattle Egrets; White-faced, White-necked and Rufous Night Herons; White and Straw-necked Ibises; Little Eagle; Whistling, Black-shouldered and Letter-winged Kites; Wedge-tailed Eagle; Spotted Harrier; Nankeen Kestrel; Brown Falcon; Red-chested Button-quail; Little Button-quail; Oriental Plover; Masked Lapwing (race: *novaehollandiae*); Banded Lapwing; Crested Pigeon; Long-billed Corella; Little Corella (race: *gymnopis*); Cockatiel; Sulphur-crested Cockatoo; Galah (race: *albiceps*); Eastern Rosella; Red-rumped Parrot; Budgerigar; Blue-winged Parrot; Turquoise Parrot; Pallid Cuckoo; Black-eared Cuckoo; Barking Owl (race: *connivens*); Southern Boobook (race: *boobook*); Barn Owl; Grass Owl; Tawny Frogmouth; Australian Owlet-nightjar; Rainbow Bee-eater; Superb Fairy-wren; Striated Fieldwren; Yellow-rumped Thornbill; Grey-crowned Babbler; Willie Wagtail; Magpie-lark; Black-faced and Dusky Woodswallows (on scattered stumps); Pied Butcherbird; Australian Magpie; Australian Raven; Forest Raven (Tas); Little Raven; Skylark; Singing Bushlark; Australian Pipit; Zebra, Double-barred, Plum-headed and Red-browed Finches; Diamond Firetail; Welcome Swallow; Fairy Martin; Little Grassbird; Golden-headed Cisticola; Rufous Songlark; Brown Songlark.

Above: Typical of the Kosciuszko High Country, snow gums peter out when the cold conditions of the tree line are reached.

Where Are They? On level to undulating High Country, such as plains and downs; 750–2250 millimetres of rain; snow cover for 1–6 months.

What Do They Look Like? They resemble a dense-growing mat of low, very dominant snow grasses appearing as downs, plains or patches.

Critical Conditions: Acidic soils with saturated or otherwise very low-aerated subsoils, which reduces tree invasion but supports shallow-rooted plants such as grasses and heath.

Best Examples: *NSW* — Barrington Tops National Park swamp area; Kosciuszko National Park; Long Plain; Currango Plain; Kiandra area; upper Snowy River; parts of the Main Range, such as Twynam area, Rolling Grounds, Ramshead Range, Cascades area. *Vic* — Hotham area; Dargo High Plains; Mount Bogong; Falls Creek area; Mount Buffalo; Mount Howitt and Wellington Plains; Mount Baw Baw. *Tas* — Cradle Mountain area; Mount Field–Mount Field West.

Sounds: Silence, interrupted on occasion by a humming wind.

Smells: Sharp, clear air.

Sensations: The clear chill of pristine, snow-covered wilderness stretching into the distance.

Above: Only a few specialised plant species survive above the tree line of the Snowy Mountains in Kosciuszko National Park.

Cold-climate Grasslands

By the end of 1839, there were 129 stations in the Monaro. Between them they were running nearly 3000 horses, 75,000 cattle and 200,000 sheep. The human population stood at 1728, made up of 889 free males, 195 free females, 640 assigned convict males, and four assigned convict females. All that was needed to take up land was a 10 Pound [$20] licence fee …

John Merritt, in *Currango Summers*, his excellent 2003 history of Currango Homestead — a fascinating historic site in Kosciuszko National Park, New South Wales.

In these early days of settlement, the Monaro Plateau had a considerably larger population than Melbourne, which had been laid out by surveyor Robert Hoddle just two years earlier. But why had the Monaro proved so attractive to pastoralists? The answer lay primarily with speargrasses (*Stipa* spp.), kangaroo and wallaby grasses and especially with the sod-tussock grasslands (*Poa* spp.), of the higher Monaro Plateau and Snowy Mountains. Despite its popularity, in some ways the Monaro was a pastoral trap, being in the rain shadow of the high Snowy Mountains section of the zig-zagging Great Divide and therefore very prone to drought. By 1834, graziers, such as Murray from Yarralumla, began moving stock onto the higher plains of sod-tussock snow grass and discovered that autumn blizzards killed more stock in just a few hours than half a year of drought. The summer pastures of the high Kosciuszko and Brindabella country drew stock from as far away as Yass, Queanbeyan, Wyalong, Urana and Bombala. A similar movement to high pastures took place on the Victorian Bogong High Plains, Wellington and Howitt Plains, and in New South Wales from the upper Hunter onto Barrington Tops and the snow grass country of New England. Even with fattening summer pastures, most Monaro stations regularly changed ownership. After 100 years, many became hand-fed lowland winter operations and fattening highland summer operations, overstocked in both seasons — a problem that increased after the 1870s, when fencing wire could concentrate stock on the "ice cream plants". Severe soil erosion and decreased biological diversity was inevitable.

Above: Vegetation blanketed by winter snow on Charlottes Pass, NSW, with Mount Townsend in the distance.

Above: *Epacris glacialis*, an alpine heath species.

Flora of Cold-climate Grasslands

Cold-climate grasslands are part of a rich embroidery of low-structured plant communities across the High Country of south-eastern Australia. Maximum distribution was reached during the grazing years, when communities with delicate, palatable plants (such as some *Carex* sedges, which scientists called "ice-cream plants") were selectively eaten out. Pastoralists regularly burned pasture at the end of summer to encourage growth of snow grasses and to reduce shrub cover. Great volumes of soil were lost and communities modified to the advantage of the grasses. About 50 years ago, grazing ceased in the Kosciuszko National Park area, protecting the Snowy Mountain catchments. Now, heath is flourishing, the grasslands are decreasing in area and the diversity of species is increasing, especially for flowering herbs and shrubs. There are more silver Snow Daisies, paler green sedges and a speckling of beautiful summer flowers. The great shadow on the horizon is global warming, which will dramatically raise the snow line and change high mountain habitats.

Classic Plants: Snow grasses (*Poa caespitosa complex*); Costin's Snow Grass; Rigid Wallaby Grass; kangaroo grasses; Common Wheatgrass; Blown Grass; White Top; Bristle Grass; Short-flowered Dryland Sedge; Button Sedge; Tufted Sedge; Dryland Sedge; Mountain Woodrush; Spreading Rope Rush; Alpine Caladenia; Tadgell's and Highland Leek-orchids; Sky Lily; Feather Buttercup; Granite Buttercup; Gunn's Alpine Buttercup; Felted Buttercup; Native Bitter-Cress; Mountain Crane's Bill; Rosetted Crane's Bill; Alpine Stackhousia; Showy Violet; Alpine Riceflower; Yellow Kunzea; Creeping Raspwort; Mueller's Snow Gentian; Dwarf, Snow and Variable Eyebrights; Thyme Speedwell; Veined and Broad Plantains; Mountain and Alpine Woodruff; Waxy Bluebell; Mud Pratia; Alpine Triggerplant; Tufted, Spoon, Gwenda's and Mountain Daisies; Herbfield and Dagger-leaf Celmisia; Alpine Cotula; Dwarf, Hairy, James's, Shiny-leafed and Woolly Billy-button; Violet Fleabane; Sticky Fleabane; Silver Cudweed; Shining Cudweed; Blue Bottle Daisy; Scaly Button; Native Dandelion; Snowpatch Daisy; Alpine Podolepis; Highland Groundsel; Small-fruited Hakea; Red Sand Spurrey; Rayless Starwort.

Above, top to bottom: During December, feathers of snow appear on Mount Feathertop in the Victorian Alps, making life difficult for all but the hardiest vegetation; Old Currango Homestead, the former home of the Taylor family of pastoralists on Tantangra Valley Plain in Kosciuszko National Park.

Above: The Highland Copperhead is commonly seen in cold-climate grasslands.

Frogs and Reptiles of the Cold-climate Grasslands

For cold-blooded animals the freezing high mountain environment presents many survival problems. There do not appear to be any geckoes inhabiting cold-climate grasslands and there is a restricted list of frogs and reptiles. The most famous and beautiful is the Southern Corroboree Frog, which really belongs to the composite habitats of alpine stream and Sphagnum bog, grassy sedgeland and adjacent woodland — different parts of its life cycle being lived in these habitats. There are two species and the northern species is associated with small grassy areas, although mostly as an understorey to alpine woodland. The southern species is disappearing quite dramatically and is already threatened by climate change because these high-altitude marginal habitats are suffering the greatest environmental impact.

Classic Frogs and Reptiles: Tasmanian Froglet; Eastern Banjo Frog; Baw Baw Frog (wetland margins); Victorian Froglet; Mountain Heath Dragon; Alpine Water Skink; Southern Water Skink (in wetland verge); Alpine Oak Skink; Mountain Log Skink (woodland verges with rock); Southern Tussock Skink; High Plains Skink; Mountain Swamp Skink; Eastern Three-lined Skink; Highland Copperhead; White-lipped Snake.

Invertebrates of the Cold-climate Grasslands

To survive the long winter, invertebrates without internal heat regulation must have adaptations that allow them to warm themselves. The simplest adaptation is a dark body colour to rapidly absorb warmth from sunlight. The Mountain Golden Cockroach is a classic example, as are the Alpine Thermocolour and Mountain Spotted Grasshoppers — all wonderfully adapted to their frigid environment.

Classic Invertebrates: Kosciuszko Funnel-web; Musgrave's Wolf Spider; trapdoor spiders; freshwater crayfish (wet edges); millipede (*Australiosoma* sp.); 60 species of butterflies in Kosciuszko National Park; the Bogong Moth; Alpine Thermocolour Grasshopper; Mountain Spotted Grasshopper; Metallic Cockroach.

There would be little strategic value in Aboriginal burning of the sod-tussock grasslands, although it is evident that fire, both accidental and lightning-initiated, did occur. Once domestic grazing began, many farm workers were crofters from the Scottish Highlands, who brought with them a heather-burning culture. It took the loss of a metre or more of soil from some parts of the Snowy Mountains, the compacting and drainage of bogs, and the entrenching of creeks before the proclamation of Kosciuszko National Park and the Snowy Mountains Scheme stopped these practices. Unfortunately, many Victorian High Plains are still grazed.

DIVERSITY OF COLD-CLIMATE GRASSLANDS

Sod-tussock grassland communities are found on high, undulating country and over broad, pound-like valley bottoms, where cold air pools behind a narrowing valley exit (usually where a creek must cut through resistant country rock). These frost hollows are typified by Nungar and Currango Plains in New South Wales. In winter, the grass is kept from freezing by blankets of snow, but once the snow thaws there are very severe frosts. Following bushfires, when the protective grass cover and its thick mat of dry "thatch" is burned off, the soil is unprotected and frost freezes moisture in the soil, shooting icy needles deep into the ground. These expanding needles break up soil structure and, on melting, loosen and collapse the topsoil, leaving it highly eroded. Before the grasses finally form dense sod again, the changing seasons produce a sequence of species mixes. The changing composition of plant food and shelter brings with it varied mixes of invertebrates.

On the higher, open snow plains (such as on the upper Snowy River) the tree line is at lower altitude and the grassland drifts into a herbfield community, with a high species diversity that is dominated by Snow Daisies, eyebrights, buttercups and others. Soil development is incredibly slow and exceedingly shallow on the highest, most exposed gravelly tops, but this is where the highest community of all grows — the feldmark of exquisite, battling "bonzai" species. Below the tree line, where the subsoil is saturated and aeration is restricted, conditions are suitable only for swamp and bog communities. If the slopes are steep, as on the track from Charlottes Pass to the Snowy River or the Blue Lake track, then both snow gums and a wet heath community can develop. In the saturated depressions of creeks, below spring lines, and in the micro-relief hollows created by near-glacial conditions thousands of years ago, are the bogs of *Carex*, Sphagnum and cushion plants. Snow grasses (*Poa caespitosa* complex) will have some members in most of these communities.

Above, left to right: White-lipped Snake; Yellow-bellied Water Skink.

Mammals of the Cold-climate Grasslands

Sod-tussock grasslands provide little or no shelter for mammals, a fact that, along with the cold, makes them not entirely suitable habitat for mammals. Those creatures that do wander onto the edges of this habitat actually belong to adjacent habitat, such as the fragile Mountain Pygmy-possum that lives in the boulder streams or the Broad-toothed Rat that occupies deep burrows and runways in the grassy, shrubby creek banks. Even the Eastern Grey Kangaroo is a transient visitor, bounding in from the shelter of woodlands.

Because there is a significant population of invertebrates (such as beetles, bugs, moths, grasshoppers, crickets, cockroaches, flies and wasps) living within the grass and its thatch, some bats may be seen sweeping low over the grasslands from adjacent woodlands.

Classic Mammals: Short-beaked Echidna; Brown Antechinus; Spotted-tailed Quoll; Eastern Quoll (Tas); Common Wombat; Eastern Grey Kangaroo; Bennett's Wallaby; Broad-toothed Rat (creek edges); Velvet-furred Rat (Tas); Bush Rat; Red Fox; Dingo; brumby; feral pig.

Above, clockwise from top: Juvenile Wedge-tailed Eagles can be identified by a rich, chestnut colouring that deepens to become almost black with age; the Little Raven ushers in late spring in alpine woodlands and large flocks are then seen hunting grasshoppers in the grasslands and gathering over the snow patches to pick at insects trapped and frozen in the snow; the Australian Magpie is a hardy and versatile bird that occupies habitat across most of the country, even in the Australian Alps during the warmer months.

Birds of the Cold-climate Grasslands

No birds occupy these grasslands all year long, but with the advent of spring birds begin to move back to the mountains. As the year warms, flowering begins, first at lower levels then towards the peaks; birds ultimately follow, arriving on the very high country in early November. A huge gathering of honeyeaters begins in the river valleys leading from the coast. However, in these high grasslands, wildlife is only ever in transit. Gang-gang Cockatoos will head for the high woodlands and in April vast flocks gather along the Murrumbidgee and Snowy tributaries for their return migration to the coastal heathlands and woodlands. Australian Pipits flit through the grasslands and few birds can match the colour of the Scarlet, Flame and Rose Robins or the Crimson Rosellas, which flash across the grasslands en route to woodlands. One wonders how these long-term behavioural patterns will change as the climate changes and the mountains become accessible all year round.

Classic Birds: Brown Goshawk; Wedge-tailed Eagle; Brown Falcon; Australian Kestrel; Stubble Quail; Latham's Snipe (in wet areas); Skylark; Welcome Swallow; Australian Pipit; Flame Robin; Common Starling; Australian Magpie; Australian Raven; Little Raven; Forest Raven (Tas).

Above, top to bottom: In summer, Eastern Grey Kangaroos move from the woodlands of the valleys to higher ground in the alpine grasslands; Common Wombats leave the shelter of the mountainous woodlands to feed on new-shooting grasslands.

Where Are They? Fens, bogs, moors and sedgelands, as systems, are not specific to geology or climate, although their species mix may be. They are restricted to wet, level to sloping positions, such as along stream flats and on slopes receiving very high rainfalls (in western Tasmania), hanging swamps on plateaus (such as Barren Grounds and Blue Mountains), coastal inter-dunes and areas of peat with perched or elevated water tables, as well as inter-dune swamps in the lower south-east of South Australia.

What Do They Look Like? *Bogs* — Very wet areas with hummocks of bright green Sphagnum and emergent *Carex*; some open water. *Button Grass* — Tawny slopes and downs under a blanket of large "grassy" tussocks, sometimes with emergent stunted tea-trees, paperbarks, Epacrids and mixes of Christmas Bells and other herbs. *Gahnia sedgeland* — Untidy, ropey tussocks mixed with other sedges and rushes (almost all are now drained).

Critical Conditions: Saturated land; fens are alkaline to neutral; bogs are an acid environment. Lomandra sedgeland is drier.

Above: Sedgelands are wet habitats, as seen around this tarn near Federation Peak in Southwest National Park, Tasmania.

Best Examples: *NSW* — Gibraltar Range, Barrington Tops and New England National Parks; Kings Tableland; Talaterang Mountain; Corang; Mount Tarn and The Castle; Morton, Kanangra–Boyd and Budderoo National Parks; Barren Grounds and Nadgee Nature Reserves; Mount Budawang; Kybeyan Range; Nunnock Swamp; Ginini Flats; Kiandra area, Main Range; Ramshead Range; head of the Snowy River; Wilkinson's Valley; Twynam Bog; Tin Mines area; Crackenback Valley; Coast Range and sedgelands. *Qld* — Mounts Banks and Hay. *Vic* — Bogong High Plains; Mount Buffalo; Mounts Wellington and Howitt; Mount Baw Baw. *SA* — Canunda National Park. *Tas* — Cradle Mountain; Barn Bluff; Mount Ossa; Frenchmans Cap Track; Southwest Track; south of Lake Pedder; Mount Anne; Federation Peak; Mount Field.

Sounds: Wind rattling the hard sedges.

Smells: Mud; earth; mould.

Sensations: Cold, wet mud.

Sedgelands

I have struggled through new country and seventy hours' continuous rain in the south-west [Tasmania]. From time to time, heavy scrub gives way to plains of button grass, whose spiny tussocks are seldom conveniently placed as "stepping stones" through the marshy peatlands in which they flourish.

Ultimately the right ridge leads upward, and the vegetation ceases to waylay the climber. High stony fells carry dwarf heaths, richeas with many-coloured bells, and exquisite pink and white boronias; there are firm cushion plants set with minute starry flowers in summer, and a multitude of berried plants and mosses, brilliant lichens, and everlasting daisies. In sheltered corries there is the red and golden Christmas Bell; there is a delicate black lily that grows in unexpected places, often on exposed ledges; there are ferns and sundews. Tarns lie close to the summits of many mountains, as in glacial country elsewhere in the world. Far below the forest is an olive-green and golden astrakhan with blue folds; endless peaks recede into the distance; often there is a glimmer from the sea that stretches uninterruptedly to Antarctica.

John Bechervaise, in *Australia: world of difference* (p. 89), published by Rigby in 1967.

Australians have a continuous love affair with trees, particularly tall trees in great forests — a love affair reflected until very recently in the type of land that dominates our national parks. Not that protecting tall trees is wrong — far from it, in fact there are too few national parks! — but by far the largest areas of the continent and those that many claim to be the "real" Australia are not forest, as this book has attempted to show. Further, human experience and research has shown that long-term environmental conditions for plants and animals swing wildly between wet, cold, dry and hot extremes, and subsequently no living

Above: Heathlands on groundwater podsol soils in Nadgee Nature Reserve, New South Wales, are sometimes (and especially about nine years after fire) thick with the sedge *Leptocarpus tenax*, which produces copious quantities of seed, prime food for the rare Ground Parrot.

Above: The sedge *Carex* is usually found growing through the yellow, mossy Sphagnum of bog communities, such as this one on a soak beside the upper Snowy River, New South Wales. *Below:* Bright green areas in and about the water at the head of the Currango Plain, New South Wales, signify the sedgeland community.

Above: Swamp Harriers cruise low over sedgeland, swooping down on large insects, small mammals, frogs and reptiles.

Birds of the Sedgelands

While sod-tussock grasslands in the High Country are relatively low in diversity, sedgelands tend to be more mixed (except in Tasmania, where they are dominated by the large tussocks of Button Grass sedge). Large seeds attract Ground Parrots and Orange-bellied Parrots, as well as the Beautiful Firetail and Red-browed Finch. The Orange-bellied Parrot uses the Tasmanian sedgelands seasonally, breeding there during summer before returning to south-west Victoria and southern South Australian coastal sedge swamps and lagoon verges in winter. This usage probably pre-dates the flooding of Bass Strait by sea-level rise. The list of birds looks large for this habitat, but that is because it has a wide climatic range: from mountain and coastal sedgelands in New South Wales and Victoria to the subalpine and lowland Button Grass sedgelands of south-west Tasmania.

Classic Birds: King and Brown Quails; Cape Barren Goose; Pacific Black Duck; Australasian Bittern; Whistling Kite; Wedge-tailed Eagle; Swamp Harrier; Nankeen Kestrel; Brown Falcon; Common and Brush Bronzewings; Red-rumped Parrot; Ground Parrot; Blue-winged Parrot; Orange-bellied Parrot; Brush Cuckoo; Pheasant Coucal; Barn Owl; White-throated Needletail; Rainbow Bee-eater; Superb Fairy-wren; Red-backed Fairy-wren; Southern Emu-wren; Striated Fieldwren; Brown Thornbill; White-eared Honeyeater (transitory); Tawny-crowned Honeyeater (trans.); Crescent Honeyeater (trans.); Scarlet Robin (trans.); Eastern Whipbird; Willie Wagtail; Magpie-lark; Australian Magpie; Black Currawong (Tas); Australian Raven; Forest Raven; Little Raven; Australian Pipit; Skylark; Zebra and Red-browed Finches; Beautiful Firetail; Welcome Swallow; Australian Reed Warbler; Tawny and Little Grassbirds.

system is more important than any other. A global truth is that an organism perfect for today's conditions may, with evolving environmental conditions, shrink in distribution and survive only in tiny refuges. Consequently, today's most overlooked system may dominate in the future; so it is with Australia's grasslands and sedgelands, both of which depend on nearly opposite extremes of wet and dry. Sedgelands are at the cool, wet end of the spectrum. A healthy landscape is always a patchwork of living communities individually rich in diversity, each like a vital organ in the "anatomy" of the planet. Modern explorer John Bechervaise gave one of the best descriptions of this tapestry of habitat ever written:

Button Grass isn't a grass but a sedge, Gymnoschoenus sphaerocephalus, *a mouthful that simply means a plant with a long, naked reed-like leaf and with a tight, spherical ball-like clump of flowers and seed on the end of a swaying, metre-long stem; like the protective button on the point of a foil [fencing sword], hence 'button grass'. I can sympathize with anyone who has had trouble pushing through the huge tangled, bronze-coloured tussocks of Button Grass, which are too far apart to step from one to another. Along the track to Frenchman's Cap, from the Frankland Hills down to the Loddon Plains, I can remember, fifty years later, our difficulties. The soil was a mixture of finely broken glistening white quartzite mixed with peaty sand and like cement slurry. Partly wading down those endlessly long slopes with the tops of the tussocks head high, the whole hill-slopes pulsing in the cold south-westerly wind like the tawny fur of a huge animal, we became uncomfortably aware that on many of the dry tussock tops were coiled shining black Island Tiger Snakes. Thankfully, they were far less active than their mainland cousins. Like their cousins, when active, they are much more interested in the frogs and freshwater crayfish which live on or below the surface of the slurry and among the tussocky root masses. For all of the imagined dangers and real difficulties for walkers, in many ways, these vast fen communities provided the breathtaking contrast to the dark and silent rainforests along the streams and in the gully heads below the gums and heaths of the better drained tops, that is the spirit of the South-West World Heritage Area.*

Above: Cape Barren Geese are native to Australia and usually inhabit coastal sedgelands. They can drink saltwater.

BUTTON GRASS TO BOGS

Button Grass is found with an increasing number of other, more warm-country sedges northwards as far as Queensland. Apart from obvious temperature change, these warmer sedgelands are wet places of hanging swamps and spring lines (as one finds high on the south and east coast ranges, from pockets in the Grampians to Mount Buffalo and Baw Baw, the Bogongs, Nadgee's Coast Range, Brown Mountain, the Kybeyan area, Badja, Budawangs, Talatarang, Barren Grounds, Madden's Plains, higher Blue Mountains areas on Kings Tableland, and about Mount Banks, the Barrington Tops and the Gibraltar Range). This habitat has special significance for two parrots: the Ground Parrot of the east, and the Orange-bellied Parrot of south-west Tasmania and coastlands west of Portland, Victoria. Both are threatened species. The former has some of its healthiest populations in New South Wales, at Nadgee, Talaterang Mountain and on the Barren Grounds — three sandstone plateaus with hanging swamps. In the Nadgee Nature Reserve the Ground Parrot obtains drought refuge on the high swamps of the Coast Range, as well as some fire protection, even though its primary food supply — the sedge, *Leptocarpus tenax* — is principally found on the lower coastal heathlands. The Orange-bellied Parrot breeds in summer on the Tasmanian sedgelands and winters on the coastal salt marshes of Victoria and South Australia.

Bogs, as distinct from fens, are found in the saturated cool to cold valley bottoms and in pond-like depressions of High County micro-relief. These communities are characterised by Sphagnum moss and *Carex* sedges. Here it is too wet for Epacrids and other wet-heath shrubs to survive, so they form a mixed community just up-slope from the bog. The dominant sedge in this community is bright-green Tufted Sedge (*Carex gaudichaudiana*), which Dr Alec Costin describes as the "ice cream plant" for cattle. Its palatability to cattle was the cause of much bog damage on the Main Range area of Kosciuszko National Park until grazing was banned. Not only

Above, left to right: Tasmanian Christmas Bells grow in wet, acidic soils of sedgelands and wet heath; the triggerplant has a tuft of fine, grass-like leaves and grows best in wet situations. This plant has evolved a cunning ambush for pollinating insects, ensuring pollen distribution and cross-pollination.

Above: A common plant group in wet, nitrogen-deficient, acidic soils is the delicate-looking sundew.

Flora of the Sedgelands

At least two plants have classic adaptations for wet habitat. "Dewy" droplets on hairs around the sundew's leaves are a concoction of sweet insect attractant, glue and plant digestive juice. An insect lured by this liquid becomes trapped by the glue. As the insect struggles to free itself, the leaf folds over it and begins to absorb the nitrogen-rich insect extract, alleviating the problem of nitrogen-deficient soil. Even the sundew is not as active as the triggerplant flower. Its tiny white anthers ripen first and carry a dusting of pollen. Then the pistil, the strong, pinkish arm with its mop-like sticky head, sets itself right back. The pollinating insect flies in, lands on the petals and searches for nectar. It probes the flower tube with its proboscis and tickles the bend of the pistil, which causes plant hormones to release the tension on the pistil and slam it down on the insect, showering it with pollen from the anthers. Simultaneously, the sticky pistil picks up pollen from the insect's visit to a previous plant. Cross-pollination is assured. This violent action can also be set off by tickling the flower with a fine straw.

Classic Plants: Short–flowered Swamp-sedge; Button Grass; Tufted Sedge; Dark Fen-sedge; *Festuca* spp.; Alpine Wallaby Grass; Water Milfoil; *Potamogeton pectinatus*; Chara; Stonewort; *Lomandra longifolia*; Giant Sword Rush (*Gahnia* spp.); Common Bullrush; Blue Wire Rush; Fen Tea-tree; Scented Paperbark; Tall Twig Rushes (*Cladium procerum* and 15 *Baumea* spp.); Spike Rushes (*Eleocharis* spp.); *Scirpus polystachus*; bottlebrushes; Alpine Bog-rush; Alpine Club-rush (*Isolepis* spp.); Grass-tree; Coral, Pink and Swamp Heath (*Sprengelia* spp.); Dog Rose; Coral Fern; sundews (*Drosera* spp.); Bladder Wort (*Utricularia* spp.); triggerplants (*Stylidium* spp.); *Richea continentis*; Dwarf and Gunn's Alpine Buttercup; Christmas Bell (*Blandfordia* spp).

Above: The freshwater crayfish *Cherax destructor* is notorious for undermining dam and creek walls with its deep tunnels.

Invertebrates of the Sedgelands

Because so many of the sedgelands are cold-country habitats, many of the invertebrates that inhabit them are dark coloured, particularly the Bog Crickets and cockroaches. Sedgelands are also in such wet areas that there is frequently surface water. Usually the muddy soil is perforated by numerous yabby and shrimp holes.

Yabbies comprise a major food source for reptiles, particularly tiger snakes. The Bog Dragonfly conducts its life history in such surface waters with a muddy bed. Leeches, of course, are prevalent and bushwalkers become accustomed to either accepting their presence, or walking with socks previously soaked in saltwater.

Classic Invertebrates: Mayflies; Bog Dragonfly; Kosciuszko Metallic Cockroach; brown and green forms of the predaceous *Austrodectes monticola* hopper; Black Bog Cricket; *Iridomyrmex* sp. (small black ants nesting in Sphagnum hummocks); freshwater crayfish (Yabbies); Mountain Shrimp (Tas); Alpine Water Skink; Mountain Swamp Skink; Latham's Snipe; Platypus.

did the cattle select and eat out the *Carex,* but, in puddling about in the bogs, they tore up the Sphagnum, creating drainage ways that dried out the bog and pounded the peaty clays into cracked, impermeable floors. Unfortunately, vital habitat areas for the stunning gold and black Southern Corroboree Frog and many invertebrates, were destroyed in this manner. However, this was only part of the impact of highland degradation by domestic stock, which set in train a sequence of events that included accelerated erosion (particularly in granite country) and re-activation of the vertical and lateral cutting by high valley wetland streams. Such physical changes ultimately destroyed wetland peat and other organic matter, as well as sediment layers down to the mineral pavement beneath.

Another consequence of grazing impacts on the migratory Japanese Snipe, which arrives in these areas exhausted after its habitual annual trans-equatorial flights. Snipes fed on invertebrates in these once-rich habitats; however, following grazing damage, these birds had to quickly find alternative food sources, or die. When one follows the succession of implications by highland range-grazing of cattle, it is easy to pinpoint widespread and even international repercussions. Unfortunately, those economists balancing the profit and loss accounts of the past rarely, if ever, looked beyond immediate monetary rewards. As nature philosopher John Muir once so well expressed: "If one removes any part of the natural system, you find that it is connected to each other part!" Here then, is a truly universal law.

Above: Red-belllied Black Snakes inhabit areas of grass tussocks close to swamps, creeks or rivers.

Frogs and Reptiles of the Sedgelands

Numerous frogs dwell in this very wet habitat, drawn to the many runnels of surface water with sedge-covered edges, as well as the litter embedded in the mud. Along with yabbies, frogs are a major food source for tiger snakes in the Button Grass sedgelands. The Alpine Water Skink, seriously threatened in Victoria due to habitat change caused by grazing, is fortunately secure in the sedgelands of Kosciuszko and Barrington Tops National Parks in New South Wales, where it is often seen sunning itself on warm boulder surfaces. Many of the skinks that favour this habitat are similarly observed. Both venomous Highland and Island Copperheads call this habitat home.

Classic Frogs and Reptiles: Georgiana's Crinia; Tasmanian Crinia; Wallum Froglet; *Heleioporus inornatus*; Western and Eastern Banjo Frog; Brown-striped Frog; Spotted Grass-frog; Sphagnum Frog; Tasmanian Tree-frog; Heath Frog; Whistling Tree-frog; Green and Golden Bell Frog; Brown Toadlet; Gray's Toadlet; Long-necked Turtle; Mountain Dragon; Lace Monitor (visitor); *Leiolopisma delicata*; *L. entrecasteauxii*; Metallic Skink (*Leiolopisma* sp.,Tas); Weasel Skink; Diamond Python; copperheads; Eastern Small-eyed Snake; White-lipped Snake; Black-bellied Swamp Snake; Black and Eastern Tiger Snakes; Red-bellied Black Snake; Eastern Brown Snake; Common Death Adder. *Alpine and Subalpine Bogs* — Southern Corroboree Frog (both colour forms: yellow and yellow-green); Southern Toadlet; Common Eastern Froglet; Smooth Froglet; Tasmanian Froglet; Baw Baw Frog; Alpine Tree-frog.

Mammals of the Sedgelands

The country pictured below is typical of most habitats — rarely are habitats pure stands of a single vegetation type. Usually, because of variable drainage and soil types, habitats are comprised of a mix of habitats and animals usually find the richest food and the best shelter at the edge of such mixes. This prime ecological effect is called the "edge effect". The marshy lowlands of Wilsons Promontory National Park are ideal for Eastern Grey Kangaroos, which use the higher, dense stands of *Banksia*, *Melaleuca* and eucalypt scrub as shelter and feed on the sedgeland. Quolls, possums and other small mammals, bats, echidnas, kangaroos and the predatory Dingo use these merged habitats to their best advantage.

Classic Mammals: Echidna; Swamp and Dusky Antechinus; White-footed Dunnart; Common Planigale; Southern Brown, Northern Brown and Eastern Barred Bandicoots; Spotted-tailed Quoll; Eastern Quoll (Tas); Tasmanian Devil; Common Wombat; Common Ringtail Possum; Eastern Pygmy-possum; Long-footed Potoroo; Tasmanian Pademelon; Western Brush Wallaby; Quokka; Swamp Wallaby; Eastern Grey Kangaroo; Ash-grey Mouse (SA); Australian Water-rat; Swamp Rat; Grassland Melomys; Eastern Chestnut Mouse; Broad-toothed Rat; Pale Field-rat; Large-footed Myotis Bat; Lesser Long-eared Bat; Little Broad-nosed Bat; Dingo; Platypus.

Above: The Common Wombat seeks out slightly drier hummocks in the wet areas for its burrows and is quite often seen across this habitat. In Tasmania it is sometimes called the "Water Badger", because it does not seem to be concerned about getting wet. *Below:* An Eastern Grey Kangaroo goes almost entirely unnoticed in the hazy light over sedgeland in Wilsons Promontory National Park, Victoria.

Where Are They?
Treeless areas on the mainland above about 1800 metres. In Tasmania they grow above 1100 metres, mainly on the tops and high slopes of the main peaks and below snow patches.

What Do They Look Like?
Meadows of low herbs and grasses with some stunted ground or rock-hugging, slow-growing shrubs; massed flowering from the thaw to midsummer.

Critical Conditions:
Snow cover for 2–6 months of the year; low summer temperatures (mean midsummer temperature of 10°C) inadequate to support greater production of plant matter. Since grazing stopped, a considerable adjustment in the flora is taking place.

Best Examples:
NSW — Walks from Charlottes Pass to Main Range and from the Thredbo Chairlift head station to Mount Kosciuszko. *Vic* — parts of Mount Bogong; Bogong High Plains; Mounts Feathertop, Buller and Howitt. Much of the Victorian herbfields are still suffering from severe grazing damage. *Tas* — Cradle Mountain; Barn Bluff; Mounts Pelion to Ossa; parts of Mount Field National Park; Ben Lomond; Mounts Anne and Barrow and high parts of the south-west.

Sounds:
Australian Pipits; Little Ravens flocking over snowpatches; roaring winter winds.

Smells:
Cold, clear air with hints of wildflower fragrance.

Sensations:
Chilled air; burning sun.

Above: Candle Heath, *Richea continentis*, grows in alpine and subalpine habitats in Kosciuszko National Park.

Alpine Herbfield and Feldmark

In general, it may be said that the high mountain country is rich in herbfields. The climax of the alpine zone on the mainland is the tall alpine herbfield indicated by large stands of snow daisy, [Celmisia longifolia costiniana]. In short alpine herbfields, the vegetation is carpet-like in the high moors and fed by melting snows. Some more adaptable short herbfield species join the 'crawling heath', Epacris petrophila and others, to battle against the harshest alpine environment, feldmark of the high, exposed tops. These herbfields are much richer in vegetation than the European alpine country.

Noted teacher of natural history Thistle Y. Harris, in *Alpine Plants of Australia* (1970).

To walk the Blue Lake track, up to the Mount Twynam saddle in Kosciuszko National Park, is to gain a vista that shows, perhaps best of all, the vegetation of Australia's High Country. Snow Gum (*Eucalyptus niphophila*) woodland at 1800 metre altitude on Charlottes Pass drops to wet heath by the Snowy River, which flows over bars of granite boulders. On the river flats are yellow-green Sphagnum bogs and spring lines up the sides are defined by bright-green mosses, ferns and Pink Triggerplants. Beyond the river, the track makes the long climb through sod-tussock grassland, broken in wetter places by pockets of heath, especially the bronze-coloured Candle Heath. In other places, stands of silver-leafed Snow Daisy — the icon of the tall alpine herbfield — are some 30 centimetres or more deep. On drier, more gravelly areas, where granites and slates are breaking down, purple, pink, mauve and gold flowers teeming with insect pollinators are set among green sods of patchy snow grass. Here are various eyebrights, billy-buttons (and other daisies), Tasman Flax-lilies, leek-orchids, buttercups, geraniums, Alpine Stackhousia, Alpine Riceflowers, Mountain Celery, and Waxy and Royal Bluebells. Some species, such as the Mountain Celery and the giant tussocks of Ribbony Grass, are making a remarkable, post-grazing recovery.

Above: A constellation of exquisite *Neopaxia* flowers, one of the cushion plants in Kosciuszko National Park, New South Wales. *Inset:* The Silver Snow Daisy (*Celmisia* sp.). *Right:* Alpine grassland on Main Range in Kosciuszko National Park during midsummer is smattered with snow grasses (*Poa* sp.), herbfield Snow Daisies and feldmark (the bare areas running along the exposed western edge of the ridge).

Above: The hardy, cold-weather-adapted Mountain Pygmy-possum (*Burramys parvus*).

Mammals of the Alpine Herbfields and Feldmark

These communities are far too extreme for any mammal but the Mountain Pygmy-possum. This tiny mammal was first discovered as a fossil from Wombeyan Caves, and given its scientific name derived from the Aboriginal name *Burra Burra*, meaning "place of rocks". It survives the freezing winter by staying under the blanket of snow and feeding on caches of seeds and fruits collected during summer. The architecture of this insulated area is of a boulder field (the "pillars") with shrubs (the "frame") growing between them. The shrubs, such as Yellow Kunzea, the *Richea* Candle Heath, Alpine Ballart and the Mountain Plum Pine, are wind-pruned, smoothing over the spaces between the boulders like a roof. Snow packs over the top of this roof, maintaining a spacious, dimly lit sheltered area beneath — the winter residence of the Mountain Pygmy-possum. In summer, they hunt invertebrates and consume the fat bodies of the Bogong Moth, which aestivates among the boulders. Sadly, this pygmy-possum has been on borrowed time for many generations as its habitat is driven up the mountain by rising snow lines. Further climate change may well push it over the brink of extinction. Other mammals seen this high on the mountains are usually visitors from lower down, although at Mount Higginbotham, the Broad-toothed Rat and Dusky Antechinus share the area along with Bush Rats, Brown Antechinus, House Mice and Eastern Pygmy-possums.

Classic Mammals: Mammals from the cold-climate grasslands and sedgelands seasonally reside in the herbfields or are visitors. Special mention is, of course, required for the Mountain Pygmy-possum.

In the saturated snowdrift run-off, some of these plants occur as stunted plants, along with Snowpatch Grass, sedges, White Purslane, Snow Buttercups and the stunning Anemone Buttercups, Alpine Marsh-marigolds, Alpine Sundews, Pennyworts, Star Plantains, Snow Wort, Creeping Daisy and Snow Daisy — all typical of the short alpine herbfield.

Beyond the Blue Lake turnoff, the track sidles up towards the Twynam saddle, which is mostly (except in December) a broad snow patch with a short herbfield lying below it. Higher up, as the slope begins to level at the saddle, chilly wind whistles. The sod-tussock grassland up here, with its Snow Daisy patches that seem to merge with the clouds, begins to thin out as soil becomes almost non-existent and conditions become more extreme. On the gravels, a titanic battle for colonisation rages, with plants pitting themselves against the icy westerly winds that are armed with wintry ice particles and abrasive summer grit. In this feldmark community, only those plants that provide the least resistance to the wind's flow can survive; most hug the ground among the stones. These low-growing plants include tightly tufted herbs like the Alpine Colobanth and the delicate pink-flowered Feldmark Snow-hebe, the ground-hugging Feldmark Buttercup and exquisite Dwarf Eyebrights hiding behind boulders or in the lee of the dense creeping canopy of Snow Heath. Snow Heath is an Epacrid that is flattened by the wind and grows along the ground, striking fresh roots from the newly extending branches and thereby slowly moving its location away from the wind as its earlier growing parts die. None of these herbland communities of herbs, grasses and low shrubs exceed 50 centimetres in depth, apart from the Alpine Plum Pine — the mainland's only alpine conifer, which clings to the lee sides of boulders forming, along with Candle Heath, dense copses over a metre deep. Feldmark is intriguingly beautiful in all of its miniature forms, truly a bonzai garden.

Shelter for animals is very scarce in this habitat, especially in winter. Only a few reptiles and some specialised invertebrates dwell here, most other species are vagrants or seasonal migrants, such as Australian Kestrels and Ravens chasing insects. Once, Aborigines moved during early summer onto the high tops to feast on Bogong Moths, the moths themselves being migrants aestivating there. About 25% of the alpine flora can trace its ancestry to that of the ancient southern supercontinent of Gondwana. Around the same percentage of alpine invertebrate fauna shows similar ancestry, suggesting that when Australia rafted northwards, approximately 50 million years ago, it brought with it entire ecosystems.

Above: Alpine Sunray, *Leucochrysum albicans* subsp. *alpinum*.

Above, top to bottom: An eyebright (*Euphrasia collina*) herbfield in the upper Snowy River valley grows on a dry site; this very exposed feldmark community of dwarf, struggling shrubs and herbs is growing near Twynam Saddle, with Sentinel Peak beyond and Grey Mare Range in the distance.

Flora of the Alpine Herbfields and Feldmark

Large numbers of visitors travel to the Australian Alps each year — in winter for snow sports and in summer to be able to walk out onto the herbfield and see it ablaze with wildflowers. With global warming, diminishing rainfall will probably dramatically affect the flowering species. The alpine herbfields and meadows are truly spectacular in their massed beauty, but are also fascinating in the life cycles presented by the plants. The triggerplant's incredible pollination strategy, the wonderful bright-green Cushion-plants, the ancient boulder-wrapped Alpine Plum Pines, Epacrid heath plants that actually "walk" away from the freezing feldmark winds, the charm of the many species of buttercup (from the exquisite Anemone Buttercup to the miniatures of the high feldmarks) — all are truly a masterpiece of nature. Then there are the endless meadows of wonderful Snow Daisies peppered here and there with Golden Buttons, and various *Craspedia*. It is said that the eye bright (*Euphrasia* spp.) got its common name from a relative plant in Britain, which, in order to attract the ladies at the Saturday night frolic, village lads would crush and rub in their eyes to make them glisten. However, the spectacular show of flowers on the Australian highland meadows (some 212 species of flowers and ferns in total) don't require any artificial stimulus to brighten the eyes, the scene alone is enough!

Classic Plants: Mountain Clubmoss; Necklace Fern; Alpine Finger-fern; Alpine Water-fern; Mother Shield Fern; Tasmanian Bladder Fern; Mountain Plum Pine; Yellow-headed, Star and Dryland Sedge; Alpine Club-rush; Mountain Hook-sedge; Spreading Rope-rush; Cushion Rush; Dwarf Wood-rush; Feldmark Wood-rush; snow grasses; Ribbony Grass; Kosciuszko Pineapple-grass; Tasman Flax Lily; Highland and Tadgell's Leek-orchid; Alpine Ballart; White Purslane; Snowpatch and Feldmark Cushion-plants; knawels; Alpine Marsh-marigold; Feldmark; Feather and Anemone Buttercups: Granite, Gunn's Alpine, Snow and Felted Buttercups; Bitter-cress; Alpine Sundew; Bidgee-widgee; Native Geraniums; Mountain Celery; Waxy and Royal Bluebells; Alpine Stackhousia; Showy Violet; Alpine Riceflower; Willow-herbs; Wreath and Small Pennyworts; Kosciuszko Aniseed; Australian Caraway; Cushion Caraway; Bog Heath; Coral Heath; Snow Heath; Carpet Heath; Mueller's Snow Gentian; Forget-me-not; Feldmark Snow-hebe; Dwarf Eyebright; Variable Eyebright; Snow Eyebright; Feldmark Eyebright; various plantains; Alpine Woodruff; Snowpatch Coprosma; Ivy Goodenia; Alpine Triggerplant; Snow-wort; Snow Daisy; Baw Baw Daisy; Tufted Daisy; Spoon Daisy; Gwenda's Daisy; Creeping Daisy; Mountain Daisy; Herbfield Celmisia; Dagger-leaf Celmisia; Alpine Cotula; Orange Billy-button; Hairy Billy-button; James's Billy-button; Shiny-leafed Billy-button; Pale Billy-button; Woolly Billy-button; Sticky Billy-button; Fleabanes; Silver Cudweed; Ford's Cudweed; Silver Ewartia (Australian Edelweiss); Button Everlasting; Blue-bottle Daisy; Scaly Button; Alpine Sunray; Snowpatch Daisy; Alpine Podolepis; Chamomile Sunray; Gunn's Groundsel; Highland Groundsel; Alpine Groundsel.

The Extremes

The Extremes

From what I have said of the Natives of New-Holland they may appear to some to be the most wretched people upon Earth, but in reality they are far more happier [sic] than we Europeans; being wholly unacquainted not only with the superfluous but the necessary Conveniences so much sought after in Europe, they are happy in not knowing the use of them. They live in a Tranquillity which is not disturb'd by the Inequality of Condition: the Earth and sea of their own accord furnishes them with all things necessary for life, they covet not Magnificent Houses, Household-stuff &c, they live in a warm and sunny Clime and enjoy a very wholsome [sic] Air. In short they seem'd to set no Value upon anything we gave them, nor would they ever part with anything of their own for any one article we could offer them; this in my opinion argues that they think themselves provided with all the necessarys of Life and that they have no superfluities.

James Cook, describing Aboriginal life in the tropical Cooktown area just one month after repairing his ship at the Endeavour River, 1770.

Habitat is only thought of as "extreme" by those who do not live there — perhaps that is what James Cook, hailing from cool, fertile, semi-industrialised Britain, meant when he wrote the above passage about Australian Aborigines. Any species surviving in a place over many generations simply comes to look upon that place as home. For a crustacean dwelling by a black smoker in the pressurised, perpetual dark of the ocean abyss, the sunny shallows of a coral reef are extreme habitat; conversely, for the coral reef inhabitant, the black smoker is an impossibly extreme environment. So what and where are these extremes, and by whose measure? These largely arbitrary places are those that do not fit the habitat types already described. Extreme habitats require the organisms that live there to have adaptations that allow them to use the habitat's peculiar resources. Such habitats may be wetlands; caves, cliffs and canyons; desert dunes; salt lakes; or isolated inland "island" refuges. However, like Cook, I am perceiving these daunting places through my own eyes, forgetting even the great diversity within our own species. Over millions of years of human evolution, we have colonised habitats with highly variant qualities. What I call extreme, other humans may call home.

Previous pages: The Arckaringa Hills south-west of Oodnadatta in South Australia's Painted Desert, a desert of extreme heat, not unlike Death Valley in America.

Above, top to bottom: Recent live and unstable dunes on the eastern edge of the Lake Mungo lunette are gradually engulfing mallee lands to the east; habitat inside the limestone cave system of Jenolan Caves is one of eternal night.

Above: The waters of Lake McKenzie in the Fraser Island World Heritage Area are extremely pure. *Right:* Peron Peninsula, part of the Shark Bay World Heritage Area, is subject to high salinity, extreme temperatures and cyclones.

EXTREME EVOLUTION

Over years of generational change, plants and animals that survive in a habitat come to fit the food, shelter and type of space provided by their habitat better than ever. However, nothing is permanent in this equation — the quality of the habitat also changes over many seasons and over the years. Some of these changes can be attributed to calamities such as fire, drought, storm, floods, earthquakes and volcanic eruption, but the most calamitous, in the long run, is climate change. Grand scale climate change alters the ecosystem's method of primary production, and it is primary production that sustains the plants that feed all animals.

The type of shelter provided changes too. Effective skin colouring for animals inhabiting a red sand dune may become a hazard in the dappled sunlight of a woodland. Changes in shelter availability are less hazardous for insects, which may produce tens of thousands of young each season, than for mammals, some of which produce just one young after maturing for eighteen years. In the hundreds of thousands of insects produced, there is almost boundless opportunity for genetic error or change to produce some young that will be able to fit the new conditions. A healthy connection between habitat and animal is the only way to ensure a healthy, reproductive animal. Some birds (such as shearwaters, stints and plovers) escape the limits imposed on them by extreme climatic conditions by undertaking annual global migrations in order to locate suitable feeding and breeding grounds to sustain their species. During the history of the Earth, countless plants and animals have become extinct, others have had the time and the genetic evolution to make a new fit; yet others have moved or migrated to attempt to discover a life-sustaining fit between their own needs and some other place. To them, their old home will now become an extreme habitat.

Accelerating climatic change may soon have all species wondering where "home" has gone. One thing is certain, climate change, especially for extreme habitats, will result in a feverish reshuffling of species. Those seeking new homes must undertake new relationships with those they cohabit with. The natural world will become a place of chaos, of revolution. One wonders if future humans will require interplanetary habitat to escape an Earth destroyed by human misuse and become, in effect, a kind of "human shearwater", migrating to more hospitable planets. Somehow, looking at other planets in our solar system, this "escapism" seems unlikely. Our best hope is to appreciate and preserve the planet we inhabit.

Left: The Painted Desert is a desiccated, arid place with no topsoil and exhumed fossil landscapes of clay, laterite and silcrete-capped hills. *Above:* Crookneck, or Mount Coonowrin, in the Glass House Mountains, Queensland, is the core of a dead volcano.

Above, clockwise from top left: Drifting coastal dunes in Coorong National Park, South Australia, are under constant attack by prevailing westerly winds; samphire dots a flat around a salt lake in Coorong National Park — a habitat of blistering heat, dehydrating salt and sand blasted by intense rainstorms; volcanic Pentecost Island, isolated in the Whitsunday Group, Great Barrier Reef Marine Park; endless, wind-polished silcrete pebbles coated with "desert varnish" stretch across Sturt's Stony Desert, near Moomba, South Australia; the Simpson Desert, near Birdsville, Queensland, receives the lowest rainfall on the continent and has few vegetation corridors; Green Island, off Cairns, Queensland, is a coral cay formed by the gradual accumulation of coral debris and subsequent vegetation — newer, less stable cays may vanish overnight in extreme cyclonic seas; limestone columns in a drifting sandy desert, Nambung National Park, Western Australia; the striated pyramids and domes of the Bungle Bungles in Purnululu National Park, Western Australia, are separated by intensely hot gorges swept by deluges during monsoons.

Where Are They? These are areas that fill with freshwater during floods and include places of permanent swamp and deeper wetlands, such as billabongs and lagoons, semi-permanent wet areas and ephemeral floodplain waters that retain cover for waterfowl breeding seasons at irregular times.

What Do They Look Like? Saturated country with patches of open water and a mix of free-floating, submerged and emergent, water-adapted vegetation. Zoned fringes of plants frequently mark earlier flood levels.

Critical Conditions: Regular and irregular floodplain; pollutant-free, freshwater flooding of high and numerous intermediate levels in some dune-covered overflow areas with a high degree of patchiness; ponds dappling the landscape are important elements, producing habitat "edge" that is valuable to amphibious and terrestrial wildlife; water source, nutrient supply (such as nitrates and phosphates), water temperature, duration, timing, frequency and intensity of flooding times are also critical elements.

Above: The Jabiru, or Black-necked Stork, is a long-legged wader that hunts for fishes, frogs and file snakes.

Right: After wet season floods, tropical freshwater wetlands become some of the most biologically productive regions of Australia. Prolific aquatic vegetation, such as numerous species of waterlilies, spike rushes and sedges, create vast quantities of grasses when they dry out. These wetlands nourish over 350,000 geese and vast numbers of ducks and other waterbirds that eat the aquatic plants, as well as an abundance of aquatic invertebrates and fishes. The largest predator here is the 6 metre long Estuarine Crocodile, which breeds in these wetlands. With low water in August, the billabongs heat up, oxygen decreases and many fish, such as Barramundi, die.

Freshwater Wetlands

The river [Macquarie] itself continued, as usual, from fifteen to twenty-five feet [4.6–7.6 metres] deep, the waters which were overflowing the plains being carried thither by a multitude of little streams … About twenty miles [32 kilometres] from where I set out [downstream from Mount Harris], there was, properly speaking, no country; the river overflowing its banks, and dividing into streams which I found had no permanent separation from the main branch, but united themselves to it on a multitude of points … Vast spaces of country clear of timber were under water, and covered with the common reed, which grew to the height of six or seven feet [1.8–2.1 metres] above the surface. After going [another] twenty miles we lost the land and trees … I was sanguine … of soon entering the long sought for Australian sea … the ocean of reeds surrounded us … There was no channel whatever among those reeds.

John Oxley, convinced of an inland sea in the Macquarie Marshes near Coonamble/Coolabah bridge site, New South Wales, on 6 July 1818.

To answer Surveyor-General John Oxley's musing, there has been no recent inland sea, but the great plains of the Riverina, the grey-clay deltaic plains of the Warrego, Culgoa, Narran and Barwon Rivers and the salt lakes of the Lake Eyre Region, in their fossils and structure, evidence watery basins of inland-sea magnitude. About a dozen times over the last century, summer floods from the northern tropical and monsoonal and southern winter rains have produced virtual temporary inland seas over these areas, sometimes in unison and most notably in 1916–17, 1920–21, 1949–51, 1955–57, 1974–76, 1983–84 and 1992–93.

The location of our continent, between 10° and 44° south latitude, places northern Australia under the influence of the rains and tropical cyclones of the north-west monsoon, from December to May. Most drainage from these prolific rains runs into the northern seas, but south of the Gulf of Carpentaria the headwaters of the Georgina and Diamantina Rivers and Thompson–Cooper Creeks rise well within the area of tropical cyclonic weather and receive at random intervals huge dumps of water, which, flowing via the Channel Country, occasionally makes it as far as Lake Eyre. In a similar fashion, headwaters of the Paroo, Warrego, Culgoa and Maranoa Rivers flood the Darling Basin when accidental, south-moving cyclonic weather drifts across them. These are all senile river systems, meandering across almost level country. Over millennia they have incised thousands of cut-offs or billabongs, anabranches and effluent channels. Natural levees have built up, with wide areas of back swamps that fill during flood-time surges. Typical wetlands fill rapidly before experiencing a period of high, stable water level; then, over months or years, according to the climatic conditions and location of the wetland, they experience a steady water loss by drainage, evaporation and infiltration.

Southern and eastern areas of Australia have more reliable rainfall, with winter rains. Until recently, many of the western rivers that rise on the Great Dividing Range, which runs south from Brisbane, Queensland, to the Grampians in Victoria, filled the Murray–Darling system to overflowing. The flooding of these rivers was usually a major annual surge with a number of lesser flood runs. These days, major surges have been capped at lower levels and most of the minor rises have been cancelled out by dam systems — a catastrophic change for the ancient River Red Gums. Most of the coastal wetlands of Queensland, New South Wales and Victoria

Above: Spike Rushes, waterlilies and Pandanus trees are characteristic of tropical wetlands.

Best Examples: *Tropical: NT* — Kakadu National Park; Fogg Dam; Adelaide River; McArthur River; Mary River. *Qld* — Townsville Common, Lakefield National Park. *WA* — Parry Lagoons Nature Reserve; Lake Gregory, Millstream–Chichester National Park; Lake Kununurra. *Temperate: Qld* — Great Sandy National Park; Nuga Nuga National Park; Bundjalung National Park. *NSW* — Ulmarra Swamp; Channel Country; Lake Innes Nature Reserve; Myall Lakes National Park; Hexham Swamps; Wingecarribee Swamp; swamps and lagoons Batemans Bay–Eden. *Vic* — Lake Wellington; Hattah Lakes National Park; Barmah Forest; Werribee Sewage Farm; lakes and wetlands Colac–Hamilton. *SA* — Piccaninnie Ponds; Bulloak Swamp; Lake Alexandrina; Upper Coorong; Kangaroo Island lagoons. *WA* — Lagoons and swamps Geraldton–Esperance. *Tas* — Moulting Lagoon. *Semi-arid and arid: NT* — Connell's Lagoon; Alice Springs and other town sewage farms; Lake Nash; wet-season river overflows. *Qld* — Diamantina Lakes; Eyre Basin Channel Country; Currawinya; Culgoa Floodplain/ National Park. *NSW* — Nocoleche Nature Reserve; Narran Lake; The Raft, Moree; Macquarie Marshes Nature Reserve; Paroo River; Menindee Lakes; Darling–Murray River and tributaries; Victoria and Fletchers Lake; Lowbidgee swamps; Coongie Lakes; Barren Box Swamp; Lake Cowal; Dalhousie Springs; seasonal south-west brackish lakes and swamps.

Sounds: Screeching cockatoos.

Smells: Sour, wet decay; sweet mud.

Sensations: Mud between the toes; stiff sedges.

Right: Seasonal wetlands on Cape York. *Right, clockwise from top left:* The waters of Lake Bowarrady, Queensland, maintain numerous waterbirds and the Broad-shelled Turtle; Eubenangee Swamp National Park wetlands, south of Babinda, Queensland; Murray River floodplain billabongs and wetlands are crucial duck hatcheries. Species take breeding cues from invertebrate food populations and water levels: some breed on rising waters, some at peak levels, still others on falling waters.

have been drained and/or seriously modified by pesticides and fertilisers. New South Wales lost 60% of its coastal wetlands in one five-year period between 1950 and 1960 as country was drained and converted into dairy and cane farms. For a continent of which 4.5 million square kilometres — more than half its area — has no permanent surface water, this loss is staggering. Yet even in this arid zone, some 65 areas become vital wetlands habitat when the highly variable climate deigns to cause deluges. Concentrations of 10,000 and more waterbirds occur in such places; when drought returns, they must seek refuge in more humid areas, even as far as the coast. As far as migratory waterbirds are concerned, the entire Australian continent must be considered their single, living habitat.

AQUATIC PRIMARY PRODUCERS

Living in an "extreme" habitat, requires aquatic plants to develop special adaptations so they can gain a supply of oxygen. Oxygen is required in order to manufacture carbohydrates, which store energy that, when consumed by animals, energises their cells. There are a great number of water-loving plants (hydrophytes) with representatives from the algae and fern families, such as the floating reddish *Azolla*, Pond Fern and Nardoo (a lover of flooded ephemeral ditches and ponds), as well as a profusion of submerged flowering plants. Aquatic plants provide abundant seed and also shelter, food and an anchor for a long list of invertebrate life that includes worms, molluscs, crustaceans, insects (including numerous larval insect phases) and spiders. Feeding off this system are vertebrates: fishes such as Bony Bream; Australian Smelt; Tasmanian Mudfish; Common Eel-tailed Catfish; Dwarf Galaxia; Cooper Creek Tandan; Lake Eyre Hardyhead; Crimson-spotted Rainbowfish; Australian Rainbowfish; Barramundi; Sailfin Glassfish; Nightfish; Barred Grunter; Black Bream; Spangled Grunter; Western Pygmy Perch; Southern Pygmy Perch; Striped Gudgeon; Western Carp Gudgeon; Purple-spotted Gudgeon; and Northern Trout Gudgeon — all in their respective territories.

TRIALS AND TRIBULATIONS OF TEMPERATURE

Tropical and temperate permanent wetlands are distinctly different, principally because tropical wetland waters are at a much higher temperature than those down south. High temperatures seriously affect the water's capacity to carry

Above: The exquisite Sacred Lotus flower commonly graces the surface of wetland waterholes.

Flora of the Freshwater Wetlands

Plant adaptations for a life lived in the water include stem and leaf structures that carry oxygen. The leaves and stems of the Spike Rush act as a kind of snorkel, carrying air, via spongy cells, down to the plant's rooting corms.

Waterlily leaves float like circular pontoons, supporting soft, flabby stems. Leaves are covered with water-proofing waxes that prevent the plant's nutrient-filled cells from absorbing water. Waterlilies provide shade and shelter for a complex system of animals, and a number of frogs find them excellent anchors for aquatic eggs and larvae, as do invertebrates. Herbivorous water snails and worms act as vacuum cleaners, ridding the lily leaves of algal growth. Beneath the leaves, numerous small fishes shelter from the light and from predatory birds, such as egrets. jacanas, grebes and Black Swans gather masses of the waterlily's spongy leaf and stem material to build their floating nests.

Classic Plants: Water Milfoils; *Zostera* eelgrasses; the pondweeds (*Potamogeton* spp.); Sea Tassels; Ribbonweeds; emergent plants such as waterlilies, Sacred Lotus, Umbrella Sedge and other sedges; reeds; Spike Rush and other rushes; Club Rushes of *Scirpus* sp.; Water Ribbons; Swamp Lily; Chara; Docks; River Red Gum; Black or Flooded Box; Coolibah; Yapunyah; Lignum; River Oak; Swamp Oak; in the tropics, various paperbarks especially Broad-leafed, Cajuput and Green Weeping Melaleucas; bottlebrushes; *Pandanus aquaticus*; Freshwater Mangrove; a watergum (*Lophostemon grandiflorous*); Riparius; Ludwigia; Wild Rice; Taro.

Right, top to bottom: The Noosa River drains the low, extensive sand plain of Great Sandy National Park, Qld; small reedy wetlands, such as these downstream of Fortescue Falls in Karijini National Park, WA, play a crucial role in sustaining wetland animal species in what is essentially a desert.

oxygen, which is necessary for animal respiration. In April, at the tail-end of the wet season with wetland waters hovering around 35°C, I have seen many tonnes of large "drowned" Barramundi floating belly-up in Kakadu's lagoons. Catfish, which can handle lower oxygen levels, then have an abundant food source, tearing at the undersides of Barramundi. Warmer waters also host a greater number of pathogens, which build-up when water flow is reduced.

The "drying out" of Australia began seriously about 8 million years ago, since then the present pattern of irregular rainfall became the norm — aside from approximately ten climatic surges from humid to arid over the past million years. Fishes such as the Murray Cod and Yellow Belly have finely tuned their breeding cycle to the water level and temperature regimes of southern rivers and associated wetland systems. For at least the past 20 million years, Australian waterfowl have lived on wetlands continuously modified by the seesawing climate. This long period of environmental testing of waterfowl, and of the attributes of other wetland vertebrates and invertebrates, gave rise to animals well-suited to these "natural" cyclical patterns. Many survival strategies emerged. Frogs filled themselves with

Frogs and Reptiles of the Freshwater Wetlands

Wetlands produce two food types that sustain reptiles in large quantities — invertebrates and frogs. Some reptiles have become beautifully adapted to hunting food in very particular habitats. One of the most interesting is Mertens' Water Monitor, which has evolved a long, vertically flattened tail that it uses to net tadpoles and small fishes in sandy pools. At the foot of Jim Jim Falls in Kakadu National Park, I witnessed this activity at a small sandy pool about 2 metres across that had been cut off by sand. The monitor placed itself across the pool, forming a moving dam to trap small fishes and tadpoles, then proceeded to slowly wrap its tail around half the prey and slide it into a tighter loop. Panicked prey attempted to escape past the monitor's nose and were deftly swallowed. The monitor devoured about half of the prey then promptly reversed the process and got most of the rest. It finally retired to a sunny bank, its swollen stomach full of fish. Because swamps abound with small vertebrates such as frogs and some rodents, they are also favoured habitats for some snake species. Wetlands are also core habitat for amphibians. Of Australia's 200 or so frog species, 75% release eggs directly into water, the rest deposit jelly-covered eggs on drier sites but require water to wash tadpoles into streams, while a few, such as the Sandhill Frog, Karri Frog, Nicholl's Toadlet and Moss Froglet develop entirely in a yolk-filled egg.

Classic Frogs and Reptiles: Masked Rock Frog; Dahl's Aquatic Frog; Rockhole Frog; Banjo Frogs; Trilling Frog; Red-groined Toadlet; Green Tree-frog; Peron's Tree-frog; Freshwater Crocodile; Estuarine Crocodile; Pig-nosed Turtle; Snake-necked Turtle; Broad-shelled Turtle; Western Swamp Turtle; Krefft's Turtle; Fitzroy River Turtle; Oblong Turtle; Eastern Water Dragon; Mertens' Water Monitor; Blue Mountains Swamp Skink; Eastern Water Skink; Red-bellied Black Snake; Mainland Tiger Snake; Eastern Brown Snake; Water Python; Olive Python; Arafura File Snake; Macleay's Water Snake; Keelback; taipan.

Invertebrates of the Freshwater Wetlands

Freshwater aquatic living systems are complex in their various relationships and dependencies. The most effective way to begin developing an understanding is to establish a small freshwater aquarium. This way you can see the system at work, understand the need for vegetable matter and see the various levels of consumer. Observing the behaviour and associations of animals in the tank can provide an understanding of how these ecosystems are sustained in nature.

Classic Invertebrates: Protozoans; ciliates; flagellates and amoebae (thousands per litre); micro-crustaceans, including water fleas, clam shrimps, seed shrimps, copepods; around 700 species of metazoans; macro-invertebrates, including dragonflies, damselflies, mayflies; true bugs; beetles; two-winged flies; caddis flies; midges; shrimps; amphipods; water mites; leeches; aquatic worms; snails; freshwater mussels; yabbies.

Above, clockwise from top left: Dahl's Aquatic Frog preys on invertebrates in tropical wetland edges that verge onto woodlands; the Pig-nosed Turtle was first described at Kakadu in the early 1970s, but is depicted in ancient Aboriginal rock paintings at Nourlangie Rock; Mitchell's Water Monitor lives in Pandanus swamps and uses its long tail to "net" water prey; the Northern Yellow-faced Turtle dwells in still-water billabongs and cut-off pools; water spiders are fleet-footed hunters; the Wetland Freshwater Crab survives the dry season in deep mud burrows; dragonflies are fast-flying predators of other insects, while their violent larvae terrorise the wetland microbes underwater; the large tropical Freshwater Prawn migrates upstream from May to June; Arafura File Snakes — the name "file" coming from its rasp-rough skin — are a major Aboriginal food source.

Above, top to bottom: The Platypus lives in cooler, temperate wetlands; a Dingo refreshes itself at a waterhole on the Thompson River, Queensland.

Mammals of the Freshwater Wetlands

Two Australian mammals are very much at home in freshwater: the Platypus in cooler temperate waters and the Water-rat in wetlands over eastern, tropical and south-western Australia. Several animals also shelter in the thick vegetation that fringes the wetlands. The Swamp Rat forms networks of runways into wet areas, while the Agile Wallaby delights in green grasses and sedges that grow in hollows when the water retreats. The Water Mouse, a *Xeromys*, lives on invertebrates around swamp margins from Fraser Island to Proserpine (Qld), and across Arnhem Land. One feral pest that does immense damage to nesting birds, mammals and the habitat is the feral pig. Pigs now exist even in desert areas with seasonal waters.

Classic Mammals: Platypus; Water-rat; False Water-rat; Swamp Rat on marginal swamp; some bats hunt in wetlands at evening, including Common Sheathtail-bat, Little Mastiff-bat, Little Northern Mastiff-bat, Greater Long-eared Bat, Arnhem Land Long-eared Bat, Large-footed Mouse-eared Bat, broad-nosed bats, flying-foxes and the Queensland Blossom Bat.

Right: A huge flock of Magpie Geese descend on Kakadu's South Alligator River floodplain.

water, buried themselves and sealed themselves in "cocoons" until rain fell. Turtles and yabbies dug deep into wetland mud to "hibernate" through the drought. Some fishes learned to wriggle deep under the wet litter of dried billabongs and appear to partially "breathe" air. Invertebrates such as Shield Shrimps produce a multitude of miniscule eggs that sit in the dry, dusty claypan, lagoon and rock hole bottoms and are only triggered into hatching and feverish activity, when submerged following rains. Mobile waterfowl have had to travel long distances to locate water and food, and waders escape seasonal drought by undertaking intercontinental flights. All of these organisms know they must slot themselves into habitats at times that will provide them with food during their highly stressful breeding period and at times when there will be enough food supplies to rear their young.

Ducks and geese provide an excellent example of this sustenance-dependent process. Each species nests when their particular food needs are best provided for. Breeding on the wetlands is wonderfully staged. To quote Dr Harry Frith, who did much to stimulate early interest in this remarkable group of birds:

> The most important breeding grounds are in the lagoons, billabongs, swamps, and creeks of the inland rivers; the Murray, Murrumbidgee, Lachlan and Darling, and the Macquarie, Gwydir, Bogan, Paroo and Bulloo. This I call the "duck hatchery of Australia". In times of very heavy rain on the catchments the effluents cannot carry the flow, and floodwaters, only a few inches deep, creep for many miles across the plains, filling every depression and claypan to form temporary, but vast expanses of breeding habitat. Duck breeding becomes extensive, the local birds are reinforced by nomads, and really great numbers of birds are produced and ultimately spread all over eastern Australia and sometimes western and northern Australia also. The very next year could be drought; the creeks will remain dry and the domestic stock that escaped drowning in one year may perish from thirst the next summer. Under these conditions there is virtually no breeding of ducks and little refuge inland, and the birds in the area must find somewhere to exist. Conservation of breeding habitat in the inland is not so much a matter of reserving swamps to provide undisturbed conditions, though no one would deny the value of this also, as of ensuring that the inland rivers continue to fluctuate in level frequently, so replenishing the lagoons, billabongs and depressions on the plains, and creating the correct breeding habitat for the different species.

Breeding for each vertebrate and invertebrate species occurs at a particular time in the flood cycle, which creates the appropriate environmental conditions for each. These conditions produce or restrict the plants and animals available as a food source, allowing ducks, ibises, herons (or Water-rats for that matter) to settle or to be forced to seek other sustaining habitat. In the case of the Grey Teal, with its diet composed of 41% wetland plant seeds and leaves, 26% terrestrial plants and 33% wetland invertebrates, it may even have to travel continent-wide.

Above, clockwise from top left: Black Swans nest along river systems, allied wetlands and coastal lagoons; the Australasian Grebe inhabits Top End billabongs; Great Egrets are mainly found in temperate and tropical regions but do venture out to semi-arid areas; Magpie Geese are native to Australia and flock to Kakadu wetlands; the elaborately patterned Purple-spotted Gudgeon is found in wet season wetlands, creeks and ponds; still, deep water by shaded banks is the preferred habitat for the Primitive Archerfish; the ornate Chequered Rainbowfish inhabits waterways in Australia's north that flow into the Arafura Sea and Gulf of Carpentaria; Salmon-tailed Catfish swim in tropical rivers, billabongs, and deeper swamps; Australian Shovelers breed in wetlands and watercourses of the Murray–Darling in Australia's south-east.

Birds of the Freshwater Wetlands

Most early studies of waterfowl were led by hunting fraternities from North America and Europe. Both areas showed the absolute dependence on the birds' annual migration — determined by obvious seasons with clearly defined flyways. When State Wildlife Services and the CSIRO began researching here, such distinctive continental flyways could not be found. Australian birds were also found to be controlled by seasonal conditions, but bird behaviour had adapted to the randomness of our semi-arid environment, where rainfall for the past 7–8 million years was almost accidental, apart from in monsoonal areas. Birds had to search for food-producing waters continent-wide. Most regularly, this "irregular" occurrence happened on the wide-reaching Murray–Darling system, which has headwaters in the south-eastern snowfields, and from delinquent tropical cyclones. Such surges of river waters, both major and minor, filled billabongs and other wetlands and produced a wide variety of plant and invertebrate food organisms. Bird species were highly selective from this menu and each species' breeding patterns became tied to certain water surges.

Damming of rivers eliminated many minor rises and it has become more and more difficult for some species to sustain their populations. As announced in 2007, with apparent increasing aridity, even conservation areas with special water-release allocations will dry up as human needs increase. The long-term future of wetlands and waterfowl are in the balance. Birds cannot change dependence and adaptive behaviours set over millions of generations and therefore cannot quickly adapt to such catastrophes.

Fishes of the Freshwater Wetlands

Australia has about 150 native freshwater fish species, of which only four are considered to be old endemics. The rest are "new" indigenous species derived from older marine species that entered the inland water systems. Through millions of generations of evolution, these became adapted to freshwater and the unique shelter and food there. Some, such as Barramundi, still return to the sea during their life histories, and many are distance travellers such as the Golden Perch, which can cover 2000 kilometres in 627 days on its trip from Victoria to Queensland via the Darling River. Such behaviour is now out of synchronisation with human-induced changes to the rivers, including irrigation, flood mitigation and pollution.

Classic Freshwater Fishes: *Old endemics:*
Queensland Lungfish; Spotted Barramundi (Qld); Northern Spotted Barramundi (WA & Qld); Salamander Fish (SW Aust.). *New indigenous fish:* Murray Cod; Golden Perch; Macquarie Perch; Silver Perch; Australian Bass; Western Carp Gudgeon; Lakes Carp Gudgeon; Spangled Perch; River Blackfish; Freshwater Mullet; Tandan Catfish; Salmon-tailed Catfish; Freshwater Herring; Desert Goby; Climbing Galaxia; Trout Cod; Sooty Grunter; Spangled Grunter; Primitive Archerfish; various rainbowfishes; Tailed Sole.

Where Are They? Scattered throughout the semi-arid and aridlands of the mainland States, particularly South Australia, Western Australia and the Northern Territory.

Critical Conditions: Ancient land surface leached of salts, which have collected in lowlands; intense summer heat; low to extremely low annual rainfall; many are the depressions of local internal drainage basins with frequently high water tables.

Best Examples: *SA* — Lakes Torrens, Eyre South, Eyre North, Frome (in Gammon Ranges National Park), Gairdner, Windabout and Hart; Pernatty and Gillies Lagoons. *WA* — Lakes Cowan, Gilmore group, Lefroy (Kambalda), King, Grace, Moore, Monger, Ballard, Austin, Anneen, McLeod and Gregory. *NT* — Amadeus chain of lakes; Curtin Springs, Lasseter Highway east of Mount Connor Lookout; Lake Lewis. *NSW* — Salt Lake (Cobham); Gum Lake group; numerous saline depressions. *Vic* — Sea Lake; Pink Lakes; numerous saline sinks.

Sounds: When dry, silence; after rains, a choir of birds.

Smells: Brine; seashore aromas.

Sensations: Glare and blistering heat.

Above: Samphire is a highly resilient plant, surviving in dried out coastal lagoons, as shown, but also in extreme salty habitats.

Flora of Inland Salt Lakes and Salinas

The salt lake surface is toxic to almost all plants except for rare algae and lichens with special cells that can hold back water from the powerful osmotic pressures. Even the beach verges are impregnated with salt and exposed to wind and sand and salt blast, powerful solar radiation and rare violent downpours. It is no surprise that most plants here will have small leaves with thick, waxy surfaces, few stomates and often a capacity to store water and an ability to separate and secrete salt.

Classic Plants: Algal mats on some salt surfaces, otherwise this habitat is largely plant-free; samphire (*Tecticornia verrucosa*); *Melaleuca* spp.; Lignum; Nitrebush; Sandhill Canegrass; Roly Poly.

Inland Salt Lakes and Salinas

Notwithstanding the flowers and the grasses, and occasional small birds, the Lake Eyre region had still cast its queer spell over us. It is like entering a vast tomb; one hesitates to break the silence … overshadowing all in the qualities of death is the very heart of the region, the great lake itself, a horrible travesty, a vast white prostrate, salt-filled ghost of a lake. Here time seems to have stood still for ages. We had seen one sluggish vein quickened in the north, the Warburton [River]. Sea and river birds had gathered there, bringing a show of life that threw into greater relief the deadness of the rest.

Charles Madigan, in *Crossing the Dead Heart*, a record of the first crossing of the Simpson Desert in 1939.

Until 1949, when torrential downpours from tropical cyclones occurred in the deep south of the Gulf of Carpentaria, the twentieth century had not produced enough rain to run the great watercourses of the Warburton and Diamantina Rivers and Cooper Creek into Lake Eyre. The years 1920–21 (and indeed most of the following two decades through to 1939) had been intensely dry and hot — influencing Madigan's perception of Lake Eyre as he made his way down its eastern edge. Early in 1974, heavy rainfall began again and for four years that "ghost of a lake" was a gleaming Prussian-blue oasis in the desert before it once again became a "travesty". Inland Australia is a country of long drought and brief respites. Wetlands are at the wet end of extreme habitats, but salt-dominated country and lakes are at the truly arid end! Not only are most salt lakes situated in the arid interior, but salt and saltwater exerts strong osmotic pressure on cells, drawing the more diluted, life-sustaining cellular fluids out of organisms and dehydrating them.

Where, however, did all this salt come from? Australia is ancient and relatively flat. North of Ooldea in South Australia, dunes 34 million years old create basin-like ranges above the Nullarbor. Over the ceaseless passage of time, the sea invaded some of these great inland basins, such as the Murravian Basin, flooding and retreating from them according to sea level and tectonic movements. Each time saltwater engulfed these basins, salt and soil infusions resulted. Over that time, too, in-flowing streams carried with them dissolved salts. In the case of Lake Eyre, an inland drainage system formed as the land sank to 16 metres or more below sea level and the large south-west Queensland and Finke Rivers carried in, over time, huge quantities of salts. While Australia dried out as it drifted northwards towards the equator, evaporation rates rose, leaving huge pans of salt-encrusted dust. About 35,000 years ago, widespread dune formation began. Dusty lake beds in the path of the westerly winds were scoured and their coarser "salty" sands piled into broad, usually single, crescent dunes that wrapped around the eastern edge — the lunette. For the rest of inland Australia, long linear dune systems were swept into place — Nature's impression of the vast, circular patterns powered by anti-cyclonic winds. However, across the ancient network of west Australian rivers, sand sheets and dunes cut channels that formed linear salt lakes comprised of old river segments.

Salt is deliquescent: it attracts water. The salty, muddy surface of most salt lakes remains damp even in the very low humidity of the inland. Over the lake's life, mud separates and sinks below the salt-encrusted surface. Beds of glistening gypsum crystals form in surrounding saline mudflats. Winds continually add salty dust to the sticky, puff-roughened surface, as well as the salt-encrusted, dehydrated corpses of dead insects such as grasshoppers, mole crickets, spiders and

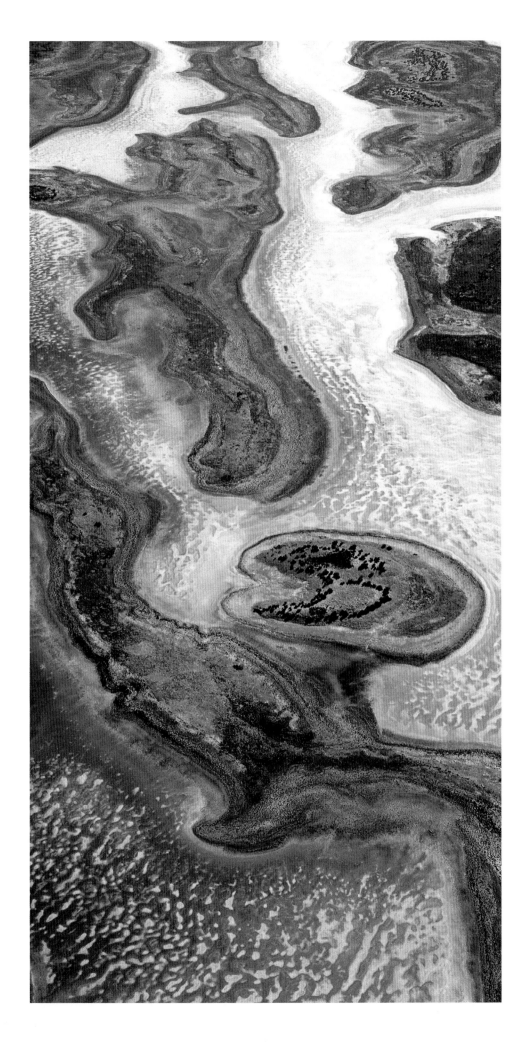

Above: The Lake Eyre Dragon has a range limited to the salt lakes around Lake Eyre in South Australia's arid inland, where its mottled white and sandy brown colouring gives it excellent camouflage for a life burrowing beneath the salt-encrusted surface. *Left:* Napperby Lake, Northern Territory, is a classic salt lake. Like many of Western Australia's salt lakes this lake follows the depression marking an old watercourse.

Frogs and Reptiles of Inland Salt Lakes and Salinas

These habitats are the most extreme, but even here there may be a great range of conditions. Most are fed by drainage systems, the gullies of which may contain waterholes with variable degrees of salinity and water temperature ranging from 5 to 35°C+ with very low oxygen levels. In or by these pools when salinity is lowest, or in the damp depths of surrounding sand dunes, frogs can be found, albeit rarely. Salt and heat dehydrate frogs, with fatal results. In effect, frogs are not present bar the rare burrowing Desert Spadefoot in adjacent sand.

Salt lakes are vast death traps for most vertebrates and invertebrates. Here, temperatures are extreme, there is total wind exposure and exposure to sunlight. On the sandy and shrubby verge are millions of salt-dried, mummified invertebrates and small vertebrates: grasshoppers, beetles, cockroaches, wasps, spiders, centipedes, finches, dragons, skinks and many more. Flying animals are caught when they misjudge the distance across these featureless flats. Once they hit the usually damp, super-salty surface they are usually doomed. A species of toe-walking dragon forages among the recent, soon-to-die victims, while others such as the world's second-largest lizard, the Perentie, a Varanid, will also seek salty morsels around the edge of its sand dune home.

Invertebrates of Inland Salt Lakes and Salinas

Summery, dry lake surfaces have little to offer the invertebrate, but when rainstorms cover the surface with brackish water vast flushes of some species occur. Mosquito wriggler larvae, midge larvae, brine shrimps, water fleas, numerous flies and even Shield Shrimps find the warm lakes of brine a habitat paradise. If the streaming channels sweep in populations of small fishes or their eggs, such as Central Australian Hardyheads and Bony Bream, then there is vast feasting for wading birds, as happens in Lake Eyre. Salt lakes are habitats of boom and bust where speed of life (or maturity) is crucial to success!

Above: Spangled Perch are common Australian fish with a wide distribution. They are very tolerant of environmental conditions, inhabiting both fresh- and saltwater at varying pH levels.

Fishes of Inland Salt Lakes and Salinas

Salt lakes range from those with a crusty salt surface to those that flood sporadically. These irregularly filled lakes may range in salinity from 1 part salt to 1000 of water to being hyper-saline at 380 parts per 1000. These systems often run from stony hills with deep rockholes that contain not only pools of freshwater but pools of fish life. They are shallow, and can become very warm (3–40°C), with oxygen levels ranging from zero to super-saturation. These are incredibly tough environmental conditions but, given enough time, variant fish ultimately evolve. Populations of 26 species in the Lake Eyre Basin boom for a short time on the masses of brine-loving insect larvae and invertebrates that erupt following freshwater rains or floods.

Classic Fishes: Australian Catfish; rainbowfishes; Spangled Grunters; Lake Eyre Hardyheads; Bony Bream; Central Australian Goby; Western Chanda; Yellow Belly.

Above: Low-growing samphire is able to withstand the salty, arid conditions around Australia's salt lakes and inland salinas where few other plants can tolerate the extreme environment.

Opposite, top: A male Orange Chat at nest. Chats protect their chicks by building nests in dense thickets of vegetation that surround some of the most inhospitable lakes in Australia. *Opposite, bottom:* During "boom" times on inland lakes, Australian Pelican populations can increase dramatically.

centipedes that live in the surrounding fleshy samphire, saltbush, Nitrebush and Dune Canegrass bordering salt flats and dunes. All long-term life in these places requires special adaptations to survive dehydration. Such modifications include the thickened skins of Shinglebacks, internal water-recycling systems in Spinifex Hopping-mice, salt-secreting systems for saltbush, and water storage in samphire.

Understanding our continental living systems requires us to look at salt lakes and salinas over the long term. After only 30 or so years of observing the region, Madigan, an eminent geographer, concluded that the place was a "vast tomb". In 1939, he glimpsed changes that might occur as he crossed the Warburton River at the end of its flood. After breaking through massive dunes blocking the river channels in 1949, the Warburton River did indeed flood the lake, sweeping in with it an entire aquatic living system. Organic mud, which quickly settled under the action of dissolving salt, brought with it the "seeds" of life: cyanobacteria, algae and zooplankton (including seed shrimps, water fleas, insect eggs and larvae, as well as the larval stages of fishes such as Central Australian Hardyhead, Bony Bream and Golden Perch). Here was the basis for a temporary ecosystem with phytoplankton as the base and Golden Perch as the top consumer. This ecosystem, however, could only survive intact providing water temperature and salinity remained at levels in which these organisms could live. Fortunately, all of these species were well-adapted to dramatic swings in temperature and salinity.

By all accounts, the volume of life in Lake Eyre's waters within a year was staggering. Australian Pelicans, cormorants, stilts, Black, Grey and Chestnut Teals, Australian Shelducks, Freckled Ducks, Silver Gulls and Whiskered Terns all enjoyed the bonanza that was 1950 on the lake. Tens of thousands of Australian Pelicans hatched on island rookeries, but the following year drought had returned, decimating the chicks and leaving, in turn, a bonanza for scavengers. By 1956, Lake Eyre was again a wasteland. This cycle returned again in 1974–78 and briefly in 1984–85 — all were caused by tropical influences. In 1992, Lake Torrens, another massive salt lake west of the Flinders Ranges, was flooded by winter rains and on one island over 10,000 Banded Stilts nested.

Above: Salt forms crusty-ridged barriers around puddles on the evaporating Lake MacDonnell in South Australia's Great Australian Bight. The saltwater that seeps into Lake MacDonnell through porous coastal dunes contains approximately 3.6% of dissolved salts. After evaporation it is about 77% sodium chloride — or salt as we know it. Salt for the world's tables is still produced by solar evaporation at Lake MacDonnell.

Birds of Inland Salt Lakes and Salinas

For millions of years this continent has been gradually dehydrating. Indigenous and migratory bird species, well adapted to earlier, more humid times, also underwent slow changes in behaviour and physiology to fit the new climate. Through repetitive trial and error, their makeup "remembered" patterns of life — the irregular monsoon floodings and abundance of food organisms in the continent's interior. These memories were incorporated into the life cycles of some species, enabling them to breed large numbers of offspring on the inland lakes to repair population losses occurring elsewhere. Many waterbirds, swimmers and waders now count salt lakes as essential parts of their habitat.

Classic Birds: Grey Teal; Chestnut Teal; Pink-eared, Hardhead, Pacific Black Ducks and Australian Shoveler; Little Black Cormorant; Australian Pelican; Intermediate and Great Egrets; White-faced and White-necked Herons; Whistling Kite; Wedge-tailed Eagle; White-bellied Sea-Eagle; Swamp Harrier; Black Falcon; Black-tailed Native Hen; Black-tailed Godwit; Marsh Sandpiper; Common Greenshank; Sharp-tailed Sandpiper; Curlew Sandpiper; Red-necked, Banded and Black-winged Stilts; Red-necked Avocet; Australian Pratincole; Red-capped Plover; Black-fronted Dotterel; Red-kneed Dotterel; Silver Gull; Caspian Tern; Gull-billed Tern; Whiskered Tern; Night Parrot.

Where Are They? Across arid Australia.

What Do They Look Like? Linear dunes, sometimes 150 kilometres long and 20 metres high with hummocks on top; long firm, windward slopes about six times the dune height, with steep, loose lee sides where sand spills over to a width of about one dune height; net-like dunes where there are random wind parabolic blowouts.

Critical Conditions: Extended periods of strong, prevailing winds; very hot summers and the occasional destabilising influences of fire and severe drought.

Best Examples: *NT* — Uluṟu National Park; Chambers Pillar; Watarrka National Park; Mount Connor Area. *Qld* — Birdsville. *NSW* — Lake Cobham Area. *WA* — Canning Stock Route; Great Sandy Desert. *SA* — Simpson Desert; Great Victoria Desert; Lake Frome area.

Sounds: Australian Ravens; Little and Torresian Crows; silence; wind in Desert Oaks and Mulga.

Smells: Dry dust; decaying carcasses; musky sweetness of Honey Grevillea and *Micromyrtus*; wet earth after storms.

Sensations: Intense glare; dust in the eyes, nose and throat; unrelieved heat; thirst.

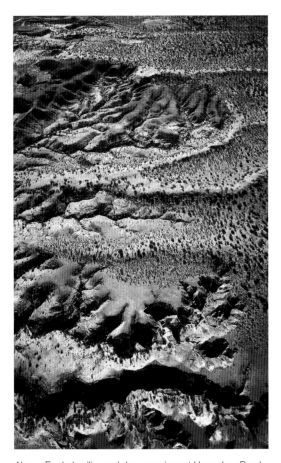

Above: Eroded gullies and dune cappings at Horseshoe Bend, Finke River, Northern Territory. *Right:* Strong winds during drought raise a swirl of dust in Finke River country, where the Mulga scrub has been destroyed by grazing stock.

Sandy Deserts

A vast succession of sand-ridges, north and south in direction and fiery red in colour, except near the channels of the great floodplains [Diamantina], where the whole land surface is bleached to a pale yellow ochre. Between the sand hills are either clay-pans or gibber plains, and away from the channels the vegetation is so sparse and lowly that it does nothing to hide the great nakedness of the land. Towards noon the heat and luminosity become terrific, and looking into the still, silent glare, I thought that no better picture of arid sterility could be painted. Yet it is by no means so.

H.H. Finlayson, zoologist, at the edge of the Simpson Desert and Sturt's Stony Desert in 1936.

Australia's extreme desert dunes were swept into place by strong anti-cyclonic winds around 40,000–30,000 years ago. Today, they are still the playthings of the wind, particularly after bushfires or severe droughts. Winnowing in the wind and saturation from time to time by intense, highly unpredictable rains has, over 30,000 years, blown and washed out the fine dusty clays into the swales, where they form the water-filled claypans in which Shield Shrimps play out their brief life cycles.

Dunes of coarser sand allow waters to sink into the dune core, where a layer of dampness survives the drought, insulated by a metre or so of loose sand and vegetation. In this layer, moisture provides for quite a diverse community of plants: grevilleas, acacias, Camel Poison Bush, Soft Spinifex and needlewood. Like all other extreme habitats, life on desert dunes requires special modifications. These plants usually have two rooting systems — a very shallow, widespread net to immediately collect whatever surface moisture falls, accounting for the very rapid response to rain showers, and deep roots that drive into the damp dune core or even deeper (as do the Mulga and Desert Oak).

Once water is drawn into the plant, it must then be conserved. Rains may not eventuate again for many months and the summers are extremely hot, with desiccating winds. To reduce dehydration, oaks have reduced their leaves to scales; Mulga and *Grevillea* species to silvery strap-like, wax-covered leaves; spinifex to very thin, tightly rolled, almost woody leaves in dense tussocks; and herbs like Parakeelya to thick, fleshy, water-storing leaves.

Animals also have their protective devices and habits, including the Thorny Devil, barking spiders, Southern Marsupial Mole and desert burrowers, along with Children's Pythons, the Woma and Western Brown Snakes.

DESERT DUNE

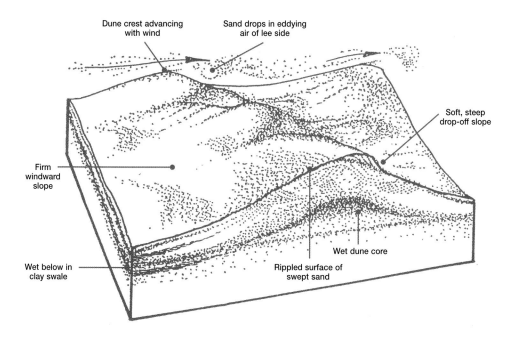

Dune crest advancing with wind

Sand drops in eddying air of lee side

Soft, steep drop-off slope

Firm windward slope

Wet below in clay swale

Rippled surface of swept sand

Wet dune core

AUSTRALIAN DUNE PATTERNS OF THE INLAND

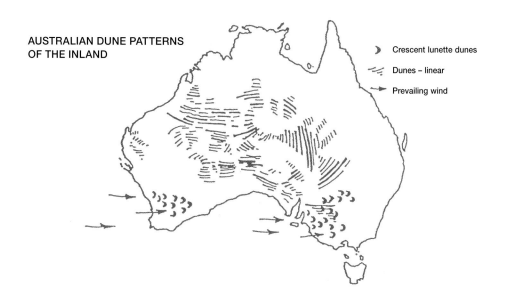

> Crescent lunette dunes

/// Dunes – linear

→ Prevailing wind

Above: Wind sculpts the red dunes into fantastic linear patterns and dislodges larger grains. Heavy winds can set an entire sand surface in motion. *Below:* Wildflowers and desert plants bloom resplendently after rain and what at first seems a barren, inhospitable landscape becomes an inland flower garden.

Birds of the Sandy Deserts

The outstanding feature of sandy desert country is irregular, unpredictable rainfall across vast areas. To survive here, larger vertebrates must, therefore, be very mobile and able to move between habitats to sustain themselves. Seed eaters and other dry food consumers must live close to water supplies. Birds are the classic mobile animals able to live such nomadic lifestyles and Budgerigars and finches are perhaps the best examples. After above-average rainfall, grasses grow rapidly, flower and seed, creating a glut of food near full claypans and waterholes. Spiny Dead Finish Acacia shrubs become loaded with grassy Zebra Finch nests, and hollows in River Red Gums by the creeks and in Desert Bloodwoods across the flood plains become nesting sites for bickering Budgerigars. With clutch sizes from four to eight eggs and as many as three broods in a good season, "Budgie" populations skyrocket. When drought returns and water evaporates, the massive green flocks begin wider and wider sweeps in search of water. Sometimes they move to a waterhole too far from the next available water, and tens of thousands, probably millions, perish. But always a core population will have selected a permanent waterhole and await the next good season before bringing forth another "plague" of Budgies.

Classic Birds: Emus; White-fronted Honeyeater; Wedge-tailed Eagle; Grey-crowned Babbler; Grey Butcherbird; Western Gerygone; Slaty-backed and Chestnut-rumped Thornbill; Mulga Parrot; Budgerigar.

Mammals of the Sandy Deserts

Sandy deserts are rarely endless dune fields. In Australia they are in fact a veneer of sand covering an older land surface that is cut and shaped from country rock, as well as mesas and tablelands of some sedimentary material, often capped with a resistant layer of silcrete, ferricrete and laterite. These (particularly silcrete which is as tough and resistant as porcelain) act as a "roof" over the tableland. Often deep recesses weathered and eroded from the softer material beneath, create cool caverns with at least a 30% higher humidity than outside. These areas are highly valuable in preserving body moisture and sheltering mammals such as Common Wallaroos, rock-wallabies, small marsupials and native rodents, as well as many reptiles. Feral goats have caused much damage by evicting native species from these cool refuges.

The Red Kangaroo, however, is a true open-country animal that has an exceedingly efficient internal water-conservation physiology and has proved successful in these dry habitats. However, in severe drought, even Red Kangaroos may be forced to move to seek out shade and water.

Classic Mammals: Marsupial moles; Greater Bilby; Spinifex Hopping-mouse; Red Kangaroo; Common Wallaroo; Striped-faced Dunnart.

Above, top to bottom: Emus travel great distances (sometimes up to 25 kilometres a day) to find sustenance. They are omnivorous, pecking at invertebrates and animal droppings when there is an absence of grass, leaves, flowers and fruit; Australia's two unusual marsupial mole species warrant their own order, Notoryctemorphia. These totally blind, spade-footed marsupials spend most of their lives underground, "swimming" through the desert soils.

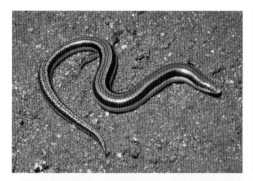

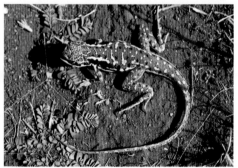

Above, clockwise from top left: The Southern Slider (*Lerista labialis*) finds solace under leaf litter or loose upper layers of sand; resembling scattered sand particles helps the Smooth Knob-tailed Gecko (*Nephrurus levis*) avoid predators; a formidable hunter, the Desert Death Adder (*Acanthophis pyrrhus*); the Crowned Gecko (*Diplodactylus stenodactylus*) seeks refuge in abandoned spider burrows or cracks in the soil; Central Military Dragon (*Ctenophorus isolepis*); the Red Tree-frog (*Litoria rubella*) can withstand extreme elements; Desert Spadefoot (*Notaden nichollsi*).

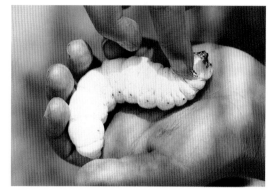

Above: The fat, white larvae of moths in the genus *Endoxyla*, and of some beetle species, are known as Witchetty Grubs and are a traditional food source for Aboriginal people.

Invertebrates of the Sandy Deserts

The soil environment in the desert is so dry and desiccated that normal processes of decomposition and return of nutrients to the ecosystem cannot take place. Thus the most crucial desert animal is the termite, which recycles the tough tissue of desert plants, particularly spinifex, and builds the mud towers that punctuate the great sandy expanse of the Tanami Desert. At Uluṟu, another termite species tunnels a subterranean honeycomb of storage cells in which to hoard trillions of neatly cut pieces of spinifex grass food. The "wet" gut of termites sustains the gut flora of bacteria and fungi, allowing this insect's digestive system to break down grass matter. Without termites, deserts would be devoid of nutrients.

In the soft dune surface, giant hairy barking spiders build their nests and forage for food. Trapdoor spiders also seek out clay-filled surfaces between the dunes. Open burrows are usually fatal during violent storms or floods, unless some kind of tight-fitting door can be attached; hence the trapdoor that can be pulled shut. Very large nocturnally foraging centipedes are also quite common. All of these animals leave a fascinating story in their tracks across the fine sandy slopes.

Classic Invertebrates: Spiders; grasshoppers; beetles; centipedes; Sand or Mole Crickets; scorpions.

Frogs and Reptiles of the Sandy Deserts

Australia's arid zone carries a very high lizard species diversity compared with arid regions elsewhere. Dragons stand extended on their very long toes, holding their bodies off the hot sand. Snakes do not have this luxury, so become almost entirely nocturnal in warmer months, spending daylight hours under logs or tussocks. Some pythons and other reptiles partially bury themselves and even "swim" through the sand.

Classic Frogs and Reptiles: Desert Spadefoot; Red Tree-frog; Woma; Children's Python; Eastern and Western Brown Snakes; King Brown Snake; Burton's Snake-lizard; Gilbert's Dragon; Central Netted Dragon; Thorny Devil; Central Military Dragon; Jacky Lizard; Desert Blue-tongue; skinks; Spiny-tailed Gecko; Crowned Gecko; Smooth Knob-tailed Gecko.

Flora of the Sandy Deserts

Two major landforms dominate the sandy desert: dune areas and the sand plains. Dunes exhibit a rich variety of vegetation in zoned patterns related to the depth of moist sand. After rapid downpours, water dissolves clays in the soil as it travels down through the sand, depositing liquid among sand grains in the dune's core. Surplus muddy water ultimately runs down the face or leaks out onto the inter-dune area forming a claypan. Soil on the dune crest will be porous and loose, ranging to a hard, clayey surface in the swale. Particular plants favour each of the soil quality and moisture regimes; thus the crest will be colonised by Camel Poison Bush, Sandhill Canegrass, *Acacia* species, Honeysuckle Spider Flower (*Grevillea juncifolia*), Sandhill Desert Bloodwood and some spinifex. The upper slopes have Rattle-pod Grevillea (*G. stenobotrya*), Mulga, mallee and denser spinifex. The lower slopes are of Desert Oak, Thryptomene, Bush Plum, Yellow Flame Grevillea (*G. eriostachya*), Needlewood (*Hakea leucoptera*), Mulla Mulla, Weeping Pittosporum, Senna, Colony Wattle and Witchetty Bush. Claypan areas have Victoria Wattle, Parakeelya, Gidgee, Desert Oaks, Umbrella Mulga, Desert Pea and Darling Pea, various *Hibiscus*, *Gossypium*, *Abutilon* and *Sida* spp, Native Tomato *Solanums* and Paddy Melons; where there has been free-standing water in the swales, Nardoo Fern will probably be present.

Classic Flora: Camel Poison Bush; Sandhill Canegrass; *Acacia* species; Honeysuckle Spider Flower (*G. juncifolia*); Sandhill Desert Bloodwood; Spinifex; Rattle-pod Grevillea (*G. stenobotrya*); Mulga; mallee; Desert Oak; Thryptomene; Bush Plum; Yellow Flame Grevillea (*G. eriostachya*); Needlewood (*Hakea leucoptera*); Mulla Mulla; Weeping Pittosporum; Senna; Colony Wattle; Witchetty Bush; Victoria Wattle; Parakeelya; Gidgee; Umbrella Mulga; Desert and Darling Peas; *Hibiscus* and *Gossypium* spp; Abutilon and Sida spp; Native Tomatoes (*Solanum* spp.); Nardoo Fern.

Above left, top to bottom: Senecio sp.; Lilac Hibiscus (*Alyogyne huegelii*); Spotted Emu Bush (*Eremophila maculata*); Rattle-pod Grevillea (*Grevillea stenobotrya*). *Above centre, top to bottom*: Greenbird Flower (*Crotalaria cunninghamii*); Crimson Turkeybush (*Eremophila latrobei*); Everlasting Daisy (*Brachyscome* sp.); Sturt's Desert Pea (*Swainsona formosa*). *Above right, top to bottom: Olearia* sp.; Honeysuckle Spider Flower (*Grevillea juncifolia*); Round-leaved Parakeelya (*Calandrinia remota*); Silver Cassia (*Senna atemisioides*). *Left:* Everlasting Daisies bloom in dune fields near Mount Augustus, Western Australia.

Above, top to bottom: Granite ridges south-west of Marble Bar, Western Australia, bloom with Sturt's Desert Pea, spinifex tussocks and Needlewood; desert dunes spring to life with Mulga and *Grevillea* tall shrubs with an understorey of spinifex hummocks, Pink Turkeybush and herbs after rain at Gascoyne Junction, Western Australia.

Where Are They? Wherever the underlying country rock has been exposed by the weather or the sea or remains exposed following earlier volcanic formation. Increased sea levels due to global warming will rejuvenate coastal cliffs. The type of rock lends specific shape to the cliffs and caverns. Sandstone and shale bedding planes produce shelving between vertical mass fall cliffs, as in the Blue Mountains (NSW) or the Grampians (Vic). Folded, shattered and faulted metamorphic rocks, such as slates and quartzites, produce abrupt hollows and sharp ledges with surfaces breaking down into rugged talus slopes, as at Simpsons Gap (NT) the Flinders Ranges (SA) the Kimberley (WA) and south-west Tasmania. Limestone with water and chemical erosion provides the greatest cave systems, as at Jenolan Caves, Yarrangobilly and Abercrombie (NSW), Nullarbor Caves (WA), Cutta Cutta Caves (NT), Mount Etna and Chillagoe Caves (Qld) and Hastings Caves (Tas).

Critical Conditions: Ledges isolated by cliffs that predators cannot climb and offering strategic views as required by Peregrine Falcons and Ospreys. Clefts and crevices that cannot be entered by predators or breached by weather or fire. Limestone caves that maintain humidity and offer stable temperatures.

Above: Dramatic stalagmite formations in Jenolan Caves, New South Wales. *Below:* The world's longest volcanic lava tubes form caves in Undara Volcanic National Park, Queensland.

Cliffs, Caves and Rocky Places

For half a mile, this gorge which is nothing more than a zig-zag cleft cuts its way right through the range. Its narrow bed is filled with water, deep and intensely cold and on either side the red jagged rocks of quartzite rise precipitously for several hundred feet.

It is upon the shady sides of these gorges that many of the most characteristic Larapintine plants have found shelter, and it is in them also that the water holes are really permanent and here also must live the fish which in times of flood are carried away to the south to stock the waterholes along the rivers.

Professor Baldwin Spencer, in *The Horn Scientific Expedition*, describing Redbank Gorge in the MacDonnell Ranges, Northern Territory, 1894.

Rocks are the framework of the landscape, over which the water, soil and living systems are draped. Different types of rock weather and erode in different ways. Some are much more resistant to chemical attack, some do not easily dissolve in water, others are very brittle, cracking and breaking up readily with temperature change, yet others simply rot. Once rocks are loosened, gravity does the rest.

One would expect, given that scientists date the Earth as some 4.6 billion years old, that the rate of erosion would have levelled the country to sea level long ago; but the planet's surface is, in fact, under constant and incredible pressures, powerful enough to cause buckling of the land's surface and to move the continent about 5 centimetres a year (and others up to 18 centimetres a year). The Earth's continental plates are from 25 to 70 kilometres thick and float on very hot, molten plastic rock. As the plates move, their edges collide and buckle, while other parts stretch and bulge. Mountainous masses are uplifted, basins form and volcanic vents release lava under pressure. Country is fractured and folded, and weathering and erosion by wind, water and ice wear it down, depositing the sediment in base-level lakes and seas, where it forms sedimentary rocks such as conglomerate, sandstone and shale. Once life on Earth began, coral beds and reefs grew on the warm, shallow-water sea floors, and their calcium carbonate skeletons later formed limestone. Beds of mineral-collecting algae settled out, along with other organic collectors, and formed other limestones and banded ironstones.

Above, clockwise from top left: Admiral's Arch, Kangaroo Island, South Australia, is a weathered cavern under a cap of old sand dune rich in calcium carbonate that is now limestone; disruptions below the Earth's surface, and the incising waters of rivers above, cleft great chasms in rock, as here at Weano Gorge in Karijini National Park, Western Australia; Kata Tjuṯa in Uluṟu–Kata Tjuṯa National Park comprises 38 weathered peaks shaped from conglomerate rock; granite tors blackened by growth of cyanobacteria and lichens on Rocky Hill south-west of Marble Bar, Western Australia; the massive terraced cliff opposite the Oxers Lookout in Joffre Gorge, Western Australia, provides prime rock-wallaby habitat.

Above: A cavernous opening in sandstone near Oenpelli, in the Northern Territory. *Below right:* Chestnut-quilled Rock-pigeons.

Flora of Cliffs, Caves and Rocky Places

Rock type and structure produces a landscape of varied resistance to weathering and erosion. The most resistant kinds are on the apex of ridges and beetling cliffs. Sloped aspects invariably produce faces that are wetter than others and these damp places attract bacteria, algae and lichen. These all help to weather the surfaces, to roughen them and to fill out any joints, bedding planes and structural faults. Soils accumulate and in damp places larger plants, such as mosses, ferns, grasses and small shrubs, begin a colonising process, providing food and special shelter for invertebrate and vertebrate consumers. Plants make these rocky places habitable for fauna but the species mix will depend upon the geographic location of the site, whether it is tropical, temperate or arid.

Classic Flora: Rock ferns; various mosses; lichens; Nodding Blue Lily; *Stypandra glauca*; *Stipa* spp.; *Danthonia* spp.; triggerplants; a number of daisies; Caustic Bush; Rock Fig; Turkeybush; Spearwood; Broad-leaved Hopbush; spinifex.

Birds of Cliffs, Cave and Rocky Places

Birds build nests in these places because they offer a strategic advantage over predators or assist in finding food. They also provide shelter from harsh environmental conditions. Thus the Peregrine Falcon nests on strategically located, secure high ledges where it gets a clear view of prey below its roost, from which it can launch an attack. The Osprey selects exposed high cliffs near a waterway, where it has a clear view of the water to assist its search for fish — an advantage judged more important than the uncomfortable exposure of chicks to the weather.

Classic Birds: Peregrine Falcon; Osprey; Rock Warblers; Welcome Swallow; Fairy Martin; Little Woodswallow; Sandstone Shrike-thrush; Superb Lyrebird; Blue-winged Parrot; White-quilled and Chestnut-quilled Rock-Pigeon; White-bellied Sea Eagle; White-faced Storm Petrel.

The country we see today is composed of a mosaic of rock types that temporarily hold their form. Their compositions and weathering create the shape of the landscape — granite, rounded form; quartzite and other metamorphic rock, jagged, chaotic landscapes as at Federation Peak, or flowing forms as in the Kimberley or Flinders Ranges; sandstones and shales in stratified layers, sometimes horizontal as in the Blue Mountains and Carnarvon Gorge, or tilted and stepped as in the Grampians; cones and spires in the igneous rock of the Glass House Mountains and Warrumbungles.

ROCKY FORTRESSES FOR FAUNA

Where the rocks are resisting erosion they are exposed as bare rock spires, peaks, cliffs, tors, ridges, mesas, buttes, tablelands and hogsbacks or cuestas — all provide very specialised habitats for plants and animals. Prior to European settlement, steep rocky slopes and cliffs broken by terraces and ledges, wherever they occurred in Australia (except in Tasmania), were the principal habitat for more than ten species of rock-wallaby. Rock-wallabies are incredibly agile, having long, balancing tails and broad hind feet with heavily treaded soles. Because aridland species live where water is frequently unobtainable, they have also developed efficient water-recycling strategies and an ability to obtain much of their water from their diet. They also shelter from daytime heat in caverns and rock talus slopes, where temperatures are 10–15 degrees cooler and humidity is up to 20% higher.

Another animal that uses hollows, shelves and slots in higher, sheer cliffs for nesting is the Peregrine Falcon. Nests built on these heights not only provide fledglings with protection from predators, they are also usually sited on cliff faces below which other birds, such as cockatoos and pigeons, have to move to water — the eyries thus become launching pads for these "express" predators to rapidly swoop down on passing prey.

Cavernous weathering of sedimentary rock and limestone creates the steady temperature, humidity and light conditions required by many bats, which form large colonies in some caves. Massive deposits of bat guano in some caves, such as at Wooltana in the Gammon Ranges of South Australia, have sustained a fertiliser industry for years. They are also wonderful repositories for fossil remains, showing lengthy periods of animal use (such as Naracoorte Caves World Heritage Area). Caves can tell a story of an animal in retreat when it comes to the carnivorous Ghost Bat, which is now found only in Northern Australia.

Mammals of the Cliffs, Caves and Rocky Places

Rock-wallabies epitomise the rocky-places habitat and this large group ranges from the cat-sized Monjon and Nabarlek to the larger Brush-tailed Rock-wallaby. The Monjon's size and rapid movements are ideal for living among the broken boulders of sandstone cliffs and among the large, dense hummocks of spinifex, and their speed helps to avoid attacks by Wedge-tailed Eagle predators. Rock-wallabies' soles are covered with a coarse non-slip tread and their sooty grey to rufous or black skin colour renders them almost invisible among the recesses of boulder streams or caverns. The Common Wallaroo is also widespread across this habitat.

Classic mammals of the rocky and cavernous climes are bats, which have special sensing adaptations to allow rapid movement and communication in places of little or no light.

Classic Mammals: Ghost Bat; Eastern Horseshoe Bat; Bent-winged Bat; Little Pied Bat; Large-footed Bat; Eastern Broad-nosed Bat; Little Mastiff-bat; Northern Quoll; Eastern Quoll; Rock Ringtail Possum; various rock-wallabies; Common Wallaroo; Stick-nest Rat; Yellow-footed Antechinus; Brown Antechinus; Mountain Pygmy-possum (Alpine Boulder Streams).

Above, clockwise from top left: Black-flooted Rock-wallaby at Simpsons Gap, MacDonnell Ranges, Northern Territory; a Northern Quoll forages among sandstone boulders at Kakadu National Park, Northern Territory; sandstone clefts in rock shelter the Rock Ringtail Possum; Ghost Bats, seen here in a sandstone cavern in Kakadu National Park are carnivorous bats, consuming lizards, small mammals and larger insects.

Frogs and Reptiles of the Cliffs, Caves and Rocky Places

Boulder piles and caverns are often used as shelter for frogs and reptiles. When the rock surface is very hot, snakes and lizards move underground. A number of pythons, such as the Oenpelli Python and Olive Python, favour rocky habitat, particularly in tropical and arid areas, where they can retreat beneath rock slabs into relative coolness. Diamond Pythons are commonly found on the sandstone escarpments around Sydney. Because reptiles depend upon the outside air temperature to regulate their body temperature, many reptiles utilise stone country seasonally.

Loose slabs are favourite places for the Ring-tailed Dragon, and many geckoes (such as the rare Giant Cave Gecko) live in sandstone caves around the Kimberley Coast. Black Pygmy Monitors are frequently seen at Uluṟu. The giant Perentie is wide-ranging and will occupy caverns beneath the hard layers of calcium carbonate in desert country.

Classic Frogs and Reptiles: Green Tree-frog; Olive Python; Copland's Rock Frog; Carpenter Frog; Oenpelli Python; Ring-tailed Dragon; Perentie; Bearded Dragon; geckoes such as the Marbled Velvet Gecko and Knob-tailed Gecko; Crevice Skinks.

Invertebrates of the Cliffs, Caves and Rocky Places

Many fascinating invertebrates use exposed rocky places and caves, including the Bogong Moth, which aestivates in summer beneath rocky slabs on the high tops of Kosciuszko National Park and is a traditional summer food for Aborigines.

Above, clockwise from top left: A monitor warms itself on sandstone at Ubirr, Kakadu, NT; large Green Tree-frogs are sometimes found in groups in the damp caverns of northern Australia; Olive Pythons are frequently seen basking on warm rocks by waterholes: dragons are commonly seen on rock screes and broken slopes.

Where Are They?

Where Are They? When considering wildlife, refuges are places of shelter, protection or safety. Since 1788, Australian habitats have suffered modification by human activities and that of our domesticated stock. Until quite recently we little understood the impact we had on our environment. Thankfully, refuges of many sizes, that we may have seen as unused, second-rate land, escaped our exploitation and are now scattered across areas of Australia.

It is clear that residual habitat refuges require protection. These relic refuges are so rare and critical to the survival of specialised species that they cannot be left to manage themselves.

Critical Conditions: Any definition cannot be of value to all species because the needs of each "refuge-dependent" species vary. A refuge requires security from invading environmental impacts, such as feral animals, fire, flood, pollution and drought for its long-term value. If a primary resource of the habitat, such as an extensive watering system, is cut off, then the refuge vanishes.

Above: Lawn Hill Gorge in Lawn Hill National Park, Queensland, is protected by its national park status and is a superb refuge for freshwater life as its headwaters and water supply are spring fed.

Refuges

Gondwana almost certainly was the birthplace of rainforests about 100 million years ago. Ancient elements have miraculously survived here [Daintree area] because Australia escaped the brunt of a massive asteroid collision in the Northern Hemisphere about 65 million years ago where the ensuing impact-winter largely wiped out rainforests. Australia also partly escaped the effects of global cooling 25 million years later because it had drifted northwards to equatorial warmth after breaking free of Antarctica. Conditions close enough to the original more tropical climates survived at least in the north to preserve ancient stocks. At the same time, the global cooling together with changes in ocean currents sharpened the climate gradient from north to south. While the warm-adapted or tropical rainforest plants and animals survived in the northern parts of Australia, new temperate forms evolved in the south.

Australia today, with its steep climatic gradients from Bamaga to Burnie, retains an array of climatic envelopes that mimic aspects of past climates, from tropical to temperate, and so now provide refuges for lineages of plants and animals originating from those times.

Dr Aila Keto, in *Conserving Australia's Rainforests — An Information Guide*, appealing for the appropriate management of Australia's rainforests of the Wet Tropics (1995).

We live in a world of environmental spontaneity, with climatic changes swinging from frigid to temperate, temperate to tropical (and the reverse), drifting continents, sea level changes and geological and tectonic upheaval. Short-term crises, such as pandemics, droughts, floods and fire, are also among the more regular and immediate stresses. Despite this, some areas of habitat form crucial elements in the planet's long-term bio-diversity — areas such as the hot, humid south-east-facing gorges and valleys tucked into a high part of the Great Divide between Cairns and Cooktown and watered by the Bloomfield, Daintree and Mossman Rivers. Other places of refuge such as the Daintree, Palm Valley, the outlying Warrumbungles, the Nandewars, the North Flinders and Hamersley

Above: Pockets of lush vegetation in Palm Valley, Finke Gorge National Park, Northern Territory, provide a natural refuge against the desert climate for remnant Cabbage Palms (*Livistona mariae*) from a cooler, more humid time. *Right*: If tree clearing ceases, this limestone outcrop on the central Queensland coastal plain may prove an effective refuge for rock-wallabies, Northern Brown Bandicoots, bats and reptiles.

Above: King Ferns on Fraser Island, Queensland, growing near Wanggoolba Creek.

Refuge Rarities — Classic Plant-refuge Stories

In one sense, the entire Australia continent is an enormous refuge. Species from Gondwana or that evolved here since, before the coming of humans some 60,000 years ago, were isolated from human-induced changes by thousands of kilometres of ocean. The rare primitive King Fern (*Angiopteris evecta*), the ancient Wollemi Pine and the palms of Palm Valley (NT) all survived the coming of "civilisation" primarily because their survival requirements were met in locations that were isolated and unsuitable for human habitation. These ancient ferns now exist only in Madagascar, the Indo-Malayan area, Wanggoolba Creek on Fraser Island and near Carnarvon Gorge, Queensland.

There are still many unanswered questions about the Wollemi Pine, a very significant cone-bearing tree discovered growing in a deep hollow in the trackless sandstone country of the north-west Blue Mountains in New South Wales. Accessible only by helicopter is a very small stand that appears to be the only remaining natural strand of a tree once dominant in the forests of Gondwana. Using cell culture, scientists at the Sydney Botanic Gardens have now reproduced tens of thousands of cultivars from this stock.

In a similar way, the Cabbage Palms of Palm Valley were sustained over millions of years in the arid Central Australian environment by waters released from the soft sandstone aquifer when those waters were unable to pass through an underlying impermeable layer. This refuge can be said to be a geological accident, saved by chance and due to its isolation from good pasture and human beings.

Right: Pockets of refuge rainforest are isolated and protected from fire, drought or destruction by the geology of surrounding rock, such as these towers of ancient sandstones, and the good fortune of geography.

Ranges, the MacDonnells and Carnarvon Gorge, provided refuges — protecting living populations of species such as Cabbage Palm (*Livistona mariae*) and innumerable species of invertebrates, reptiles, birds and mammals (particularly rock-wallabies). Yet, even in these havens, plants and animals are vulnerable to disasters that can destroy entire populations. Rock-wallabies, in their numerous separate communities, are a good example of the fragility of isolated communities because recruiting individuals from other communities is hard across inhospitable spaces. If the local population perishes, it marks the end of the species in that site.

Now, human intervention is accelerating environmental change at a rate greater than ever. Converting vast areas from woodland and forest to artificial single-species grassland of wheat, oats, cane and maize; controlling river flow and temperature by dam construction; use of fire and irrigation; the "introduced" movement of species about the world; the extraction of minerals; the removal of forests; fuels; and, of course, consumption of certain species have all accelerated animal extinction. Much of this change, all due to the space-hogging growth of a single species of primate — *Homo sapiens* — remains beyond the capacity of other species to counter by adaptation. We are acting as plague organisms and our population and economic growth is, in the long term, unsustainable.

However, we humans can excel at manufacturing outcomes. If we effectively use all of the resources of our cumulative cultural memories and organise our thought processes, we should be able to minimise the harmful affects of our existence. We could limit our own population and industrial growth, which is "fuelling" the destruction of the planet. We could urgently establish legislative protection for viable refuges of natural communities, recognising species conservation as a primary purpose, with recreation as a secondary benefit. Natural ecosystems are continental things, yet their loss affects the entire planet. Human political boundaries must not interfere with the issue of overseeing the global welfare of this planet's biodiversity.

In Australia, under the Commonwealth Constitution, nature conservation is largely a State affair, with only very recent federal involvement. Even so, many of our natural systems are gradually becoming well protected, although their safety is often secured for recreational purposes in noisy political lobbies, rather than as a consequence of their faunal or floral worth. Only over billions of years of genetic and biological evolution did the human species evolve. If anything in nature should be held sacred by *Homo sapiens*, it is biodiversity — our "creator", so to speak. We endanger the diversity of this planet at the peril of our own future.

Rock-wallabies in the Refuge

This refuge is a typical rock-wallaby habitat where two great pieces of land in western New South Wales, south-west of White Cliffs, have been thrust together under enormous pressure and crumpled, lifting up hard quartzite and sandstone ranges. Several large sheep stations have common boundaries in these ranges and overstocking has left its legacy. Native animals found their arid habitat becoming more arid, rockholes in the ranges became silted, feral goats became a competitor for food and water and occupied the cooler, humid shelters in caverns, driving Common Wallaroos and rock-wallabies out.

In the 1890s, copper was discovered here and a mining town established. A dam was constructed in a nearby gorge, Hodges Overshot. This soon filled with sand and mud and its wall became a new waterfall with a deep plunge pool beneath. Rock-wallabies found themselves vulnerable to increased predation from Wedge-tailed Eagles in the greatly thinned cover, and to becoming fresh meat for the miners. When the mine closed, sheep and goats ruled the ranges, demanding more and more output from the desperate habitat. Fortunately, a caring manager was appointed and contacted the CSIRO and the 1960s Fauna Protection Panel, which recommended immediate protection for this near-extinct population. Eventually the Coturaundee Nature Reserve was established — thus, the story of one typical refuge area and its struggle for survival. Whether this refuge can maintain its precious Yellow-footed Wallaby population through the years of global warming ahead, only time will tell.

Above, clockwise from top left: Yellow-footed Rock-wallaby, Flinders Ranges, SA; Black-footed Rock-wallaby, the Pilbara, WA; Mareeba Rock-wallabies, Atherton Tableland, Qld; the exquisite Monjon in the Western Australian Kimberley; Nabarlek at home in Arnhem Land, NT; Brush-tailed Rock-wallaby, Warrumbungles, NSW; Short-eared Rock-wallaby, Kakadu, NT. *Right:* Three Yellow-footed Rock-wallabies sunning on a cold August morning, "Moolawatana", north Flinders Ranges, SA. Fossils provide evidence of long-distance migration of rock-wallabies between suitable habitat. Now land clearing and fencing has reduced the ability of isolated populations to travel and interbreed, creating distinct species in remote populations.

Recommended Reading & Bibliography

Australian Forests

Adam, P. (1994) *Australian Rainforests*, Oxford Biogeography Series No. 6, Oxford University Press, Melbourne.

Boland, D.J. et al (1985) *Forest Trees of Australia*, Nelson CSIRO, Canberra.

Breeden, S. (1999) *Australian World Heritage Tropical Rainforest – A Natural History Guide*, Steve Parish Publishing, Brisbane.

Cooper, W. & Cooper, W.T. (1994) *Fruits of the Rainforest*, Reader's Digest Press, Sydney.

Figgis, P. & Meier, L. (1985) *Rainforests of Australia*, Weldons Geo, Sydney.

Goldstein, W. (ed) (1977) *Rainforests, Parks and Wildlife* Vol. 2 No. 1, NSW National Parks & Wildlife Service, Sydney.

Lunney, D. (ed) (2004) *Conservation of Australia's Forest Fauna*, Royal Zoological Society of NSW, Sydney.

Nix, H.A. & Switzer, M.A. (1991) *Kowari 1 – Rainforest Animals,* Australian National Parks & Wildlife Service, Canberra.

Australian Wildlife

Allen, G. (1989) *Freshwater Fishes of Australia*, TFH Publications, Sydney.

Clyne, D. (1999) *Wildlife of Australia*, New Holland, Sydney.

Cogger, H.G. (1979) *Reptiles and Amphibians of Australia*, Reed, Sydney.

Edgar, G.J. (2005) *Australian Marine Life – The Plants and Animals of Temperate Waters*, New Holland, Sydney

Frith, H.J. (1969) *Kangaroos*, Cheshire, Melbourne.

Gomman, M.F., Glover, J.C., & Kuiter, R. (ed) (1994) *The Fishes of Australia's South Coast*, State Print, Adelaide.

Green, K. & Osborne, W. (1994) *Wildlife of the Australian Snow Country*, Reed, Sydney.

Hadlington, P. (1987) *Termites*, UNSW Press, Sydney.

Healey, J. (ed) (1997) *Encyclopedia of Australian Wildlife*, Reader's Digest, Sydney.

Kuiter, R. (1999) *A Guide to the Sea Fishes of Australia*, New Holland, Sydney.

Morcombe, M. (2000) *Field Guide to Australian Birds*, Steve Parish Publishing, Brisbane.

Reid, A.J. et al (1973–75) *Birds of Victoria*, Vol. 1–5, Gould League of Victoria, Melbourne.

Schodde, R. & Tidemann, S. (1990) *Complete Book of Australian Birds*, Reader's Digest, Sydney.

Simpson, K. & Day, N. (1993) *Field Guide to the Birds of Australia*, Penguin Books, Sydney.

Slater, P. (2000) *Encyclopedia of Australian Wildlife*, Steve Parish Publishing, Brisbane.

Slater, P. & Fox, A.M. (1995) *First Field Guide*, Vols. 1–6, Steve Parish Publishing, Brisbane.

Strahan, R. (ed) (1983) *The Australian Museum Complete Book of Australian Mammals*, Angus & Robertson, Sydney.

Sutherland, S. (ed) (1993) *Australia's Dangerous Creatures*, Reader's Digest, Sydney.

Underhill, D. (ed) (1989) *The Australian Wildlife Year*, Reader's Digest, Sydney.

Basic Science

Baines, J. (1981) *Australian Plant Genera: a Dictionary of Australian Plant Genera*, Society for the Growing of Australian Plants, Sydney.

Buchsbaum, R. (1938) *Animals Without Backbones*, University of Chicago Press, Chicago.

Burroughs, W.J. (1999) *The Climate Revealed*, Cambridge University Press, Melbourne.

Hamblin, K. & Christiansen, E.H. (1995) *Earth's Dynamic Systems* [7th edition or later], Prentice Hall, New Jersey.

Mayr, E. (2001) *What Evolution Is*, Phoenix, London.

McKenzie, N.D, Jaqueler, R.I. & Brown, K (2004), *Australian Soils and Landscapes*, CSIRO, Melbourne.

Reader, J. (1986) *The Rise of Life: the First 3.5 Billion Years*, Knopf, New York.

Reader, J. & Croze, H. (1977) *Pyramids of Life*, Collins, Melbourne.

Selby, J. (1984) *Geology of the Adelaide Environment*, South Australian Government Printer, Adelaide.

Twidale, C.R. (1978) *Analysis of Landforms*, John Wiley & Sons, Brisbane.

Twidale, C.R. & Campbell, C.M. (2005) *Australian Landforms*, Rosenberg, Sydney.

Watts, D. (1971) *Principles of Biogeography*, McGraw Hill, Sydney.

White, M. (1999) *Reading the Rocks*, Kangaroo Press, Sydney.

Conservation of Nature

Anon. (nd) *The Trials of Tribulation*, The Douglas Shires Wilderness Action Group, Mossman.

Dombrovskis, P. & Brown, R. (1983) *Wild Rivers*, Peter Dombrovskis Pty Ltd, Hobart.

Fox, A.M. et al (1993) *Wilderness*, Steve Parish Publishing, Brisbane.

Frith, H.J. (1979) *Wildlife Conservation*, Angus & Robertson, Sydney.

Groom, A. (1951) *One Mountain After Another* [Lamington National Park], Angus & Robertson, Sydney.

Suzuki, D. & McConnell, A. (2002) *The Sacred Balance*, Greystone Books, Vancouver.

Tranter, D.J. (2006) *Nature and Society – Patterns in Space and Time*, Seaview, Adelaide.

Webb, L.J., Whitelock, D. & Le Gay Brereton, J. (1969) *The Last of Lands*, Jacaranda Press, Brisbane.

Discovering the Nature of Australia

Angas, G.F. (1847) *Savage Life and Scenes in Australia and New Zealand*, Two Volume Facsimile Edition, Library Board of South Australia, Adelaide.

Anon. (1838) *A Month in the Bush of Australia*, Facsimile Edition, Library Board of South Australia, Adelaide.

Carnegie, D.W. (1898) *Spinifex and Sand*, C. Arthur Pearson, London.

Dovers, S. (ed) (1994) *Australian Environmental History — Essays and Cases*, Oxford University Press, Melbourne.

Durack, M. (1959) *Kings in Grass Castles*, Corgi, Sydney.

Feeken, E.H.J. & Gerda, E.E. Feeken, (1970) *The Discovery and Exploration of Australia*, Thomas Nelson & Son, Melbourne.

Finlayson, H.H. (1936) *The Red Centre*, Angus & Robertson, Sydney.

Giles, E. (1889) *Australia Twice Traversed From 1872–1876*, Two Volume Facsimile Edition, Double Day, Sydney.

Goldstein, W. (ed) (1979) *Australia's 100 years of National Parks*, NSW National Parks & Wildlife Service, Sydney.

Hancock, W.K. (1972) *Discovering Monaro: A Study of Man's Impact on his Environment*, Cambridge University Press, Melbourne.

Hodgkinson, C. (1845) *Australia from Port Macquarie to Moreton Bay*, Boone, London.

Leichhardt, L. (1847) *Journal of an Overland Expedition from Moreton Bay to Port Essington*, Facsimile Edition, Double Day, Sydney.

Madigan, C.T. (1946) *Crossing the Dead Heart*, Georgian House, Melbourne.

Mitchell, T.L. (1839) *Three Expeditions into Eastern Australia*, Two Volume Facsimile Edition, Library Board of South Australia, Adelaide.

Oxley, J. (1820) *Journals of Two Expeditions into the Interior of New South Wales*, Facsimile Edition, Public Library Board of South Australia, Adelaide.

Paszkowski, L. (1997) *Sir Paul Edmund de Strzelecki*, Arcadia, Melbourne.

Sorenson, E.S. (1911) *Life in the Australian Backblocks*, Facsimile Edition, Currey O'Neil, Melbourne.

Spencer, B (1896) *The Horn Expedition 1894*, Four Volume Facsimile Edition, Corkwood Press, Bundaberg.

Stone, D. I. & Garden, D. S. (1978) *Squatters and Settlers*, Reed, Sydney.

Sturt, C. (1849) *Expeditions into Central Australia*, Two Volume Facsimile Edition, Library Board of South Australia, Adelaide.

Uren, M. & Stephens, R. (1945) *Waterless Horizons — Edward John Eyre*, Robertson & Mullins, Melbourne.

Vader, J. (2002) *Red Gold: the Tree that Built a Nation*, New Holland, Sydney.

Grasslands and Herbfields

Cogger, H.G. & Cameron, E.E. (1985) *Arid Australia*, Australian Museum, Sydney.

Costin, A., Gray, M., Totterdell, C. & Wimbush, D. (2000) *Kosciuszko Alpine Flora*, CSIRO Collins, Canberra.

Frith, H.J. (1969) *Kangaroos*, Cheshire, Melbourne.

Latz, P. (1995) *Bushfires and Bush Tucker: Aboriginal Plant Use in Central Australia*, IAD Press, Alice Springs.

Moore, R.M. (ed) (1970) *Australian Grasslands*, ANU Press, Canberra.

Mountford, C.P. (1962) *Brown Men and Red Sand*, Angus & Robertson, Sydney.

Guide Books

Anon. (nd) *The Reader's Digest Illustrated Guide to Australian Places*, Reader's Digest, Sydney.

Barca, M. (2002) *Explore Historic Australia*, Viking Penguin, Sydney.

Bunny, J. (ed) (1996) *Explore Australia: Four Wheel Drive*, Viking Penguin, Melbourne.

Fox, A.M. (2000) *National Parks of Australia*, New Holland, Sydney.

Gill, P. & Burke, C. (2001) *Whale Watching in Australian and New Zealand Waters*, Reader's Digest, Sydney.

Klinge, S. (2000) *Classic Walks of Australia*, New Holland, Sydney.

Lockwood, L., Wilson, J. & Fagg, M. (2001) *Botanic Gardens of Australia*, New Holland, Sydney.

Lord, S. & Daniel, G. (ed) (1993) *Bushwalks in the Sydney Region* Vol. 1 & 2, National Parks Association of NSW, Sydney.

Moffat, A. (ed) (1996) *Off the Beaten Track: a Guide to 155 Scenic Tours in Australia*, Reader's Digest, Sydney.

Moffat, A. (ed) (1999) *Reader's Digest Book of the Road: the Complete Driver's Atlas and Touring Guide to Australia*, Reader's Digest, Sydney.

Molyneux, B. (1985) *Bush Journeys*, Nelson, Melbourne.

Moon, R. & Moon, V. (1989) *Cape York: An Adventurer's Guide*, Kakirra Adventure Publications, Melbourne.

Moon, R. & Moon, V. (1989) *The Kimberley: an Adventurer's Guide*, Kakirra Adventure Publications, Melbourne.

Recher, H. (ed) (1976) *Scenic Wonders of Australia*, Reader's Digest, Sydney.

Ross, Z. et al (2003) *Eyewitness Travel Guides: Australia*, Dorling Kindersley, London.

Schaefer, K. (1985) *Environment Explorer*, Methuen, Sydney.

Heathlands

Coaldrake, J.E. (1961) *The Ecosystem of the Coastal Lowlands (Wallum) of Southern Queensland*, CSIRO, Australian Bulletin No. 283, Canberra.

Fox, A.M. (1997) *Mungo National Park Guidebook*, Beaten Track Press, Queanbeyan.

Fox, A.M. (1978) *The 72 Fire of the Nadgee Nature Reserve*, NSW National Parks & Wildlife Service, Sydney.

Haigh, C. (ed) (1981) *Heaths in New South Wales*, NSW National Parks & Wildlife Service, Sydney.

Ingwersen, F. (1976) *Vegetation of the Jervis Bay Territory*, Department of Capital Territories Conservation Series 3, Canberra.

Kikkawa, J., Ingram G.J. & Dwyer, P.D. (1979) "Vertebrate fauna of Australian heathlands" in Specht, R.L. (ed) *Heathlands and Related Shrublands of the World*, Elsevier, Amsterdam.

Specht, R.L. (1981) "Australian Heathlands" in Groves, R.H. (ed) *The Vegetation of Australia*, Cambridge University Press, Melbourne.

Marine, Estuarine and Coastal Wetlands

Andrew, N. (ed) (1999) *Under Southern Seas: The Ecology of Australia's Rocky Reefs*, UNSW Press, Sydney.

Bennett, I. (1981) *The Great Barrier Reef*, Landsdowne, Sydney.

Berry, P.F., Bradshaw, S.T. & Wilson, B.R. (1990) *Research in Shark Bay*, Western Australian Museum, Perth.

Chapman, D.M., Geary, M., Roy, P. S. & Thom, B. (1982) *Coastal evolution and coastal erosion in New South Wales*, Coastal Council of NSW, Sydney.

Cooper, S. (ed) (2002) *Fish Australia*, Viking Penguin, Melbourne.

Dakin, W. (1960) *Australian Seashores*, Angus & Robertson, Sydney.

Edgar, G.J. (2001) *Australian Marine Habitats in Temperate Waters*, New Holland, Sydney.

Edgecombe, J. (1987) *Lord Howe Island — World Heritage Area*, Australian Environmental Publications, Sydney.

Edwards, H. (1999) *Shark Bay Through Four Centuries, 1616 to 2000*, Edwards, Geraldton.

Gamlin, L. (1995) *Secrets of the Sea*, Reader's Digest, Sydney.

Gray, W. (1993) *Coral Reefs and Islands: a Natural History of a Threatened Paradise*, David & Charles, Devon.

Heatwole, H. (1981) *A Coral Island: The Story of One Tree Reef*, Collins, Sydney.

Landy, J. (1993) *A Coastal Diary*, Macmillan, Sydney.

Laughlin, G. (1997) *The User's Guide to the Australian Coast*, New Holland, Sydney.

Parish, S. (1995) *Photographing Australia's Great Barrier Reef*, Steve Parish Publishing, Brisbane.

Pullan, R. (ed) (1983) *Reader's Digest Guide to the Australian Coast*, Reader's Digest, Sydney.

Thom, B.G. et al (1992) *Coastal Geomorphology and Quaternary Geology of the Port Stephens Myall Lakes Area*, ANU Press, Canberra.

Slater, P. (nd) *Amazing Facts about Australian Marine Life*, Steve Parish Publishing, Brisbane.

Stevenson, R. & Talbot, F. (eds) (1994) *Islands*, Reader's Digest, Sydney.

Wilson, B.R. & Gillett, K. (1974) *Australian Shells*, Reed, Sydney.

Woodroffe, C.D., Chappell, J., Thom, B. & Willensky, E. (1986) *Geomorphological Dynamics and Evolution of the South Alligator Tidal River*

and Plains, Northern Territory, Northern Australian Research Unit ANU, Darwin.

Zann, L.P. (ed) (1995) *Our Sea, Our Future*, Great Barrier Reef Marine Park Authority, Townsville.

Natural History of Australia

Anon. (1981) *Flora of Australia,* Volume I — Introduction, Bureau of Flora and Fauna, Canberra.

Anon. (1987) *Fauna of Australia,* Volume I — General articles, Bureau of Flora and Fauna, Canberra.

Archer, M. & Clayton, G. (1984) *Vertebrate Zoogeography and Evolution in Australasia*, Hesperian Press, Perth.

Archer, M., Hand, S. & Godthelp, H. (1991) *Riversleigh*, Reed, Sydney.

Auslig (1992) *The Ausmap Atlas of Australia*, Cambridge University Press, Melbourne.

Berra, T.M. (1998) *A Natural History of Australia*, UNSW Press, Sydney.

Fox, A.M. & Parish, S. (1984) *Australia's Wilderness Experience*, Rigby, Adelaide.

Leeper, G.W. (1960) *The Australian Environment*, CSIRO and Melbourne University Press, Melbourne.

Morrison, R (2002) *Australia: Land Beyond Time*, New Holland, Sydney.

Neidjie, B., Davis, S. & Fox, A.M. (1985) *Kakadu Man*, Mybrood Publishing, Queanbeyan.

Read, I.G. (1987) *The Bush*, Reed, Sydney.

Sutherland, L. (1995) *The Volcanic Earth*, UNSW Press, Sydney.

Vickers-Rich, P. & Rich, T.H. (1993) *Wildlife of Gondwana*, Reed, Sydney.

White, M.E. (1986) *The Greening of Gondwana*, Reed, Sydney.

White, M.E. (1994) *After the Greening*, Kangaroo Press, Sydney.

Regional Environmental Guides

Calder, J. (1987) *The Grampians: a Noble Range*, Victorian National Parks Association, Melbourne.

Corbett, D. (1987) *Geology and Scenery of South Australia*, Wakefield Press, Adelaide.

Costin, A. (1954) *A Study of the Ecosystems of the Monaro Region of New South Wales*, NSW Government Printer, Sydney.

Good, R.B. (1992) *Kosciusko Heritage*, NSW National Parks & Wildlife Service, Sydney.

Good, R.B. (ed) (1989) *Scientific Significance of the Australian Alps*, Australian Alps National Parks Liaison Committee and the Australian Academy of Science, Canberra.

Green, K. & Osborne, W. (1994) *Wildlife of the Australian Snow Country*, Reed, Sydney.

Lavery, H.J. (ed) (1978) *Exploration North: a Natural History of Queensland*, Lloyd O'Neil, Brisbane.

Main, B.Y. (1967) *Between Wodjil and Tor*, Jacaranda Landfall Press, Perth.

Marshall, J. & Drysdale, R. (1963) *Journey Among Men* [Kimberley], Hodder & Staughton, London.

Miles, G. (2000) *Kakadu Wildlife*, Barker Souvenirs Publishers, Darwin.

Morris, I. (1996) *Kakadu National Park*, Steve Parish Publishing, Brisbane.

Twydale, C.R., Tyler M.J. & Davies, M. (ed) (1979) *Natural History of Kangaroo Island*, Royal Society of South Australia, Adelaide.

Twydale, C.R., Tyler M.J. & Davies, M. (ed) (1985) *Natural History of the Eyre Peninsula*, Royal Society of South Australia, Adelaide.

Tyler M.J., Twydale, C.R., Ling, J.K. & Holmes, J.W. (eds) (1983) *Natural History of the South East*, Royal Society of South Australia, Adelaide.

Watson, C. (ed) (1985) *Pigeon House and Beyond*, Budawang Committee, Sydney.

Watson, C. (ed) (1988) *Fitzroy Falls and Beyond*, Budawang Committee, Sydney.

Scrubland and Shrubland

Frith, H.J. (1962) *The Mallee Fowl*, Angus & Robertson, Sydney.

Moore, R.M. (ed) (1970) *Australian Grasslands*, ANU Press, Canberra.

Extreme Habitats

Crabb, P. (1997) *Murray–Darling Basin Resources*, Murray–Darling Basin Commission, Canberra.

Fox, A.M. & Parish, S. (1983) *Of Birds and Billabongs*, Rigby, Adelaide.

Frith, H.J. (1968) *Waterfowl in Australia*, Angus & Robertson, Sydney.

Williams, W.D. (ed) (1998) *Wetlands in a Dry Land: Understanding for Management — Workshop Proceedings*, Environment Australia, Canberra.

Vegetation Guides

Beadle, N.C., Evans, O.D. & Carolin, R.C. (1972) *Flora of the Sydney Region*, Reed, Sydney.

Brock, J. (2001) *Native Plants of Northern Australia*, New Holland, Sydney.

Brock, J. (1988) *Top End Native Plants*, Brock, Darwin.

Chippendale, G. & Wolf, L. (1981) *The Natural Distribution of Eucalyptus in Australia*, Australian National Parks & Wildlife Service, Canberra.

Cochrane, G.R., Fuhrer, B.A., Rotherham, E.R. & Willis, J.H. (1973) *Flowers and Plants of Victoria*, Reed, Sydney.

Costermans, L. (1981) *Native Trees and Shrubs of South Eastern Australia*, Weldon, Sydney.

Costin, A., Gray, M., Totterdell, C. & Wimbush, D. (2000) *Kosciuszko Alpine Flora*, CSIRO Collins, Canberra.

Cunningham, G.M., Mulham, W.E., Milthorpe P. & Leigh, J. (1971) *Plants of Western New South Wales*, Soil Conservation Service, Sydney.

Elliot, R. (1984) *A Field Guide to the Grampians Flora*, Algona Publications, Melbourne.

Fuller, L. (1982) *Wollongong's Native Trees*, Weston, Kiama.

Galbraith, J. (1967) *Wildflowers of Victoria*, Longmans, Melbourne.

Harris, T.Y. (1970) *Alpine Plants of Australia*, Angus & Robertson, Sydney.

Jessop, J. (ed) (1981) *Flora of Central Australia*, The Australian Systematic Botany Society, Reed, Sydney.

Keith, D. (2004) *Ocean Shores to Desert Sands — The Native Vegetation of NSW and ACT*, NSW National Parks and Wildlife Service, Sydney.

Lovelock, C. (1993) *Field Guide to the Mangroves of Queensland*, Australian Institute of Marine Science, Townsville.

Nevill, S. & Mcquoid, N. (1998) *Guide to the Wildflowers of South Western Australia*, Simon Nevill, Perth.

Nicholson, N. & Nicholson, H. (1985–94) *Australian Rainforest Plants* Volumes 1–4, Terania Rainforest Nursery, Lismore.

Petheram, R.J. & Kok, B. (1986) *Plants of the Kimberley Region of Western Australia*, UWA Press, Perth.

Sainty, G.R. & Jacobs, S.W.L. (1981) *Waterplants of New South Wales*, Water Resources Commission of NSW, Sydney.

Simmons, M. (1982) *Acacias of Australia*, Nelson, Melbourne.

Specht, R.L. (1972) *The Vegetation of South Australia*, South Australian Government Printer, Adelaide.

Urban, A. (1990) *Wildflowers and Plants of Central Australia*, Southbank Editions, Melbourne.

Whibley, D.J.E. (1980) *Acacias of South Australia*, South Australian Government Printer, Adelaide.

Williams, J.B., Harden, G. & McDonald, W.J.F. (1984) *Trees and Shrubs in Rainforests of New South Wales and Southern Queensland*, UNE Press, Armidale.

Williams, K.A.W. (1979) *Native plants: Queensland*, Vol. 1, Williams, Brisbane.

Wrigley, J. & Fagg, M. (1989) *Banksias, Waratahs and Grevilleas*, Collins, Melbourne.

Woodlands and Savanna

Boomsma, C.D. (et al) (ud) "The Native Forest and Woodland Vegetation of South Australia" (Bulletin 25), Government Printer of South Australia, Adelaide.

Wallace, H.R. (ed) (1986) *The Ecology of the Forests and Woodlands of South Australia*, Government Printer of South Australia, Adelaide.

Glossary

A

Accretion An increase, by natural growth, of sediments to form beds of sandstone, shale and mudstone.

Alga (pl. algae) A group of non-flowering plants, including seaweeds, usually living in water.

Angiosperm A flowering plant, e.g. Waratah.

Aquifer A permeable stratum or layer below the Earth's surface through which ground water moves or may be stored.

Arboreal Pertaining to trees, e.g. brushtail possums are arboreal animals, living in trees.

Awn A bristle-like appendage on a seed, e.g. the appendage on speargrass seeds.

B

Bacteria A large group of single-celled or filamentous organisms without a well-defined nucleus surrounded by a thin wall or membrane.

Bedding plane A surface separating layers of sedimentary rock.

Billabong An Aboriginal word, *billa* meaning river, *bong* meaning dead, e.g. may be a lagoon and is a river-meander cut-off.

Bivalve shell A shellfish cover in two parts united by a hinge, such as that of a pipi, oyster or mussel.

Braided stream A stream with a complex network of channels separated by bars and islands, e.g. Cooper Creek Channel Country.

Biomass The total mass of organisms living in a particular place or living system.

Biotic community A community of living things, often considered to be animal but also including plants, e.g. a shoreline rockpool's living contents, including fish, molluscs, sea stars, seaweeds, crustaceans etc.

C

Calcium carbonate Chemical composition of $CaCO_3$ — the mineral in limestone, corals and mollusc shells.

Canopy The leafy ceiling of a plant, plants or forest.

Carnivore A meat-eating animal, such as the Eastern Quoll or Wedge-tailed Eagle.

Chlorophyll The green-coloured plant material that is the catalyst in converting carbon dioxide and water into carbohydrates (sugars) using the energy of light.

Chloroplast The package within plant cells that holds the grains of chlorophyll and is thought to be the remains of a bacteria that joined with plant cells for their mutual benefit early in the story of life, billions of years ago.

Closed forest A forest where the tree canopies are so close that the tree tops all link up, blocking out the sky. These closed forests in Australia are the rainforests and mangrove forests.

Community A group of organisms that have common needs and that are usually interdependent, e.g. forest community, saltbush community.

Continental plate Vast sections of the Earth's crust that form the continents and that slowly drift about the planet's surface, e.g. the Indo–Australian Plate.

Corolla The petals of a flower.

Cotyledon A dormant leaf in a seed, usually containing a food store for the germinating seed.

Country rock The rock beneath the landscape, e.g. Hawkesbury sandstone under Katoomba.

Crab holes Deep, wide hollows that form in heavy cracking clays when they dry out, e.g. on the blacksoil plains of the Darling River.

Cycles The process that moves water and minerals about the planet, e.g. evaporation, condensation (clouds), rainfall, running streams, ocean, evaporation, wind-driven vapour, cooling and condensation.

Cycle of erosion The process that describes the weathering and erosion of land, transport of the sediment to a place of deposition (ocean), followed by uplift of a new mountain range, which is then once again eroded and transported etc.

D

Dicotyledon A group of flowering plants with seeds that have two cotyledons, e.g. peas, wattles and grevilleas.

Deciduous Natural organisms that lose part of their bodies/form, e.g. trees that shed their leaves in winter or eucalypts that shed their bark in summer.

Dry sclerophyll forests These forests (and dry sclerophyll woodlands) grow on sites that are dry for long periods, where the trees are more widely spaced than those of wet forests and where much light penetrates to the forest floor (where shrubs and grasses predominate).

E

Ecology The study of the relationships between an organism and its physical environment and other organisms, such as plants and animals, living nearby.

Ecosystem The structure of sustainable relationships between plants and animals identifiable as a coherent living system. See diagram for this structure.

Edge effect The edge between two adjoining communities or ecosystems. These are usually the richest living areas, providing shelter and food between the two systems.

Emergent A plant that stands above the general canopy of a community or above the water surface, as opposed to floating or submerged, e.g. Moreton Bay Fig tree in a rainforest.

Endemic Unique to a particular place, e.g. kangaroos are endemic to Australia.

Epiphyte A plant growing on a surface other than on soil or water, e.g. on other plants such as elkhorns, or on rock faces (Pencil Orchids).

Epicormic Nature of buds concealed beneath the protective bark of trunks and branches of some eucalypts, e.g. bloodwoods.

Environment The physical factors that affect growth; often the term is used to include the organisms that impact on the life of the plant or animal.

F

Fault A surface along which a rock body has broken and been displaced, frequently providing alignment for rivers and mountains.

Fermentation A process involved in the decomposition of plant matter

producing heat as a by-product, e.g. nest mounds of the Malleefowl.

Fold Bend or flex in a rock resulting from intense lateral pressure.

Food chain The chain of feeders in an ecosystem, commencing with herbivores through omnivores to carnivores, with waste products and dead participants being recycled by decomposers back into the soil.

Forest A close-growing stand of trees where the trunks are longer than the depth of the crown of the tree, e.g Sherbrook Forests Mountain Ash. Types include closed forest, rainforest, tall open forest (wet eucalypt forest) and open forest (dry eucalypt forest).

Fungi A major group of seedless living organisms without chlorophyll that disperse by spores, feeding not from roots but by mycelium, which absorb nutrients from dead or living tissue of other plants and animals.

G

Gilgai A pattern of hollows usually on flat country with soils that shrink when dry and swell when wet.

Gondwana The supercontinent that originally included Antarctica (the core of Gondwana), Australia, South America, Africa, India and New Zealand before break-up and continental drift.

Gymnosperm Seed plants that are cone bearers, i.e. not flowering plants (conifers, cycads etc.).

H

Habitat The place where a species of animal lives, providing food, shelter and special space requirements, e.g. cool rivers (Platypus) or temperate rainforest (Albert's Lyrebird).

Heath A low, species-rich, closed community of shrubs, and sometimes scrub (which is then called Wallum).

Herb A plant that does not produce a woody stem, e.g. Snow Daisy.

Hypersaline An environment with extreme salt levels contained in the soil beyond levels plants can normally survive at, e.g. mudflats behind tropical mangrove swamps.

I

Invertebrates Animals without backbones, including spiders, insects, sponges and crustaceans.

J

Joint A fracture in a rock along which no appreciable movement has occurred.

K

Karst topography A landscape characterised by sinks, solutions valleys (canyons, gorges), caverns and other features produced by groundwater activity, e.g. Cooleman, Bungonia, Chillagoe, Nullarbor.

L

Larva A very immature stage in the life cycle of some animals, e.g. a butterfly's caterpillar.

Larval (adj.) An immature phase in an animal's life, many of which make up zooplankton and early insect phases.

Lignotuber A woody growth at or below ground level in some eucalypts, particularly mallee, beneath the bark of which, following stress or trauma, protected dormant buds can shoot to the top of the tree.

M

Macropod *Macro* = large, *pod* = foot. A group including all of the kangaroo family, i.e. kangaroos, wallabies, wallaroos and potoroos.

Marine bank A bank of sand or shelly or coral rubble built by wave and current action in the sea.

Metamorphic The nature of a group of rocks that have been changed by heat and/or pressure, e.g. schist and slate from "cooked" shale and mudstone, quartzite from sandstone or gneiss from granite.

Metamorphosis The process of change, e.g. insect metamorphosis = egg to larvae to chrysalis to adult form (such as the moth).

Mollusc An invertebrate characterised by a calcareous shell of one, two or more pieces that wholly or partly encloses a soft body, e.g. chitons, snails, bivalves, squids and octopuses etc.

Monocotyledon A group of flowering plants with seeds that usually only has one cotyledon, e.g. grass, palms.

Mosaic of communities Any significant area where there are variable environmental conditions (available water, temperature, drainage, soils etc.) that produce a pattern of communities as in a mosaic.

N

Nectar The sweet liquid attractant produced by flowering plants to attract insects, birds and mammals so as to transfer pollen (male) to the female stigmas of other flowers of the same species.

Node The area of a stem from which a leaf, root or branch might shoot.

O

Organic Nature of living material.

P

Parasite Organism living on or in, and deriving nourishment from, another organism (the host), e.g. mistletoe.

Perennial Growing over many years.

Plankton Small living organisms drifting and/or swimming in water; plants = phytoplankton, animals = zooplankton.

Photosynthesis The process by which the plant leaf combines water and carbon dioxide using the energy of the sun to produce carbohydrate (sugars). *See also* chlorophyll and chloroplast.

Phyllode A stem modification where it flattens, contains chloroplasts and functions as a leaf, e.g. acacias.

Plant succession A sequence of plant species that occurs in the colonisation of a landscape, e.g. on coastal sand dunes.

Plate tectonics The process by which continental plates drift and, in collision with adjacent plates, either plunge beneath these plates (subduct) or crumple, generating earthquakes and mountain ranges.

Prehensile The nature of an animal's anatomy, most commonly tails and feet, that aids and assists in climbing.

R

Regime A condition, usually a sequence of happenings or characteristics, related to the frequency of other events happening, e.g. flood regimes in a river or temperature regimes.

Recycle The process that allows the renewal and reuse of things used, e.g. recycling water and nutrients in the soil.

Respiration The activity of living cells that use oxygen to power cellular activity to maintain life.

Rhizome An underground stem, sometimes storing starches, e.g. the rhizome of waterlilies and spike rushes.

S

Savanna Country covered with a scattering of trees and a ground storey of grasses, frequently sustained by fire.

Sedimentary Nature of rock formed by the accumulation and consolidation of sediment, e.g. sandstone, shale, mudstone and conglomerate.

Sclerophyll A type of plant, usually with thickened leaves that are hard and leathery (*sclero* = hard, *phyllon* = leaf), with wax coatings protecting the plant from loss of water.

Scrubland A community of low trees, usually growing densely, e.g. Mulga scrub, Brigalow scrub.

Shrubland A community more open than heathland and with less species, e.g. bluebush/saltbush shrubland.

Soil A complex living community of micro-organisms, invertebrates and small vertebrates mixing soil minerals and organic matter, forming a number of strata or horizons in the soil, ranging from organic at the top to pure mineral at the bottom.

Spike An arrangement of flowers along a stem with very short connecting stalks, e.g. Mulga and many other wattles.

Spore A primitive unicellular or few-celled asexual or sexual reproductive unit not containing an embryo, e.g. fern spores.

Stomate The pore space through which gasses are exchanged with the atmosphere (oxygen and carbon dioxide) located on the leaf surfaces.

Strata A layer in sedimentary rocks, parts of which have a common history.

Succession A successive process of colonisation of landscape by plants and animals.

Swale The valley between adjacent sand dunes.

Swash The rush of water onto a beach after a wave breaks.

Symbiosis The process whereby one organism joins with another of a different species for the common benefit of both, e.g. algae and fungi living together to form lichen, and algae and a polyp living together to form reef-building coral.

T

Terrestrial Living on land.

Tuber A storage root that contains carbohydrate for later use by the plant, e.g. yam.

Turbidity Mud and other impurities carried by running water.

V

Vertebrates Animals with backbones.

W

Weathering The process by which rocks are chemically altered or physically broken into fragments as a result of exposure to atmospheric agents, organic fluids and the pressures and temperatures at or near the Earth's surface, with little or no transportation of the loosened or altered materials.

Wet sclerophyll forest These forests, typically growing in damp, fertile locations, are tall with long, unbroken trunks and a ferny understorey.

Woodland A landscape of moderately close trees where the trees are not interlocked, allowing the canopy to be hemispherical with branches spreading from the trunk close to the ground. The ground storey of woodland is usually covered by grass and/or shrubs.

X

Xeromorphic A plant with adaptations for growth under dry or arid conditions.

Index

Ribbony Grass 292, 295
Richea 127, 156, 158
    Candle Heath 294
    continentis 289, 292
    pandanifolia 156, 158
Richmond, George 10
Richmond
    Range 129, 142
    River 142
Ridge-fruited Mallee 225
Ridge-tailed Monitor 231, 274
Rigid Wallaby Grass 283
Ring-necked Parrot 194
Ring-tailed Dragon 206, 212, 231, 269, 274, 323
Ringed
    Brown Snake 206, 212, 231, 242, 269, 274
    Thin-tailed Gecko 147
ringtail possums 46, 77, 183, 185, 188, 241, 253
Riparius 306
River
    Blackfish 309
    Buttercup 278
    Mangrove 76, 86, 88
    Oak 186, 306
    Red Gum 118, 186, 187, 190, 192, 194, 195, 197, 204, 208, 210–212, 233, 243, 278, 281, 302, 316
    White Gum 120
Riverina 196, 242, 302
Riverine woodlands 174, 186, 192, 194
Roaring Forties 32
Robust
    Ctenotus 227, 237, 241
    Frog 138
    Skink 269
    Striped Skink 280
    Velvet Gecko 192, 237
    Whistlefrog 167
Rock
    Fern 322
    Fig 167, 172, 322
    Flathead 57, 96
    Lily 158
    Oyster 70, 96
    Parrot 241, 253
    Ringtail Possum 167, 168, 173, 323
    Striped Skink 274
    Warbler 322
rock-wallaby 321, 323, 327
Rocket Froglet 46, 88
Rockhampton 32, 44, 262
Rockhole Frog 307
rockpool 53
Rocky coasts 48–57
    birds 54–55
    fishes 57
    flora 54
    formation 50–52
    habitat 52–54
    invertebrates 55
    threats 48
    zones 53, 55
Rocky Hill 321
rodents 147, 154
Roe, John Septimus 176
Rolleston 170
Rolling Grounds 282
Roly Poly 310
Roma 202, 206, 236
Roper River 80, 202
Rose Darwinia 225
Rose Robin 145, 153, 160, 285
Rose-crowned
    Fruit-Dove 145, 164, 169, 172
    Pigeon 132, 138, 145, 163
Roseate Tern 65
Rosen's Snake 200, 231
Rosetted Crane's Bill 283

Rosewood 146, 152, 197, 212, 235, 239
Ross River 210
Rosy Riceflower 254
Rottnest Island 50, 75, 90
Rough
    Barked Apple 189
    Burr Daisy 278
    Flutemouth 92
    Honey Myrtle 255
    Knob-tail Gecko 231
    Possumwood 158
    -scaled Snake 147, 154
    Speargrass 278
    Tree Fern 123, 134, 150, 152, 158
Round
    Hill 222
    Mountain 184
    Yam 167
Round-leaf Pigface 225
Round-leaved Parakeelya 318
Royal
    Acacia 211
    Albatross 37
    Bluebell 292, 295
    Hakea 250
    National Park 170, 198, 211, 249, 250, 252
    Society 277
Rubus probus 133
Ruby Saltbush 223, 225, 235
Ruddy Turnstone 65
Rufous
    Bettong 200, 207, 269, 279
    Bristlebird 241
    Fantail 77, 115, 124, 138, 145, 151, 153, 169, 172, 258
    Fieldwren 244, 275
    Hare-wallaby 232, 273
    Night Heron 77, 79, 258, 268, 281
    Owl 138, 169
    Scrub-bird 151, 153
    Songlark 207, 214, 233, 268, 281
    Treecreeper 201
    Whistler 115, 201, 207, 214, 224, 233, 275
Rufous-banded Honeyeater 79, 169, 172
Rufous-crowned Emu-wren 275
Rufous-throated Honeyeater 207
Rufus Rat-kangaroo 114
Ruppia spp. 88
Russell Falls 122
Russell Island 58, 58–59
Rusty
    Dragon 274
    Jacket 204
Rusty-topped Delma 172, 231

S

Sacred
    Kingfisher 65, 76, 77, 124, 151, 172, 207, 214, 215, 241
    Lotus 306
Sago Pondweed 88
Sailfin Glassfish 304
sailfish 36
Salamandar 309
salinas 298, 301, 302, 310–313
saline mudflats 310
Salmon
    Gum 197, 198, 204, 239
    Holes 51
Salmon-tailed Catfish 309
salt 296, 310–313
    lakes 298, 302, 310–313
saltbush 216, 220, 223, 229, 235, 242–244, 245, 312
Saltbush Bill J.P 242
saltmarsh 76
samphire 72, 74, 76, 79, 80, 301, 310, 312
sand

crickets 310, 317
dollars 70
Flathead 97
Hopper 46
Mallee 223, 225
Monitor 227, 231, 274
Octopuses 90, 96
Palm 204, 205
Plain Gecko 274
sand-mining 44–45
Sandalwood 228, 235, 237
Sandhill
    Bloodwood 272, 273
    Canegrass 310, 318
    Desert Bloodwood 318
    Dunnart 272, 273
    Frog 307
Sandpaper Fig 172
Sandspurrey 278
Sandstone Shrike-thrush 322
sandy desert 301, 314–318
Sandy Inland Mouse 213, 226, 232, 273
Saratoga 168
Sarcocornia spp. 79
Sargassum spp. 36, 54
Sarsaparilla 238, 239
Sassafras 123, 127, 150–152, 158
Satin
    Bowerbird 124, 138, 145, 153, 241
    Flycatcher 241
Satinash 132, 136, 162
Saucer Scallop 96
savanna 202, 204, 206–208, 211, 279
Sawn Rocks 170
Sawpit Creek 110
Scaevola Fanflower 46
scallops 39, 70, 90
Scaly
    241, 258
    Button 278, 283, 295
    Tree Ferns 136
Scaly-breasted Lorikeet 115, 134, 145
Scarlet
    Banksia 255
    Gum 204, 266
    Honeyeater 88, 258
    Pear Gum 225
    Robin 115, 124, 153, 160, 253, 266, 275, 285, 288
Scarlet-chested Parrot 214, 233, 244, 275
Scented Paperbark 88, 289
Schizophrys spp. 70
Schomburgk's Striped Skink 274
Scirpus spp. 306
    polystachus 289
scorpionfish 69
scorpions 272, 317
Scott, Keith 122, 130
Scott National Park 122
Scottsdale 110
Screw
    Palm 166
    Shells 70
Scribbly Gum 178, 179, 197, 199, 224, 225, 227, 230–233, 235–237, 239–242
Scrub
    Beefwood 151
    Breadfruit 136
    Python 138, 167
    She-oak 255
Scrub-robin 223, 224, 241
scrublands 196, 216, 218, 227, 228, 230, 238–241
Scrubtit 156, 160
Sea
    anemone 68, 71, 97
    cucumber 90, 96, 166
    fans 70
    hares 55, 70, 97

jellies 36, 38, 70, 96
Lake 310
Lettuce 53, 54
level 40, 58, 61, 72, 78, 82, 84, 96
pens 97
Rocket 46
Rush 88
slugs 70
snakes 58, 66
squirts 70, 96
Tassel 88, 306
Trumpeter 96
urchins 53, 55, 70, 97
whips 55, 70
Worm 46
seagrass 34, 64, 67, 76, 79, 86, 90, 92, 92, 92, 92, 93, 94, 96, 97
seahorses 97
Seal
    Bay 47, 50, 67
    Rocks 50, 82, 84, 172
Searcy, Alfred 80
seaweed 42, 50, 52, 54
Seawrack 88
sedge 82, 86, 88, 248, 251, 253, 255, 257, 302, 304, 306, 308
sediment 34, 42, 72, 74, 78, 82, 90, 93, 94, 96
sedimentary rocks 14
seed shrimps 70, 307, 312
Sefton Bush 223, 225
segmented worms 70
Semaphore Crab 77
Senecio sp. 318
Senna 223, 318
    atemisioides 318
Sentinel Peak 295
Serengeti Plain 276
Sergeant Major 69
Sesbania benthamiana 204
Seven Spirits Bay 61
Shark Bay 23, 42, 43, 67, 72, 90, 92, 94, 96, 220, 221, 232
    Snake 96
    World Heritage Area 298
Shark Mackerel 36
sharks 36, 38
Sharp-snouted Delma 227, 231, 274
Sharp-tailed Sandpiper 313
She-oak 123
shearwater 300
sheep 218, 220, 223, 224, 226, 228, 229, 242, 244, 245
Shelburne Bay 45
Shell Beach 94
shelly cheniers 80
Shepherd's Ironwood 136
Shield
    Bug 184
    Fern 158
    Shrimps 308, 311, 314
Shingleback 192, 200, 206, 212, 221, 222, 227, 231, 237, 242, 269, 274, 312
Shining
    Bronze-Cuckoo 115, 121, 124, 145, 153, 160, 237
    Cudweed 283
    Flycatcher 169
    Gum 120, 123, 158
Shiny-leafed Billy-button 283, 295
Shipwreck Coast 50
Shivery Grass 278
Shoemaker Frog 231, 274
Shore
    Crab 55
    Oaks 64, 74
    Slater 46
Short-beaked Echidna 125, 147, 154, 161, 170, 185, 192, 200, 207, 213, 226, 232, 237, 240, 245, 253, 259,

Acknowledgements

Wild Habitats of Australia has been a work in progress for a lifetime. My role has been as a lifelong naturalist. I am not a researcher; I am an observer, a listener and a reader. Therefore, first I must acknowledge my father, who insisted that the most important question in life is, "Why is it so?" Obtaining the answer frequently got him into trouble and kept his pocket empty, but what an adventurous life that made for a school principal! It meant plenty of travel, particularly to places like the Warrumbungles, where I was born, and the far south coast. Somehow, becoming a teacher seemed the next logical step and I came under the influence of two wonderful mentors: Principal of Balmain Teachers' College, George Cantello, an inspiring man with hundreds of anecdotes of his rich teaching life, and Allen Strom, who changed my life by introducing me to the Australian environment and showing me that understanding it depended upon four things: geology of the country; geomorphic processes; how plants and animals evolve their form, behaviour and relationships to adapt to the country; and that humans, too, colonise land and adapt to the country's natural resources and the impact of utilising those resources.

My life became centred around uncovering these themes. Sixteen years of environmental teaching saw me transferred to the Wildlife Service of New South Wales, directed at the time by Allen Strom, who again rejuvenated my interest and understanding of nature. Later with the new National Parks and Wildlife Service of NSW, and later still, the federal service, I spent more than 60% of my time in the field. Highlights were reorganising the kangaroo management program and planning for Kakadu and Uluru. I worked beside many remarkable colleagues and researchers from the CSIRO and Australia's universities and I preyed compulsively on their work. Some who were particularly inspiring were Drs Alan Newsome, Bill Poole, Harry Frith, John Calaby, Len Webb, Alec Costin, Dane Wimbush, John Le Gay Brereton, Roger Good, Dan Lunney, Harry Recher, Russell Ward, Dorothy Tunbridge, John Harris, David Keith, David Tranter, Neil McKenzie and Jeffrey Clyde. Many more were mentors so far as understanding nature goes — Bill Neidjie, Ian Morris, Greg Miles, Jane Moore, George Chaloupka, Wendy Goldstein, Margo Warnett, John Dorman, John Sinclair, Nick Newland, Mylo Dunphy and his dad Myles, Don Johnstone, Alan Morris, Charles Boyd, Fred Hersey, Theo Livanes, Richard Woldendorp and, of course, old friend and photographer par excellence Steve Parish. There are so many more — farmers and graziers, men and women of great heart and hospitality, who were always keen to share their experiences. Along with these were the managers and rangers in our parks and reserves, my colleagues around the continent, as well as all of the friends in the old Caloola Club and the National Parks Association and the various crews on the *Coral Princess* cruises.

This book is the result of much reading of other people's works, and I have been the interpreter of it only. Any error or misinterpretation is entirely my responsibility. I must make a special note of appreciation for my family, who suffered an absentee husband and father for so much of my learning experience. Now, I hope that my children and their children will appreciate this book as a written memory of what this natural world of ours was like in 2007. Thanks also the Steve Parish Publishing image library team and talented book designers, and finally, a word of appreciation for my editor Karin Cox who had the challenging job of restraining my words to these always-too-small spaces. Like Steve Parish and I, she realises just how much bigger this work would have been had my passion for writing this homage to nature remained unrestrained.

ALLAN FOX

Photographic Credits

Photography: Steve Parish

Photographic assistance: Ken Stepnell: pp. 47 (centre right), 89 (Long-footed Frog), 115 (top left, centre left, centre & bottom), 117 (bottom centre), 124 (top left), 147 (bottom right), 154 (top centre & top right), 160 (top & centre), 169 (bottom centre), 183 (bottom), 194 (top right & bottom right), 195 (top left & right), 200 (Black-headed Python & Western Blue-tongue), 201 (top left, bottom left & right), 212 (bottom), 227, 231 (top right, centre left & right), 241 (top left, top right & bottom left), 253 (centre left, centre right & bottom), 258 (bottom), 259 (Green and Golden Bell Frog), 265 (centre right & bottom), 269 (both right), 274 (Central Military Dragon, Variegated Dtella, Leopard Skink & Thorny Devil), 280, 285 (centre), 288 (top), 311 (right), 313 (top), 323 (Black-footed Rock-wallaby); Ron & Valerie Taylor: pp. 28–29, 39, 95 (centre).

Additional photography: Kelvin Aitken/ANTPhoto.com: p. 95 (top); Fredy Mercay/ANTPhoto.com: p. 313 (bottom); Bruce Thomson/ANTPhoto.com: p. 316 (bottom); Stanley Breeden: p. 317 (Witchetty Grub); Michael Cermak: pp. 125 (all right), 133, 139 (top right), 144 (forest leech & Green Tree Ant), 153 (bottom right), 184 (centre right), 231 (top left), 272 (bottom left & right), 290 (left), 307 (water spider, Wetland Freshwater Crab & dragonfly), 312 (top); CSIRO: p. 23 (bottom) & 184 (centre left); Allan Fox: pp. 12, 19, 42 (centre left), 44 (top), 45 (top left & right), 61, 75 (bottom right), 86 (bottom), 87 (top & centre right), 88 (top), 89 (bottom left), 90, 104–105, 140 (left), 143 (top right), 144 (bottom right), 145 (left), 146 (centre top left, centre left & centre right), 150, 153 (Sydney Funnel-web Spider), 155 (top), 163 (left), 164 (top & bottom left), 165, 166 (top), 167 (right), 173 (both right), 179 (all right), 180 (top), 186 (left, Nos. 1 & 4–5), 187 (Nos. 6–7 & 9–15), 192 (top), 196, 197 (centre, bottom left & bottom right), 205 (top left), 206 (all left), 208 (left), 211 (bottom centre), 213 (left), 220 (centre & bottom), 222 (top & bottom), 224 (top), 228 (both), 229 (top & bottom right), 230 (top), 233 (bottom), 234 (centre & bottom right), 236 (bottom right), 237–238, 251 (bottom left & right), 252 (centre & bottom), 265 (top), 266 (top), 270, 271 (Mount Connor & burning spinifex hummocks), 274 (Trilling Frog), 276–277, 278 (bottom), 279 (bottom), 282 (bottom left), 283 (top left & bottom), 287, 292 (right & inset), 293, 295, 298 (top), 311 (left), 312 (bottom left), 314 (bottom right), 315 (top), 317 (Central Military Dragon), 321 (centre), 324 (right), 327 (Yellow-footed Rock-wallabies, right); Greg Harm: pp. 283 (top right), 292 (left), 294 (bottom), 310; Jiri Lochman/Lochman Transparencies: p. 327 (Monjon); M & I Morcombe: pp. 226 (Western Barred Bandicoot), 245 (bottom right), 253 (top right); Ian Morris: pp. 138 (right), 173 (bottom left & centre), 212 (top), 226 (Fat-tailed Dunnart), 241 (both right), 279 (centre), 307 (Dahl's Aquatic Frog, Arafura File Snake & Mitchell's Water Monitor), 317 (Southern Slider, Desert Death Adder, Crowned Gecko, Red Tree-frog & Desert Spadefoot), 323 (Rock Ringtail Possum & monitor), 324 (right), 327 (Yellow-footed Rock-wallaby & Nabarlek); Gary Bell/OceanwideImages.com: pp. 36 (bottom), 37 (top & bottom right), 64 (bottom), 67 (bottom right); Rudie Kuiter/OceanwideImages.com: pp. 31 (bottom), 33 (bottom), 38 (top & bottom left); Peter Slater: p. 233 (top right); Len H. Smith: p. 121 (top left); Steve Swanson: p. 284; Martin Willis: p. 117 (all left & centre top), 145 (top), 201 (top right & bottom centre), 268 (centre right), 322 (bottom).